S0-ABC-122

How to Use the *Reading and Study Workbook A*

Did you know that learning to study more effectively can make a real difference in your performance at school? Students who master study skills are more confident and have more fun learning. This book, the *Reading and Study Workbook* for *Prentice Hall Biology,* is designed to help you acquire the skills that will allow you to study biology more effectively. Your active participation in class and use of this book can go a long way toward helping you achieve success in biology.

The *Reading and Study Workbook* can be used to
- preview a chapter,
- learn key vocabulary terms,
- master difficult concepts, and
- review for chapter and unit tests.

The *Reading and Study Workbook* concentrates on the key concepts presented in each chapter of the textbook. Each chapter in the *Reading and Study Workbook* is divided into the same numbered sections as in the textbook. By completing each section after you have read the section in the textbook, you will be better able to understand and remember the important points made in the chapter. In addition, your ability to tie information together in order to see the "big picture" in biology will be greatly improved.

Each chapter in the *Reading and Study Workbook* begins with a two-page chapter summary. This review material stresses the key concepts and facts you should focus on in that particular chapter. As you read the chapter review, try to relate the material you have read in the chapter to the material stressed in the summary. If parts of the summary are not clear to you, go back to that part of the section in the textbook and read it again.

An alternate way of using the chapter summary is to read it before you read the chapter in the textbook. In that way you will be alerted to the important facts contained in the chapter. Used in this manner, the summary can be a prereading guide to the chapter material.

Following the chapter summary, you will find specific workbook activities designed to help you read and understand the textbook. Completing these worksheets will help you master the key concepts and vocabulary in each section.

Each lesson in the *Reading and Study Workbook* provides questions to help you under-stand the content found under each of the main headings in the textbook. Diagrams, charts, and word puzzles provide a variety of formats to help you master key terms.

An activity that focuses on a particular reading strategy for each chapter is also provided. These activities will help improve your reading skills. Strategies include
- outlining,
- sequencing information,
- identifying cause and effect, and
- identifying main ideas and supporting details.

The final part of each chapter consists of Vocabulary Reviews. The Vocabulary Reviews take a variety of formats including flowcharts, crossword puzzles, labeling diagrams, multiple-choice questions, and matching exercises.

Contents

Chapter 1 The Science of Biology

Summary 1
1–1 What Is Science? 3
1–2 How Scientists Work 5
1–3 Studying Life 8
1–4 Tools and Procedures 10
Vocabulary Review 12

Chapter 2 The Chemistry of Life

Summary 13
2–1 The Nature of Matter 15
2–2 Properties of Water 17
2–3 Carbon Compounds 19
2–4 Chemical Reactions and Enzymes 22
Vocabulary Review 24

Chapter 3 The Biosphere

Summary 25
3–1 What Is Ecology? 27
3–2 Energy Flow 29
3–3 Cycles of Matter 32
Vocabulary Review 34

Chapter 4 Ecosystems and Communities

Summary 35
4–1 The Role of Climate 37
4–2 What Shapes an Ecosystem? 39
4–3 Biomes 41
4–4 Aquatic Ecosystems 45
Vocabulary Review 48

Chapter 5 Populations

Summary 49
5–1 How Populations Grow 51
5–2 Limits to Growth 54
5–3 Human Population Growth 56
Vocabulary Review 58

Chapter 6 Humans in the Biosphere

Summary 59
6–1 A Changing Landscape 61
6–2 Renewable and Nonrenewable Resources 63
6–3 Biodiversity 66
6–4 Charting a Course for the Future 69
Vocabulary Review 70

Chapter 7 Cell Structure and Function

Summary.. 71
7–1 Life Is Cellular.. 73
7–2 Eukaryotic Cell Structure.............................. 75
7–3 Cell Boundaries.. 80
7–4 The Diversity of Cellular Life......................... 83
Vocabulary Review.. 84

Chapter 8 Photosynthesis

Summary.. 85
8–1 Energy and Life.. 87
8–2 Photosynthesis: An Overview........................... 89
8–3 The Reactions of Photosynthesis....................... 91
Vocabulary Review.. 94

Chapter 9 Cellular Respiration

Summary.. 95
9–1 Chemical Pathways...................................... 97
9–2 The Krebs Cycle and Electron Transport................ 100
Vocabulary Review... 104

Chapter 10 Cell Growth and Division

Summary... 105
10–1 Cell Growth.. 107
10–2 Cell Division.. 108
10–3 Regulating the Cell Cycle............................ 111
Vocabulary Review... 112

Chapter 11 Introduction to Genetics

Summary... 113
11–1 The Work of Gregor Mendel............................ 115
11–2 Probability and Punnett Squares...................... 117
11–3 Exploring Mendelian Genetics......................... 119
11–4 Meiosis.. 122
11–5 Linkage and Gene Maps................................ 125
Vocabulary Review... 126

Chapter 12 DNA and RNA

Summary... 127
12–1 DNA.. 129
12–2 Chromosomes and DNA Replication...................... 132
12–3 RNA and Protein Synthesis............................ 134
12–4 Mutations.. 137
12–5 Gene Regulation...................................... 139
Vocabulary Review... 142

Chapter 13 Genetic Engineering

Summary... 143
13–1 Changing the Living World............................ 145
13–2 Manipulating DNA..................................... 147
13–3 Cell Transformation.................................. 150
13–4 Applications of Genetic Engineering.................. 152
Vocabulary Review... 154

Chapter 14 The Human Genome
Summary...155
14–1 Human Heredity..157
14–2 Human Chromosomes...160
14–3 Human Molecular Genetics..163
Vocabulary Review..166

Chapter 15 Darwin's Theory of Evolution
Summary...167
15–1 The Puzzle of Life's Diversity..................................169
15–2 Ideas That Shaped Darwin's Thinking.............................171
15–3 Darwin Presents His Case..173
Vocabulary Review..176

Chapter 16 Evolution of Populations
Summary...177
16–1 Genes and Variation...179
16–2 Evolution as Genetic Change.....................................182
16–3 The Process of Speciation.......................................184
Vocabulary Review..186

Chapter 17 The History of Life
Summary...187
17–1 The Fossil Record...189
17–2 Earth's Early History...192
17–3 Evolution of Multicellular Life.................................195
17–4 Patterns of Evolution...198
Vocabulary Review..200

Chapter 18 Classification
Summary...201
18–1 Finding Order in Diversity......................................203
18–2 Modern Evolutionary Classification...............................205
18–3 Kingdoms and Domains..207
Vocabulary Review..210

Chapter 19 Bacteria and Viruses
Summary...211
19–1 Bacteria..213
19–2 Viruses...217
19–3 Diseases Caused by Bacteria and Viruses.........................220
Vocabulary Review..222

Chapter 20 Protists
Summary...223
20–1 The Kingdom Protista..225
20–2 Animallike Protists: Protozoans................................227
20–3 Plantlike Protists: Unicellular Algae...........................230
20–4 Plantlike Protists: Red, Brown, and Green Algae.................233
20–5 Funguslike Protists...236
Vocabulary Review..238

Chapter 21 Fungi

Summary..239
21–1 The Kingdom Fungi..241
21–2 Classification of Fungi..244
21–3 Ecology of Fungi...248
Vocabulary Review..250

Chapter 22 Plant Diversity

Summary..251
22–1 Introduction to Plants...253
22–2 Bryophytes...256
22–3 Seedless Vascular Plants...259
22–4 Seed Plants..262
22–5 Angiosperms—Flowering Plants.....................................266
Vocabulary Review..268

Chapter 23 Roots, Stems, and Leaves

Summary..269
23–1 Specialized Tissues in Plants....................................271
23–2 Roots..274
23–3 Stems..276
23–4 Leaves...279
23–5 Transport in Plants..281
Vocabulary Review..284

Chapter 24 Reproduction of Seed Plants

Summary..285
24–1 Reproduction With Cones and Flowers..............................287
24–2 Seed Development and Germination.................................292
24–3 Plant Propagation and Agriculture...............................294
Vocabulary Review..296

Chapter 25 Plant Responses and Adaptations

Summary..297
25–1 Hormones and Plant Growth..299
25–2 Plant Responses..302
25–3 Plant Adaptations..304
Vocabulary Review..306

Chapter 26 Sponges and Cnidarians

Summary..307
26–1 Introduction to the Animal Kingdom...............................309
26–2 Sponges...313
26–3 Cnidarians..315
Vocabulary Review..318

Chapter 27 Worms and Mollusks

Summary 319
27–1 Flatworms 321
27–2 Roundworms 324
27–3 Annelids 326
27–4 Mollusks 329
Vocabulary Review 332

Chapter 28 Arthropods and Echinoderms

Summary 333
28–1 Introduction to the Arthropods 335
28–2 Groups of Arthropods 338
28–3 Insects 341
28–4 Echinoderms 344
Vocabulary Review 346

Chapter 29 Comparing Invertebrates

Summary 347
29–1 Invertebrate Evolution 349
29–2 Form and Function in Invertebrates 353
Vocabulary Review 356

Chapter 30 Nonvertebrate Chordates, Fishes, and Amphibians

Summary 357
30–1 The Chordates 359
30–2 Fishes 361
30–3 Amphibians 365
Vocabulary Review 368

Chapter 31 Reptiles and Birds

Summary 369
31–1 Reptiles 371
31–2 Birds 374
Vocabulary Review 378

Chapter 32 Mammals

Summary 379
32–1 Introduction to the Mammals 381
32–2 Diversity of Mammals 385
32–3 Primates and Human Origins 387
Vocabulary Review 390

Chapter 33 Comparing Chordates

Summary 391
33–1 Chordate Evolution 393
33–2 Controlling Body Temperature 395
33–3 Form and Function in Chordates 397
Vocabulary Review 400

Chapter 34 Animal Behavior

Summary...401
34–1 Elements of Behavior...403
34–2 Patterns of Behavior 406
Vocabulary Review 408

Chapter 35 Nervous System

Summary...409
35–1 Human Body Systems 411
35–2 The Nervous System 413
35–3 Divisions of the Nervous System 415
35–4 The Senses 417
35–5 Drugs and the Nervous System 420
Vocabulary Review 422

Chapter 36 Skeletal, Muscular, and Integumentary Systems

Summary...423
36–1 The Skeletal System 425
36–2 The Muscular System...428
36–3 The Integumentary System 431
Vocabulary Review 434

Chapter 37 Circulatory and Respiratory Systems

Summary...435
37–1 The Circulatory System 437
37–2 Blood and the Lymphatic System..................................440
37–3 The Respiratory System..442
Vocabulary Review 446

Chapter 38 Digestive and Excretory Systems

Summary...447
38–1 Food and Nutrition..449
38–2 The Process of Digestion 452
38–3 The Excretory System..456
Vocabulary Review 458

Chapter 39 Endocrine and Reproductive Systems

Summary...459
39–1 The Endocrine System 461
39–2 Human Endocrine Glands..464
39–3 The Reproductive System 467
39–4 Fertilization and Development...................................470
Vocabulary Review 472

Chapter 40 The Immune System and Disease

Summary...473
40–1 Infectious Disease...475
40–2 The Immune System..477
40–3 Immune System Disorders 480
40–4 The Environment and Your Health 482
Vocabulary Review 485

Summary

1–1 What Is Science?

Science is an organized way of using evidence to learn about the natural world. Scientific thinking usually begins with observation, which is the process of gathering information about events or processes in a careful, orderly way. The information gathered from observations is called data. Quantitative data are expressed as numbers, obtained by counting or measuring. Qualitative data are descriptive and involve characteristics that can't usually be counted. Scientists use data to make inferences. An inference is a logical interpretation based on prior knowledge or experience.

After making first observations, a researcher will propose one or more hypotheses. A hypothesis is a proposed scientific explanation for a set of observations. Scientists generate hypotheses using prior knowledge, logical inference, and informed, creative imagination. Scientific hypotheses must be proposed in a way that enables them to be tested. Some hypotheses are tested by performing controlled experiments. Other hypotheses are tested by gathering more data. The conclusions researchers draw from experiments or data must be valid. To be valid, a conclusion must be based on logical interpretation of reliable data.

1–2 How Scientists Work

Conducting a scientific investigation involves a series of steps. The first step is asking a question. The second step involves forming a hypothesis. The third step in conducting a scientific investigation is setting up a controlled experiment. Whenever possible, a hypothesis should be tested by an experiment in which only one variable is changed at a time. All other variables should be kept unchanged. This type of experiment is called a controlled experiment. The variable that is deliberately changed is called the manipulated variable. The variable that is observed and

that changes in response to the manipulated variable is called the responding variable.

The fourth step in conducting a scientific investigation is recording and analyzing results. The fifth step is drawing a conclusion. A key assumption in science is that experimental results can be reproduced.

Sometimes, controlled experiments are not possible. When researchers design alternative investigations, they try to maintain the rigorous thinking associated with a controlled experiment. As evidence from numerous investigations builds up, a particular hypothesis may become so well supported that scientists consider it a theory. In science, a theory is a well-tested explanation that unifies a broad range of observations.

1–3 Studying Life

Although living things vary greatly, all living things share eight characteristics:

1. Living things are made up of units called cells. A cell is a collection of living matter enclosed by a barrier that separates the cell from its surroundings. Cells are the smallest units of an organism that can be considered alive.

2. Living things reproduce. In sexual reproduction, cells from two different parents unite to produce the first cell of the new organism. In asexual reproduction, a single-celled organism divides in half to form two new organisms.

3. Living things are based on a universal genetic code. The directions for inheritance are carried by a molecule called DNA.

4. Living things grow and develop. Multicellular organisms typically go through a process called development. As cells divide, they change in shape and structure in a process called differentiation.

5. Living things obtain and use materials and energy. The combination of chemical reactions through which an organism builds up or breaks down materials as it carries out its life processes is called metabolism.

6. Living things respond to their environment. Organisms detect and respond to stimuli from their environment. A stimulus is a signal to which an organism responds.

7. Living things maintain a stable internal environment. The process by which they do this is called homeostasis.

8. Taken as a group, living things change over time. Change over time in living things is called evolution.

Biology is divided into different fields of study. Some fields focus on the study of living systems at different levels. These levels include, from smallest to largest: molecules, cells, groups of cells, organisms, populations, communities, ecosystems, and the biosphere.

1–4 Tools and Procedures

Most scientists use the metric system when collecting data. The metric system is a decimal system of measurement whose units are based on certain physical standards and are scaled on multiples of 10. A revised version of the original metric system is called the International System of Units, or SI.

The simplest way to find out whether factors in an experiment changed or remained the same is to record data in a table and then make a graph.

A microscope is a device that produces magnified images of structures that are too small to see with the unaided eye. Light microscopes produce magnified images by focusing visible light rays. Compound light microscopes allow light to pass through the specimen and use two lenses to form an image. Electron microscopes use beams of electrons to produce magnified images. Biologists use two main types: the transmission electron microscope (TEM) and the scanning electron microscope (SEM).

A cell culture is a group of cells that develops from a single cell placed in a dish containing a nutrient solution. Cell fractionation is a technique in which cells are broken into pieces and different cell parts are separated for study.

Whenever you work in your biology laboratory, it's important for you to follow safe practices. The single most important rule for your safety is simple: Always follow your teacher's instructions and the textbook directions exactly. Because you may be in contact with organisms you cannot see, it is essential that you wash your hands thoroughly after every scientific activity.

Chapter 1 The Science of Biology

Section 1–1 What Is Science? (pages 3–7)

🔑 **Key Concept**
- What is the goal of science?

What Science Is and Is Not (page 3)

1. What is the goal of science? The goal of science is to investigate and understand nature, to explain events in nature, and to use those explanations to make useful predictions.

2. What is science? Science is an organized way of using evidence to learn about the natural world.

Thinking Like a Scientist (page 4)

3. What is observation? Observation is the process of gathering information about events or processes in a careful, orderly way.

4. The information gathered from observation is called _____ data _____.

5. Complete the table about types of data.

TYPES OF DATA

Type	Data Involves . . .	Example
Quantitative	Numbers	Accept all reasonable examples. One example may be: The manatee has one scar on its back.
Qualitative	Characteristics that cannot be easily measured or counted	Accept all reasonable examples. One example may be: The scar appears old.

6. What is an inference? An inference is a logical interpretation based on prior knowledge and experience.

Explaining and Interpreting Evidence (page 5)

7. What is a hypothesis? A hypothesis is a proposed scientific explanation for a set of observations.

_____

8. In science, a hypothesis is useful only if it can be _____tested_____.

9. Is the following sentence true or false? A hypothesis should be stated in such a way that it can never be proved wrong. _____false_____

10. What are three sources from which hypotheses may arise?

   a. From prior knowledge

   b. From logical inferences

   c. From informed, creative imagination

11. Circle the letter of each of the following that may be an outcome of testing a hypothesis.

   (a.) The hypothesis is partly true but needs to be revised.

   (b.) The hypothesis is wrong.

   (c.) The hypothesis is supported.

   d. The hypothesis is of no value.

Science as a Way of Knowing (page 6)

12. What do scientists assume about the universe?

They assume that the universe is a system in which basic natural laws apply.

_____

13. What are some qualities that are desirable in a scientist? Qualities include openness,
skepticism, and a recognition that science has limits.

_____

Science and Human Values (page 7)

14. Is the following sentence true or false? A community must use its shared values to make decisions about scientific issues. _____true_____

Section 1–2 How Scientists Work (pages 8–15)

🔑 Key Concepts
- How do scientists test hypotheses?
- How does a scientific theory develop?

Designing an Experiment (pages 8–10)

1. The idea that life can arise from nonliving matter is called
   _____spontaneous generation_____.

2. What was Francesco Redi's hypothesis about the appearance of maggots?
   Flies produce maggots.

3. What are variables in an experiment? They are factors that can change.

4. Ideally, how many variables should an experiment test at a time? It should test only one
   variable at a time.

5. What is a controlled experiment? A controlled experiment is an experiment in which one
   variable is changed while the other variables are controlled.
   _____

6. The illustration below shows the beginning of Redi's experiment. Complete the
   illustration by showing the outcome.

Redi's Experiment on Spontaneous Generation

Uncovered jars

Covered jars

Several
days pass.

Maggots appear

No maggots appear

7. Complete the table about variables.

VARIABLES

Type of Variable	Definition
Manipulated variable	The variable that is deliberately changed in an experiment
Responding variable	The variable that is observed and changes in response to the manipulated variable

8. In Redi's experiment, what were the manipulated variable and the responding variable?
The manipulated variable was the presence or absence of the gauze covering, and the
responding variable was whether maggots appear.

9. For what do scientists use the data from a controlled experiment? They use it to evaluate
the hypothesis and draw a conclusion.

10. When scientists look for explanations for specific observations, what do they assume
about nature? They assume that the patterns in nature are consistent.

Repeating Investigations (pages 10–13)

11. Why do scientists assume that experimental results can be reproduced?
A key assumption in science is that nature behaves in a consistent manner.

12. What did Anton van Leeuwenhoek discover? He discovered a world of tiny moving objects,
which he called "animalcules," in rainwater, pond water, and dust.

13. What did John Needham conclude from his test of Redi's findings? He concluded that the
little animals in a bottle of gravy could only have come from the juice of the gravy.

14. What did Spallanzani do to improve upon Redi's and Needham's work? He boiled two
containers of gravy, assuming that the boiling would kill any microorganisms that were present.

15. How did Pasteur settle the spontaneous generation argument? He designed a special
flask to show that as long as broth was protected from microorganisms, it remained free of living
things.

When Experiments Are Not Possible (page 14)

16. In animal field studies, why do scientists usually try to work without making the animals aware that humans are present? <u>To learn how animals in the wild interact, it is</u> <u>necessary to observe the animals without disturbing them.</u>

_____

17. When a controlled experiment is not possible, why do scientists try to identify as many relevant variables as possible? <u>They identify as many as possible so that most variables are</u> <u>controlled.</u>

How a Theory Develops (pages 14–15)

18. In science, what is a theory? <u>A theory is a well-tested explanation that unifies a broad range</u> <u>of observations.</u>

19. Is the following sentence true or false? A theory may be revised or replaced by a more useful explanation. _____<u>true</u>_____

Reading Skill Practice

A flowchart can help you remember the order in which a set of events has occurred or should occur. On a separate sheet of paper, create a flowchart that represents the process that Redi carried out in his investigation of spontaneous generation. This process is explained under the heading Designing an Experiment on pages 8–10. For more information about flowcharts, see Organizing Information in Appendix A of your textbook.

Students' flowcharts should begin with Redi's proposal of a hypothesis and end with his drawing a conclusion about how maggots are produced.

Section 1–3 Studying Life (pages 16–22)

👁 **Key Concepts**
- What are some characteristics of living things?
- How can life be studied at different levels?

Introduction (page 16)

1. What is biology? <u>Biology is the science that seeks to understand the living world.</u>

_____

Characteristics of Living Things (pages 16–20)

2. What is a cell? <u>A cell is a collection of living matter enclosed by a barrier that separates the cell</u>
<u>from its surroundings.</u>

_____

3. Circle the letter of each sentence that is true about cells.
   - **(a.)** A cell is the smallest unit of an organism that can be considered alive.
   - **(b.)** A multicellular organism may contain trillions of cells.
   - c. A living thing that consists of a single cell is a multicellular organism.
   - **(d.)** Organisms are made up of cells.

4. What are two types of asexual reproduction?
   - a. <u>A single-celled organism divides in half to form two new organisms.</u>
   - b. <u>A portion of an organism splits off to form a new organism.</u>

5. Living things are based on a universal _____<u>genetic code</u>_____.

6. Circle the letter of each sentence that is true about living things.
   - a. The life cycle of many organisms involves development.
   - **(b.)** For bacteria, growth is mostly a simple increase in size.
   - **(c.)** Each type of organism has a distinctive life cycle.
   - **(d.)** Cells may change in number but never differentiate.

7. Why does an organism need energy and a constant supply of materials?
   <u>An organism uses energy and materials to grow, develop, and reproduce.</u>

_____

8. What is metabolism? <u>It is the combination of reactions through which an organism builds up</u>
   <u>or breaks down materials as it carries out its life processes.</u>

_____

_____

9. Is the following sentence true or false? All organisms respond to the environment in exactly the same ways. _____false_____

10. What is homeostasis? It is the process by which organisms keep their internal conditions fairly constant._____

_____

11. A group of organisms that changes over time is said to _____evolve_____.

Branches of Biology (pages 20–21)

Match the different kinds of biologists with the focus of their study.

	Kinds of Biologists	Focus of Study
c	12. Zoologist	a. Plants
a	13. Botanist	b. Ancient life
b	14. Paleontologist	c. Animals

15. Label each of the illustrations below according to the level of study represented.

Population	Biosphere	Cells

16. The largest level of biological study is the _____biosphere_____.

Biology in Everyday Life (page 22)

17. What kinds of information can the study of biology provide about matters affecting human society? Biology helps you understand all forms of life and helps you understand what affects the quality of your life._____

_____

Section 1–4 Tools and Procedures (pages 24–28)

👉 **Key Concepts**
- What measurement system do most scientists use?
- How are light microscopes and electron microscopes similar? How are they different?

A Common Measurement System (page 24)

1. Why do scientists need a common system of measurement? <u>Researchers need to</u>
<u>replicate one another's experiments, and most experiments involve measurements.</u>
_____

2. When collecting data and doing experiments, what system of measurement do most
scientists use? <u>Metric system</u>

3. What is the metric system? <u>The metric system is a decimal system of measurement whose</u>
<u>units are based on certain physical standards and are scaled on multiples of 10.</u>
_____

4. Complete each equation by writing the correct number or metric unit.
   a. 1000 meters = 1 <u>kilometer</u>
   b. 1 liter = <u>1000</u> milliliters
   c. 1 gram = <u>1000</u> milligrams
   d. 1000 kilograms = 1 <u>metric ton</u>

Analyzing Biological Data (page 25)

5. When scientists collect data, what are they often trying to find out? <u>They are trying to</u>
<u>find out whether certain factors changed or remained the same.</u>
_____

6. What does a graph of data make easier to recognize and understand than a table of
data? <u>A pattern</u>

Microscopes (pages 25–26)

7. What are microscopes? <u>Microscopes are devices that produce magnified images of structures</u>
<u>that are too small to see with the unaided eye.</u>

8. What are compound light microscopes? <u>They are microscopes that allow light to pass</u>
<u>through the specimen and use two lenses to form an image.</u>
_____

9. How do chemical stains make light microscopes more useful? <u>They can show specific</u>
<u>structures in the cell.</u>

10. What are the two main types of electron microscopes?

    a. Transmission electron microscopes (TEMs)

    b. Scanning electron microscopes (SEMs)

11. Compare how a TEM and an SEM produce images. A TEM shines a beam of electrons through a thin specimen, whereas an SEM scans a narrow beam of electrons back and forth across the surface of a specimen.

12. How must samples be prepared for observation by an electron microscope? Samples must be preserved and dehydrated.

Laboratory Techniques (page 27)

13. A group of cells grown in a nutrient solution from a single original cell is called a(an) cell culture .

14. What technique do biologists use to separate one part of a cell from the rest of the cell? Cell fractionation

Working Safely in Biology (page 28)

15. What is the single most important rule for your safety while working in a laboratory? Always follow your teacher's instructions and the textbook directions exactly.

Chapter 1   The Science of Biology

Vocabulary Review

Completion   *Fill in the blanks with terms from Chapter 1.*

1. The process of gathering information about events or processes in a careful, orderly way is called _____observation_____.

2. The information gathered from observations is called _____data_____.

3. A(An) _____inference_____ is a logical interpretation based on prior knowledge or experience.

4. A(An) _____hypothesis_____ is a proposed scientific explanation for a set of observations.

5. In a(an) _____controlled_____ experiment, only one variable is changed at a time, while all other variables are kept unchanged.

6. The variable that is deliberately changed in a controlled experiment is called the _____manipulated_____ variable.

7. A(An) _____theory_____ is a well-tested explanation that unifies a broad range of observations.

8. In _____asexual_____ reproduction, the new organism has a single parent.

9. A(An) _____stimulus_____ is a signal to which an organism responds.

10. The _____metric_____ system is a decimal system of measurement whose units are based on certain physical standards and are scaled on multiples of 10.

Matching   *In the space provided, write the letter of the definition that best matches each term.*

___g___ **11.** biology

___e___ **12.** microscope

___a___ **13.** cell

___f___ **14.** cell fractionation

___d___ **15.** homeostasis

___b___ **16.** metabolism

___c___ **17.** cell culture

a. a collection of living matter enclosed by a barrier that separates it from its environment

b. combination of chemical reactions through which an organism builds up or breaks down materials

c. a laboratory technique in which a group of cells develops from a single cell

d. process of keeping an organism's internal conditions constant

e. a device that produces magnified images of structures that are too small to see with the unaided eye

f. a laboratory technique in which cells are separated into cell parts

g. the science that seeks to understand the living world

© Pearson Education, Inc., publishing as Pearson Prentice Hall.

Summary

2–1 The Nature of Matter

The basic unit of matter is the atom. The subatomic particles that make up atoms are protons, neutrons, and electrons. Protons and neutrons have about the same mass. Protons are positively charged particles (+), and neutrons carry no charge. Protons and neutrons together form the nucleus, at the center of the atom. The electron is a negatively charged particle (–). Atoms have equal numbers of electrons and protons, and therefore atoms do not have a charge.

A chemical element is a pure substance that consists entirely of one type of atom. The number of protons in an atom of an element is the element's atomic number. Atoms of an element can have different numbers of neutrons. Atoms of the same element that differ in the number of neutrons they contain are known as isotopes. Because all the isotopes of an element have the same number of electrons, they all have the same chemical properties.

A chemical compound is a substance formed by the chemical combination of two or more elements in definite proportions. Atoms in compounds are held together by chemical bonds. An ionic bond is formed when one or more electrons are transferred from one atom to another. A covalent bond forms when electrons are shared between atoms. The structure that results when atoms are joined together by covalent bonds is called a molecule. Unequal sharing of electrons creates regions of positive and negative charges in molecules. Slight attraction can develop between the oppositely charged regions of nearby molecules. Such intermolecular forces of attraction are called van der Waals forces.

2–2 Properties of Water

The water molecule (H_2O) is neutral. Yet, the oxygen end of the molecule has a slight positive charge, and the hydrogen end has a slight negative charge.

A molecule in which the charges are unevenly distributed is called a polar molecule. Polar molecules can attract each other. The attraction between the hydrogen atom on one water molecule and the oxygen atom on another water molecule is called a hydrogen bond. Cohesion is an attraction between molecules of the same substance. Adhesion is an attraction between molecules of different substances.

A mixture is a material composed of two or more elements or compounds that are physically mixed together—the substances are not chemically combined. A solution is a mixture in which all the components are evenly distributed throughout the mixture. In a solution, the substance that is dissolved is called the solute. The substance in which the solute dissolves is called the solvent. Water is the greatest solvent on Earth.

A water molecule can react to form ions. A water molecule (H_2O) can form a hydrogen ion (H^+) and a hydroxide ion (OH^-). The pH scale indicates the concentration of H^+ ions in a solution. Pure water has a pH of 7. An acid is any compound that forms H^+ ions in solution. Acidic solutions contain higher concentrations of H^+ ions than pure water. A base is a compound that produces OH^- ions in solution. Basic, or alkaline, solutions contain lower concentrations of H^+ ions than pure water and have pH values above 7.

2–3 Carbon Compounds

Organic chemistry is the study of all compounds that contain bonds between carbon atoms. Carbon compounds are also called organic compounds. Many of the molecules in living things are so large that they are known as macromolecules. Macromolecules are formed in a process called polymerization. Smaller units, called monomers, join together to form macromolecules, or polymers.

Four groups of organic compounds found in living things are carbohydrates, lipids, nucleic acids, and proteins. Carbohydrates are compounds made up of carbon, hydrogen, and oxygen atoms. Living things use carbohydrates as their main source of energy. Plants and some animals use carbohydrates in structures. Starches and sugars are examples of carbohydrates.

Lipids are made mostly from carbon and hydrogen atoms. Fats, oils, and waxes are lipids. Lipids are used in living things to store energy. Some lipids are important parts of biological membranes and waterproof coverings. Lipid molecules are made up of compounds called fatty acids and glycerol.

Nucleic acids contain hydrogen, oxygen, nitrogen, carbon, and phosphorus. Nucleotides are the monomers that make up nucleic acids. Each nucleotide consists of a 5-carbon sugar, a phosphate group, and a nitrogenous base. Nucleic acids store and transmit hereditary, or genetic, information. There are two kinds of nucleic acids: ribonucleic acid (RNA) and deoxyribonucleic acid (DNA).

Proteins contain nitrogen as well as carbon, hydrogen, and oxygen. Proteins are polymers of molecules called amino acids. Some proteins control the rate of reactions and regulate cell processes. Some are used to form bones and muscles. Others transport substances into or out of cells or help to fight disease.

2–4 Chemical Reactions and Enzymes

A chemical reaction is a process that changes one set of chemicals (reactants) into another set of chemicals (products). Chemical reactions always involve the breaking of bonds in reactants and the formation of new bonds in products.

Some chemical reactions release energy, and other reactions absorb energy. Chemical reactions that release energy often occur spontaneously. Every chemical reaction needs energy to get started, and that starting energy is called activation energy.

A catalyst is a substance that speeds up the rate of a chemical reaction. Catalysts work by lowering a reaction's activation energy. Enzymes are proteins that act as biological catalysts. Enzymes speed up chemical reactions by lowering activation energies. In an enzyme-catalyzed reaction, the reactants are known as substrates. The substrates bind to a site on the enzyme called the active site.

Name_____ Class_____ Date_____

Chapter 2 The Chemistry of Life

Section 2–1 The Nature of Matter (pages 35–39)

🔑 Key Concepts
- What three subatomic particles make up atoms?
- How are all of the isotopes of an element similar?
- What are the two main types of chemical bonds?

Atoms (page 35)

1. The basic unit of matter is called a(an) _____atom_____.
2. Describe the nucleus of an atom. It is the center of an atom, made up of protons and neutrons.
3. Complete the table about subatomic particles.

SUBATOMIC PARTICLES

Particle	Charge	Location in Atom
Proton	Positive	Nucleus
Neutron	Neutral	Nucleus
Electron	Negative	Surrounding nucleus

4. Why are atoms neutral despite having charged particles? Atoms have equal numbers of electrons and protons, and these subatomic particles have equal, but opposite, charges.

Elements and Isotopes (page 36)

5. What is a chemical element? A chemical element is a pure substance that consists entirely of one type of atom.
6. What does an element's atomic number represent? It represents the number of protons in an atom of the element.
7. Atoms of the same element that differ in the number of neutrons they contain are known as _____isotopes_____.
8. How are isotopes identified? Isotopes are identified by their mass number.
9. Why do all isotopes of an element have the same chemical properties? They have the same chemical properties because they have the same number of electrons.

Reading and Study Workbook 15

Chemical Compounds (page 37)

10. What is a chemical compound? A chemical compound is a substance formed by the
chemical combination of two or more elements in definite proportions.

_____

11. What does the formula for table salt indicate about that compound?
The formula for table salt, NaCl, indicates that the elements from which table salt

forms—sodium and chlorine—combine in a 1:1 ratio.

_____

_____

Chemical Bonds (pages 38–39)

12. What holds atoms in compounds together? Chemical bonds _____

13. Complete the table about the main types of chemical bonds.

CHEMICAL BONDS

Type	Formed when . . .
Covalent bond	Electrons are shared between atoms
Ionic bond	One or more electrons are transferred from one atom to another

14. What is an ion? An ion is an atom that is positively or negatively charged because it has lost or
gained electrons.

_____

15. Is the following sentence true or false? An atom that loses electrons has a negative
charge. _____false_____

16. The structure that results when atoms are joined together by covalent bonds is called
a(an) _____molecule_____.

17. Circle the letter of each sentence that is true about covalent bonds.

 a. When atoms share two electrons, it is called a double bond.

 b. In a water molecule, each hydrogen atom forms a single
covalent bond.

 c. Atoms can share six electrons and form a triple bond.

 d. In a covalent bond, atoms share electrons.

18. The slight attractions that develop between oppositely charged regions of nearby
molecules are called _____van der Waals forces_____.

Section 2–2 Properties of Water (pages 40–43)

Key Concepts
- Why are water molecules polar?
- What are acidic solutions? What are basic solutions?

The Water Molecule (pages 40–41)

1. Is the following sentence true or false? A water molecule is neutral. _____ true _____

2. Why is a water molecule polar? There is an uneven distribution of electrons between the oxygen and hydrogen atoms. _____

_____

3. Circle the letter of each sentence that is true about hydrogen bonds.

   a. A hydrogen bond is stronger than an ionic bond.

   b. The attraction between the hydrogen atom on one water molecule and the oxygen atom on another water molecule is an example.

   c. A hydrogen bond is stronger than a covalent bond.

   d. They are the strongest bonds that form between molecules.

4. Complete the table about forms of attraction.

FORMS OF ATTRACTION

Form of Attraction	Definition
Cohesion	Attraction between molecules of the same substance
Adhesion	Attraction between molecules of different substances

Solutions and Suspensions (pages 41–42)

5. What is a mixture? A mixture is a material composed of two or more elements or compounds that are physically mixed together but not chemically combined. _____

_____

6. A mixture of two or more substances in which the molecules of the substances are evenly mixed is called a(an) _____ solution _____.

7. The greatest solvent in the world is _____ water _____.

8. What is a suspension? A suspension is a mixture of water and nondissolved substances that are so small they do not settle out. _____

9. Complete the table about substances in solutions.

SUBSTANCES IN SOLUTIONS

Substance	Definition	Saltwater Solution
Solute	Substance that is dissolved	Table salt
Solvent	Substance in which the solute dissolves	Water

Acids, Bases, and pH (pages 42–43)

10. Why is water neutral despite the production of hydrogen ions and hydroxide ions?

It is neutral because the number of positive hydrogen ions produced is equal to the number of

negative hydroxide ions produced.

_____

11. What does the pH scale indicate? It indicates the concentration of H$^+$ ions in solution.

_____

12. On the pH scale below, indicate which direction is increasingly acidic and which is increasingly basic.

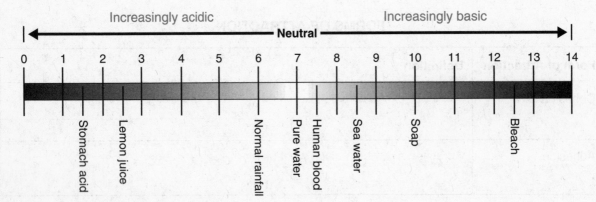

13. How many more H$^+$ ions does a solution with a pH of 4 have than a solution with a pH of 5? _____10 times_____

14. What is an acid? An acid is any compound that forms H$^+$ ions in solution.

15. Is the following sentence true or false? Strong bases have pH values ranging from 11 to 14. _____true_____

16. What are buffers? Buffers are weak acids or bases that can react with strong acids or bases to prevent sharp, sudden changes in pH.

_____

Name_____ Class_____ Date _____

Section 2–3 Carbon Compounds (pages 44–48)

🔑 **Key Concept**
- What are the functions of each group of organic compounds?

The Chemistry of Carbon (page 44)

1. How many valence electrons does each carbon atom have? Each carbon atom has four electrons.

2. What gives carbon the ability to form chains that are almost unlimited in length? A carbon atom can bond to other carbon atoms.

Macromolecules (page 45)

3. Many of the molecules in living cells are so large that they are known as macromolecules.

4. What is the process called by which macromolecules are formed? Polymerization

5. When monomers join together, what do they form? Polymers

6. What are four groups of organic compounds found in living things?
   a. Carbohydrates
   b. Lipids
   c. Nucleic acids
   d. Proteins

Carbohydrates (pages 45–46)

7. What atoms make up carbohydrates? Carbon, hydrogen, and oxygen atoms make up carbohydrates.

8. Circle the letter of each sentence that is true about carbohydrates.
   (a.) Starches and sugars are examples of carbohydrates.
   (b.) Living things use them as their main source of energy.
   c. The monomers in sugar polymers are starch molecules.
   (d.) Plants and some animals use them for strength and rigidity.

9. Single sugar molecules are also called monosaccharides.

10. Circle the letter of each monosaccharide.
    (a.) galactose   (c.) glucose
    b. glycogen   (d.) fructose

11. What are polysaccharides? They are large macromolecules formed from monosaccharides.
_____

12. How do plants and animals store excess sugar? Plants use a polysaccharide called plant
starch, whereas animals use a polysaccharide called glycogen.
_____

Lipids (pages 46–47)

13. What kinds of atoms are lipids mostly made of? They are made mostly of carbon and
hydrogen atoms.
_____

14. What are three common categories of lipids?

a. Fats _____   b. Oils _____   c. Waxes _____

15. Many lipids are formed when a glycerol molecule combines with compounds
called _____ fatty acids _____.

16. Circle the letter of each way that fats are used in living things.

(a.) As parts of biological membranes

(b.) To store energy

c. To give plants rigidity

(d.) As chemical messengers

17. Complete the table about lipids.

LIPIDS

Kind of Lipid	Description
Saturated	Each carbon atom in a lipid's fatty acid chain is joined to another carbon atom by a single bond.
Unsaturated	There is at least one carbon-carbon double bond in a fatty acid.
Polyunsaturated	A lipid's fatty acids contain more than one double bond.

Nucleic Acids (page 47)

18. Nucleic acids contain what kinds of atoms? They contain hydrogen, oxygen, nitrogen,
carbon, and phosphorus atoms.

19. The monomers that make up nucleic acids are known as ____nucleotides____.

20. A nucleotide consists of what three parts? It consists of a nitrogenous base, a phosphate
group, and a 5-carbon sugar.
_____

21. What is the function of nucleic acids in living things? <u>Nucleic acids store and transmit</u> <u>hereditary, or genetic, information.</u>

_____

22. What are two kinds of nucleic acids?

a. <u>Ribonucleic acid (RNA)</u>

b. <u>Deoxyribonucleic acid (DNA)</u>

Proteins (pages 47–48)

23. Proteins contain what kinds of atoms? <u>They contain nitrogen, carbon, hydrogen, and</u> <u>oxygen atoms.</u>

_____

24. Proteins are polymers of molecules called _____<u>amino acids</u>_____.

25. What are four roles that proteins play in living things?

a. <u>Some control the rate of reactions and regulate cell processes.</u>

b. <u>Some are used to form bones and muscles.</u>

c. <u>Some transport substances into or out of cells.</u>

d. <u>Some help to fight diseases.</u>

Reading Skill Practice

You can often increase your understanding of what you've read by making comparisons. A compare-and-contrast table helps you to do this. On a separate sheet of paper, make a table to compare the four groups of organic compounds you read about in Section 2–3. You might use the heads Elements, Functions, and Examples for your table. For more information about compare-and-contrast tables, see Organizing Information in Appendix A.

Students' tables should include the basic information about carbohydrates, lipids, nucleic acids, and proteins.

Section 2–4 Chemical Reactions and Enzymes (pages 49–53)

Key Concepts

- What happens to chemical bonds during chemical reactions?
- How do energy changes affect whether a chemical reaction will occur?
- Why are enzymes important to living things?

Chemical Reactions (page 49)

1. What is a chemical reaction? It is a process that changes one set of chemicals into another set of chemicals.

2. Complete the table about chemicals in a chemical reaction.

CHEMICALS IN A CHEMICAL REACTION

Chemicals	Definition
Reactants	The elements or compounds that enter into a chemical reaction
Products	The elements or compounds produced by a chemical reaction

3. Chemical reactions always involve changes in chemical _____bonds_____.

Energy in Reactions (page 50)

4. What is released or absorbed whenever chemical bonds form or are broken?
   _____Energy_____

5. What do chemical reactions that absorb energy need to occur? They need a source of energy.

6. Chemists call the energy needed to get a reaction started the ____activation energy____.

7. Complete the graph of an energy-releasing reaction by adding labels to show the energy of the reactants, the energy of the products, and the activation energy.

© Pearson Education, Inc., publishing as Pearson Prentice Hall.

Name_____ Class_____ Date _____

Enzymes (pages 51–52)

8. What is a catalyst? A catalyst is a substance that speeds up the rate of a chemical reaction.

_____

9. Proteins that act as biological catalysts are called _____enzymes_____.

10. What do enzymes do? Enzymes speed up chemical reactions that take place in cells.

_____

11. From what is part of an enzyme's name usually derived? It is derived from the reaction it catalyzes.

_____

Enzyme Action (pages 52–53)

12. The reactants of enzyme-catalyzed reactions are known as _____substrates_____.

13. Why are the active site and the substrates in an enzyme-catalyzed reaction often compared to a lock and key? The active site and the substrates have complementary shapes, and the fit is very precise.

_____

14. The binding together of an enzyme and a substrate forms a(an) _____enzyme-substrate complex_____.

15. How do most cells regulate the activity of enzymes? Most cells contain proteins that help turn key enzymes "on" or "off" at critical stages in the life of the cell.

_____

_____

© Pearson Education, Inc., publishing as Pearson Prentice Hall.

Vocabulary Review

Crossword Puzzle   *Use the clues below to fill in the spaces in the puzzle with the correct words.*

Across

1. element or compound that enters into a chemical reaction
4. process that changes one set of chemicals into another
7. positively charged subatomic particle
8. substance formed by the chemical combination of two or more elements in definite proportions
11. positively or negatively charged atom
12. carbon compound that stores and transmits genetic information
14. the center of an atom
16. bond formed when electrons are shared between atoms
17. macromolecule formed when monomers join together

Down

2. negatively charged subatomic particle
3. compound that produces hydroxide ions in solution
5. bond formed when one or more electrons are transferred from one atom to another
6. monomer of nucleic acid
9. monomer of protein
10. compound that forms hydrogen ions in solution
13. atom of same element that differs in number of neutrons compared with other atoms of the element
15. basic unit of matter

Summary

3–1 What Is Ecology?

Ecology is the scientific study of interactions among organisms and between organisms and their environment. Earth's organisms live in the biosphere. The biosphere consists of the parts of the planet in which all life exists. It includes land; water; and air, or atmosphere.

Ecology includes the study of all the different levels of life, ranging from the individual organism to the biosphere. Above the level of the individual organism is the species. A species is a group of organisms so similar to one another that they can breed together and produce fertile offspring. A group of individuals that belong to the same species and live in the same area is called a population. A collection of different populations that live together in an area is referred to as a community. An ecosystem includes all the organisms that live in a particular place, together with their physical environment. A group of ecosystems that have the same climate and similar dominant communities is called a biome.

Ecologists use three basic methods of research: observing, experimenting, and modeling. Observing often leads to questions and hypotheses. Experimenting can be used to test hypotheses. Experimenting may be done in a laboratory or in the natural world. Modeling helps ecologists understand complex processes.

3–2 Energy Flow

All organisms need to obtain energy from their environment to power life processes. Sunlight is the main energy source for life on Earth. Organisms that can capture energy from sunlight or chemicals and use that energy to produce food are called autotrophs, or producers. Only plants, some algae, and certain bacteria are producers. On land, plants are the main autotrophs.

The process in which autotrophs use light energy to make food is called photosynthesis. In photosynthesis, light provides the energy needed to turn carbon dioxide and water into oxygen and carbohydrates. The process in which autotrophs use chemical energy to produce carbohydrates is called chemosynthesis. Chemosynthesis is performed by only certain types of bacteria.

Organisms that rely on other organisms for their energy and food are called heterotrophs. Heterotrophs are also referred to as consumers. There are many different types of heterotrophs. Herbivores, such as cows, obtain energy by eating only plants. Carnivores, such as snakes, eat only animals. Omnivores, such as humans, eat both plants and animals. Detritivores, such as earthworms, feed on plant and animal remains and other dead matter. Decomposers, such as fungi, break down organic matter.

Energy flows through an ecosystem in one direction. It flows from the sun or from inorganic compounds, first to autotrophs and then to heterotrophs. A food chain is a series of steps in which organisms transfer energy by eating and being eaten. A food web links together all the food chains in an ecosystem. Each step in a food chain or food web is called a trophic level. Producers make up the first trophic level. Consumers make up higher trophic levels. Each consumer depends on the trophic level below it for energy.

An ecological pyramid is a diagram that shows the relative amounts of energy or matter contained within each trophic level in a food chain or food web. Types of ecological pyramids are energy pyramids, biomass pyramids, and pyramids of numbers. Energy pyramids show how much energy is available within each trophic level. Only about 10 percent of the energy available within one trophic level is transferred to organisms at the next trophic level.

Biomass pyramids show the biomass, or total amount of living tissue, within each trophic level. A pyramid of numbers shows the relative number of individual organisms at each trophic level.

3–3 Cycles of Matter

Matter, unlike energy, is recycled within and between ecosystems. Matter is passed from one organism to another and from one part of the biosphere to another through biogeochemical cycles. These cycles connect biological, geological, and chemical processes. Matter can cycle through the biosphere because biological systems do not use up matter; they only change it.

All living things require water to survive. Water cycles between the ocean, atmosphere, and land. Several different processes are involved in the water cycle, including evaporation and transpiration. Evaporation is the process in which water changes from a liquid to a gas. Transpiration is the process in which water evaporates from the leaves of plants.

All the chemical substances that an organism needs to survive are called nutrients. Like water, nutrients cycle within and between ecosystems.

The three most important nutrient cycles are the carbon, nitrogen, and phosphorus cycles. Carbon is a key ingredient of living tissue. Processes involved in the carbon cycle include photosynthesis and human activities such as burning. Nitrogen is needed by all organisms to build proteins. Processes involved in the nitrogen cycle include nitrogen fixation and denitrification. In nitrogen fixation, certain bacteria convert nitrogen gas into ammonia. In denitrification, other bacteria convert nitrogen compounds called nitrates back into nitrogen gas. Phosphorus is needed for molecules such as DNA and RNA. Most of the phosphorus in the biosphere is stored in rocks and ocean sediments. Stored phosphorus is gradually released into water and soil, where it is used by organisms.

The primary productivity of an ecosystem is the rate at which organic matter is created by producers. One factor that controls primary productivity is the amount of available nutrients. When an ecosystem is limited by a single nutrient that is scarce or cycles very slowly, this substance is called a limiting nutrient. If an aquatic ecosystem receives a large quantity of a limiting nutrient, there may be a sudden increase in the amount of algae, called an algal bloom.

Section 3–1 What Is Ecology? (pages 63–65)

🔑 **Key Concepts**
- What different levels of organization do ecologists study?
- What methods are used to study ecology?

Interactions and Interdependence (page 63)

1. What is ecology? It is the scientific study of interactions among organisms and between organisms and their environment.

_____

2. What does the biosphere contain? It contains the combined portions of the planet in which all of life exists, including land, water, and atmosphere.

_____

Levels of Organization (page 64)

3. Why do ecologists ask questions about events and organisms that range in complexity from an individual to the biosphere? They ask those questions to understand relationships within the biosphere.

_____

4. Complete the table about levels of organization.

LEVELS OF ORGANIZATION

Level	Definition
Species	A group of organisms so similar to one another that they can breed and produce fertile offspring
Population	A group of individuals that belong to the same species and live in the same area
Community	An assemblage of different populations that live together in a defined area
Ecosystem	A collection of all the organisms that live in a particular place, together with their physical environment
Biome	A group of ecosystems that have the same climate and dominant communities

5. What is the highest level of organization that ecologists study? The highest level is the entire biosphere itself.

Ecological Methods (page 65)

6. What are the three basic approaches scientists use to conduct modern ecological research?

a. Observing   b. Experimenting   c. Modeling

7. Why might an ecologist set up an artificial environment in a laboratory? An ecologist might do that to imitate and manipulate conditions that organisms would encounter in the natural world.

8. Why are many ecological phenomena difficult to study? They occur over long periods of time or on large spatial scales.

9. Why do ecologists make models? They make models to gain insight into complex phenomena.

10. Is the following sentence true or false? An ecological model may consist of a mathematical formula. _____true_____

Section 3–2 Energy Flow (pages 67–73)

Key Concepts
- Where does the energy for life processes come from?
- How does energy flow through living systems?
- How efficient is the transfer of energy among organisms in an ecosystem?

Producers (pages 67–68)

1. What is at the core of every organism's interaction with the environment?
   At the core is its need for energy to power life's processes.

2. What source of energy do organisms use if they don't use the sun's energy?
   Such organisms rely on the energy stored in inorganic chemical compounds.

3. What are autotrophs? They are organisms that can capture energy from sunlight or chemicals
   and use that energy to produce food.

4. Why are autotrophs also called producers? They make their own food.

5. What do autotrophs do during photosynthesis? They use light energy to power chemical
   reactions that convert carbon dioxide and water into oxygen and energy-rich carbohydrates such
   as sugars and starch.

6. For each of the following, write which kind of autotroph is the main producer.
   a. Land: Plants
   b. Upper layers of ocean: Algae
   c. Tidal flats and salt marshes: Photosynthetic bacteria

7. What is chemosynthesis? It is the process by which organisms use chemical energy to
   produce carbohydrates.

8. Where do bacteria that carry out chemosynthesis live? They live in remote places, such as
   volcanic vents on the deep-ocean floor and hot springs in Yellowstone Park. They also live in more
   common places, such as tidal marshes along the coast.

Consumers (pages 68–69)

9. Heterotrophs are also called _____consumers_____.

10. Plant and animal remains and other dead matter are collectively called
    _____detritus_____.

11. Complete the table about types of heterotrophs.

TYPES OF HETEROTROPHS

Type	Definition	Examples
Herbivore	Heterotroph that obtains energy by eating only plants	Cows, rabbits
Carnivore	Heterotroph that eats animals	Snakes, dogs, owls
Omnivore	Heterotroph that eats both plants and animals	Humans, bears, crows
Detritivore	Heterotroph that feeds on plant and animal remains and other dead matter	Mites, earthworms, snails, crabs
Decomposer	Heterotroph that breaks down organic matter	Bacteria, fungi

Feeding Relationships (pages 69–71)

12. How does energy flow through an ecosystem? It flows through an ecosystem in one direction, from the sun or inorganic chemicals to autotrophs (producers) and then to various heterotrophs (consumers).

13. Complete the table about feeding relationships.

FEEDING RELATIONSHIPS

Relationship	Description
Food Chain	A series of steps in which organisms transfer energy by eating and being eaten
Food Web	A network of complex interactions formed by the feeding relationships among the various organisms in an ecosystem

14. What does a food web link together? It links together all the food chains in an ecosystem.

15. What is a trophic level? It is a step in a food chain or a food web.

16. In a food web, what organisms make up the first trophic level? Producers

17. What does a consumer in a food chain depend on for energy? It depends on the trophic level below it.

Ecological Pyramids (pages 72–73)

18. What is an ecological pyramid? It is a diagram that shows the relative amounts of energy or matter contained within each trophic level in a food chain or food web.

19. Why is it that only part of the energy stored in one trophic level is passed on to the next level? That is because organisms use much of the energy that they consume for life processes.

Name_____ Class_____ Date_____

20. Complete the energy pyramid by writing the source of the energy for the food web and how much energy is available to first-, second-, and third-level consumers.

Heat

Heat

Heat

Heat

Heat

Light or chemical energy

0.1%   Third-level consumers

1%   Second-level consumers

10%   First-level consumers

100% Producers

21. What is biomass? It is the total amount of living tissue within a trophic level.

22. What does a biomass pyramid represent? It represents the amount of potential food available for each trophic level in an ecosystem.

23. What does a pyramid of numbers show? It shows the relative number of individual organisms at each trophic level.

24. Why can each trophic level support only about one tenth the amount of living tissue of the level below it? That is because each trophic level harvests only about one tenth of the energy from the level below.

Reading Skill Practice

When you read about complex topics, writing an outline can help you organize and understand the material. Outline Section 3–2 by using the headings and sub-headings as topics and subtopics and then writing the most important details under each topic. Do your work on a separate sheet of paper.

Students' outlines should have four major topics, matching the four blue headings of the section. Details include all the highlighted vocabulary terms as well as the important concepts discussed under each heading.

Section 3–3 Cycles of Matter (pages 74–80)

🔑 **Key Concepts**
- How does matter move among the living and nonliving parts of an ecosystem?
- How are nutrients important in living systems?

Introduction (page 74)

1. What are the four elements that make up over 95 percent of the body in most organisms? The four are oxygen, carbon, hydrogen, and nitrogen.

Recycling in the Biosphere (page 74)

2. How is the movement of matter through the biosphere different from the flow of energy? Unlike the one-way flow of energy, matter is recycled within and between ecosystems.

3. Matter moves through an ecosystem in _____biogeochemical cycles_____.

4. What do biogeochemical cycles connect? They connect biological, geological, and chemical aspects of the biosphere.

The Water Cycle (page 75)

5. Water can enter the atmosphere by evaporating from the leaves of plants in the process of _____transpiration_____.

6. Circle the letter of each process involved in the water cycle.
   (a.) precipitation   (b.) evaporation   (c.) runoff   d. fertilization

Nutrient Cycles (pages 76–79)

7. What are nutrients? They are all the chemical substances that an organism needs to sustain life.

8. What are the three nutrient cycles that play especially prominent roles in the biosphere?
   a. Carbon cycle
   b. Nitrogen cycle
   c. Phosphorus cycle

9. Why is carbon especially important to living systems? It is a key ingredient of living tissue.

10. What are three large reservoirs where carbon is found in the biosphere?
    a. As carbon dioxide gas in the _____atmosphere_____
    b. As dissolved carbon dioxide in the _____oceans_____
    c. As coal, petroleum, and calcium carbonate rock found _____underground_____

11. In what process do plants use carbon dioxide? Photosynthesis

Name_____ Class_____ Date _____

12. Why do all organisms require nitrogen? They require it to make amino acids, which in turn are used to build proteins.

13. What is nitrogen fixation? It is the process by which bacteria convert nitrogen into ammonia.

14. What is denitrification? It is the process by which some soil bacteria convert nitrates into nitrogen gas.

15. What role does denitrification play in the nitrogen cycle? The process releases nitrogen into the atmosphere once again.

16. Circle the letter of each sentence that is true about the phosphorus cycle.

(a.) Phosphate is released as rocks and sediments wear down.

(b.) Plants absorb phosphate from the soil or from water.

c. Phosphorus is abundant in the atmosphere.

d. Organic phosphate cannot move through food webs.

17. Why is phosphorus essential to living things? It forms part of important life-sustaining molecules such as DNA and RNA.

Nutrient Limitation (page 80)

18. What is the primary productivity of an ecosystem? It is the rate at which organic matter is created by producers.

19. If a nutrient is in short supply in an ecosystem, how will it affect an organism?
It will limit an organism's growth.

20. When is a substance called a limiting nutrient? It is called that when an ecosystem is limited by a single nutrient that is scarce or cycles very slowly.

21. Why do algal blooms occur? They occur when an excess of nutrients is available. As a result, producers grow and reproduce more quickly.

© Pearson Education, Inc., publishing as Pearson Prentice Hall.

Chapter 3   The Biosphere

Vocabulary Review

Matching   *In the space provided, write the letter of the definition that best matches each term.*

___d___ **1.** biosphere

___a___ **2.** community

___g___ **3.** autotroph

___i___ **4.** chemosynthesis

___b___ **5.** detritivore

___f___ **6.** biomass

___c___ **7.** transpiration

___j___ **8.** denitrification

___h___ **9.** biome

___e___ **10.** trophic level

a. collection of different populations that live together in an area

b. consumer that feeds on plant and animal remains and other dead matter

c. process in which water evaporates from the leaves of plants

d. combined parts of the planet in which all life exists

e. each step in a food chain or food web

f. total amount of living tissue within a trophic level

g. organism that can capture energy and use it to produce food

h. group of ecosystems that have the same climate and similar dominant communities

i. process in which organisms use chemical energy to produce carbohydrates

j. process in which bacteria convert nitrates into nitrogen gas

True or False   *Determine whether each statement is true or false. If it is true, write* true *in the space provided. If the statement is false, change the underlined word or words to make the statement true.*

___ecosystem___ **11.** A(An) <u>species</u> is a collection of all the organisms that live in a particular place, together with their physical environment.

___photosynthesis___ **12.** The process in which autotrophs use light energy to make carbohydrates is called <u>nitrogen fixation</u>.

___omnivores___ **13.** Heterotrophs that eat both plants and animals are referred to as <u>carnivores</u>.

___true___ **14.** A(An) <u>food web</u> links together all the food chains in an ecosystem.

___primary production___ **15.** The rate at which organic matter is created by producers is called the <u>limiting nutrient</u> of an ecosystem.

___true___ **16.** <u>Ecology</u> is the scientific study of interactions among organisms and between organisms and their environment.

___population___ **17.** A(An) <u>community</u> is a group of individuals that belong to the same species and live in the same area.

___producers___ **18.** Autotrophs are also called <u>consumers</u>.

___decomposers___ **19.** Organisms that break down organic matter are called <u>herbivores</u>.

___true___ **20.** The process in which water changes from a liquid to a gas is called <u>evaporation</u>.

© Pearson Education, Inc., publishing as Pearson Prentice Hall.

Summary

4–1 The Role of Climate

Weather is the condition of Earth's atmosphere at a particular time and place. Climate is the average yearly condition of temperature and precipitation in a region. Climate is caused by latitude, winds, ocean currents, and the shape and height of landmasses. Climate affects ecosystems, because all organisms have certain needs for temperature and other aspects of climate.

Temperature on Earth stays within a range suitable for life due to the greenhouse effect. The greenhouse effect is the trapping of heat by gases in the atmosphere.

Differences in latitude determine the angle of sunlight striking Earth. This angle determines how much of the surface is heated. Differences in heating result in three main climate zones: polar, temperate, and tropical. Unequal heating of Earth's surface also causes winds and ocean currents. Winds and currents move heat through the biosphere.

4–2 What Shapes an Ecosystem?

Organisms in ecosystems are influenced by both biological, or biotic, and physical, or abiotic, factors. Biotic factors include all the living things with which organisms interact. Abiotic factors include temperature, soil type, and other nonliving factors. The area where an organism lives is called its habitat. A habitat includes both biotic and abiotic factors.

A niche consists of all the physical and biological conditions in which an organism lives and the way in which the organism uses those conditions. For example, a niche includes what an organism eats and how it gets its food.

Organisms in communities may interact in one of three ways: competition, predation, or symbiosis. Competition occurs when organisms try to use the same resources, or necessities of life. Competition often results in one organism dying out.

This is the basis of the competitive exclusion principle. This principle states that no two species can occupy the same niche in the same habitat at the same time. Predation occurs when one organism (the predator) captures and eats another (the prey). Symbiosis occurs when two species live closely together in one of three ways: mutualism, commensalism, or parasitism. In mutualism, both species benefit from the relationship. In commensalism, one species benefits and the other is neither helped nor harmed. In parasitism, one species benefits by living in or on the other and the other is harmed.

As an ecosystem ages, older inhabitants gradually die out and new organisms move in. The series of predictable changes that occurs in a community over time is called ecological succession. Primary succession occurs on bare rock surfaces where no soil exists. The first species to live in an area of primary succession are called pioneer species. Secondary succession occurs when a disturbance changes a community without removing the soil.

4–3 Biomes

A biome is a group of communities on land that covers a large area and is characterized by certain soil and climate. Within a biome, there may be microclimates. A microclimate is the climate of a small area that differs from the climate around it. Species may be found over a large or small area, depending on their tolerance. Tolerance is the ability to survive and reproduce under difficult conditions.

There are ten major biomes: tropical rain forest, tropical dry forest, tropical savanna, desert, temperate grassland, temperate woodland and shrubland, temperate forest, northwestern coniferous forest, boreal forest (or taiga), and tundra. Each biome has a unique set of abiotic factors and a characteristic collection of organisms.

In tropical rain forests, the tops of tall trees form a covering, called the canopy. Shorter trees and vines form another layer, called the understory. In other forests, trees may be deciduous, meaning they shed their leaves during a particular season each year. Coniferous forests have trees called conifers that produce seed cones. Temperate forests have soils rich in humus, which forms from decaying leaves and makes soil fertile. Tundra is characterized by permafrost, a layer of permanently frozen subsoil. Some areas, such as mountains and polar ice caps, do not fall neatly into the major biomes.

4–4 Aquatic Ecosystems

Aquatic ecosystems are determined mainly by the depth, flow, temperature, and chemistry of the water. In many aquatic ecosystems, tiny organisms called plankton are common. Plankton consist of phytoplankton and zooplankton. Phytoplankton are single-celled algae that use nutrients in water to produce food. They form the base of many aquatic food webs. Zooplankton are animals that feed on phytoplankton.

Freshwater ecosystems include flowing-water ecosystems (rivers and streams), standing-water ecosystems (lakes and ponds), and freshwater wetlands (bogs and swamps). In wetlands, water either covers the soil or is present at or near the surface for at least part of the year.

Estuaries are wetlands formed where rivers meet the sea. They contain a mixture of fresh and salt water. Most of the food produced in estuaries enters food webs as tiny pieces of organic matter, or detritus. Salt marshes are temperate estuaries. Mangrove swamps are tropical estuaries.

Marine ecosystems are found in the ocean. The ocean can be divided into zones based on how much light penetrates the water. The photic zone is the well-lit upper layer of water where photosynthesis can occur. The aphotic zone is the permanently dark lower layer of water where only chemosynthesis can occur.

The ocean also can be divided into three zones based on depth and distance from shore: the intertidal zone, coastal ocean, and open ocean. The intertidal zone is exposed to the rise and fall of tides each day. This may lead to zonation, or horizontal distribution of different types of organisms. Coastal ocean is the relatively shallow border of water that surrounds the continents. Kelp forests and coral reefs are found in coastal ocean. Open ocean consists of the rest of the ocean. Nutrients are scarce in open ocean, and fish are the dominant animals. The ocean floor is the benthic zone. Organisms that live on the ocean floor are called benthos.

Section 4–1 The Role of Climate (pages 87–89)

⊂⊃ Key Concepts

- How does the greenhouse effect maintain the biosphere's temperature range?
- What are Earth's three main climate zones?

What Is Climate? (page 87)

1. How is weather different from climate? Weather is the day-to-day condition of Earth's
atmosphere at a particular time and place, whereas climate is the average, year-to-year conditions
of temperature and precipitation in a particular region.

_____

_____

2. What factors cause climate? Factors include the trapping of heat by the atmosphere, the
transport of heat by winds and ocean currents, and the amount of precipitation that results. The
shape and elevation of landmasses also contribute to global climate patterns.

_____

_____

The Greenhouse Effect (pages 87–88)

3. Circle the letter of the world's insulating blanket.

   a. oxygen   (b.) the atmosphere   c. the oceans   d. solar energy

4. Complete the illustration of the greenhouse effect by showing in arrows and words what happens to the sunlight that hits Earth's surface.

5. What effect do carbon dioxide, methane, and a few other atmospheric gases have on Earth's temperature? They trap heat energy and maintain Earth's temperature range.

6. What is the greenhouse effect? It is the retention of heat by the layer of greenhouse gases.

The Effect of Latitude on Climate (page 88)

7. Why does solar radiation strike different parts of Earth's surface at an angle that varies throughout the year? Earth is a sphere that is tilted on its axis.

8. Circle the letter of where the sun is almost directly overhead at noon all year.

   a. the North Pole   **b.** China   (**c.**) the equator   **d.** the South Pole

9. Why does Earth have different climate zones? It has different climate zones as a result of differences in latitude and thus the angle of heating.

10. Complete the table about Earth's three main climate zones.

MAIN CLIMATE ZONES

Climate Zone	Location	Climate Characteristics
Polar zones	Areas around North and South poles	Cold areas
Temperate zones	Between the polar zones and the tropics	Ranges from hot to cold, depending on the season
Tropical zones	Near the equator	Almost always warm

Heat Transport in the Biosphere (page 89)

11. What force drives winds and ocean currents? The unequal heating of Earth's surface drives winds and ocean currents.

12. The process in which water rises toward the surface in warmer regions is called _____upwelling_____ .

13. Circle the letter of each sentence that is true about ocean currents.

   (**a.**) Patterns of heating and cooling result in ocean currents.

   (**b.**) Ocean currents transport heat within the biosphere.

   (**c.**) Surface water moved by winds results in ocean currents.

   d. Ocean currents have no effect on the climate of landmasses.

Name_____ Class_____ Date_____

Section 4–2 What Shapes an Ecosystem? (pages 90–97)

Key Concepts
- How do biotic and abiotic factors influence an ecosystem?
- What interactions occur within communities?
- What is ecological succession?

Biotic and Abiotic Factors (page 90)

1. Complete the table about factors that influence ecosystems.

FACTORS THAT INFLUENCE ECOSYSTEMS

Type of Factor	Definition	Examples
Biotic factors	Biological influences on organisms within an ecosystem	Birds, trees, mushrooms, bacteria; the whole ecological community
Abiotic factors	Physical, or nonliving, factors that shape ecosystems	Climate, wind, nutrient availability, soil type, sunlight

2. What do the biotic and abiotic factors together determine? Together they determine the survival and growth of an organism and the productivity of the ecosystem in which the organism lives.

The Niche (pages 91–92)

3. What is a niche? A niche is the full range of physical and biological conditions in which an organism lives and the way in which the organism uses those conditions.

4. In what ways is food part of an organism's niche? Its niche includes the type of food the organism eats, how it obtains its food, and which other species use the organism for food.

5. Circle the letter of each sentence that is true about niches.
   a. Different species can share the same niche in the same habitat.
   b. No two species can share the same niche in the same habitat.
   c. Two species in the same habitat have to share a niche to survive.
   d. Different species can occupy niches that are very similar.

Community Interactions (pages 92–93)

6. When does competition occur? It occurs when organisms of the same or different species attempt to use an ecological resource in the same place at the same time.

7. What is a resource? It is any necessity of life, such as water, nutrients, light, food, or space.

8. What is often the result of direct competition in nature? There is often a winner and a loser, with the losing organism failing to survive.

9. What is the competitive exclusion principle? No two species can occupy the same niche in the same habitat at the same time.

10. What is predation? It is an interaction in which an organism captures and feeds on another organism.

11. When predation occurs, what is the organism called that does the killing and eating, and what is the food organism called? The one that kills and eats is called the predator, and the food organism is called the prey.

12. What is symbiosis? It is any relationship in which two species live closely together.

13. Complete the table about main classes of symbiotic relationships.

MAIN CLASSES OF SYMBIOTIC RELATIONSHIPS

Class	Description of Relationship
Mutualism	Both species benefit from the relationship.
Commensalism	One member of the association benefits, and the other is neither helped nor harmed.
Parasitism	One organism lives on or inside another organism and harms it.

14. The organism from which a parasite obtains nutritional needs is called a(an) _____host_____.

15. Circle the letter of each sentence that is true of parasites.
   a. They generally weaken but do not kill their host.
   b. They obtain all or part of their nutritional needs from the host.
   c. They neither help nor harm the host.
   d. They are usually smaller than the host.

Ecological Succession (pages 94–97)

16. What is ecological succession? It is the series of predictable changes that occurs in a community over time.

17. What is primary succession? It is succession that occurs on surfaces where no soil exists.

18. The first species to populate an area when primary succession begins are called _____pioneer species_____.

19. When a disturbance changes a community without removing the soil, what follows? Secondary succession follows.

20. An area that was once referred to as a climax community may appear to be permanent, but what might cause it to undergo change? Long-term climate change and introduction of nonnative species can profoundly affect such a community.

Section 4–3 Biomes (pages 98–105)

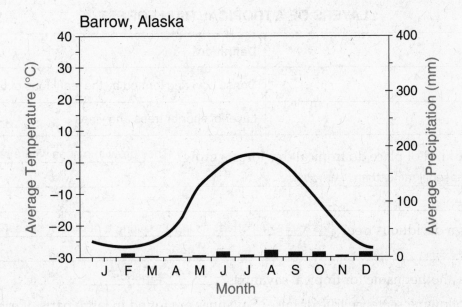 **Key Concept**
- What are the unique characteristics of the world's major biomes?

Introduction (page 98)

1. What is a biome? It is a complex of terrestrial communities that covers a large area and is characterized by certain soil and climate conditions and particular assemblages of plants and animals.

Biomes and Climate (page 98)

2. What does a climate diagram summarize? It summarizes a region's climate, including temperature and precipitation.

3. Complete the climate diagram by adding labels to the bottom and both sides of the graph to show what the responding variables are.

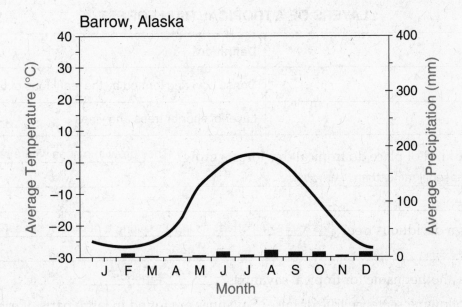

4. On a climate diagram, what does the line plot, and what do the vertical bars show? The line plots changes in temperature through the months of a year, and the vertical bars show the amount of precipitation each month of a year.

5. What is a microclimate? It is a climate within a small area that differs significantly from the climate around it.

The Major Biomes (pages 99–104)

6. Circle the letter of each sentence that is true about how each of the world's major biomes is defined.

(a.) Each is defined by a unique set of abiotic factors.

(b.) Each has a characteristic ecological community.

c. Each is defined by the country it is in.

(d.) Each is particularly defined by climate.

Use the map in Figure 4–11 on page 99 of your textbook to match the biome with its geographic distribution.

Biome	Geographic Distribution
_b_ 7. Tropical rain forest	a. Forest biome that occurs almost exclusively in the Northern Hemisphere
_c_ 8. Tundra	b. Biome that occurs on or near the equator
_a_ 9. Boreal forest	c. Biome that occurs near or above 60°N latitude

10. Complete the table about layers of a tropical rain forest.

LAYERS OF A TROPICAL RAIN FOREST

Layer	Definition
Canopy	Dense covering formed by the leafy tops of tall trees
Understory	Layer of shorter trees and vines

11. In what kind of place do tropical dry forests grow? They grow in places where rainfall is highly seasonal rather than year-round.

12. What is a deciduous tree? It is a tree that sheds its leaves during a particular season each year.

13. What is another name for tropical savannas? Grasslands

14. Is the following sentence true or false? Savannas are found in large parts of eastern Africa. true

15. Circle the letter of each sentence that is true about deserts.

a. They are hot, day and night.

(b.) The soils are rich in minerals but poor in organic material.

(c.) Cactuses and other succulents are dominant plants.

d. Reptiles are the only wildlife.

16. What amount of annual precipitation defines a desert biome? A desert biome is defined by having annual precipitation of less than 25 centimeters.

17. What factors maintain the characteristic plant community of temperate grasslands?
Periodic fires and heavy grazing by large herbivores maintain the characteristic plant community.

18. Why is fire a constant threat in temperate woodland and shrubland? Fire is a constant
threat because of the growth of dense, low plants that contain flammable oils.

19. Communities that are dominated by shrubs are also known as _____chaparral_____.

20. What kinds of trees do temperate forests contain? They contain a mix of deciduous and
coniferous trees.

21. What is a coniferous tree? It is a tree that produces seed-bearing cones, and most have
leaves shaped like needles.

22. What is humus? It is a material formed from decaying leaves and other organic matter that
makes soil fertile.

23. What is the geographic distribution of the northwestern coniferous forest?
It is found on the Pacific coast of northwestern United States and Canada, from northern
California to Alaska.

24. Boreal forests are also called _____taiga_____.

25. What are the seasons like in a boreal forest? Winters are bitterly cold, but summers are mild
and long enough to allow the ground to thaw.

26. Circle the letter of each sentence that is true about boreal forests.
   a. Dominant plants include spruce and fir.
   b. They have very high precipitation.
   c. They have soils that are rich in humus.
   d. Dominant wildlife includes moose and other large herbivores.

27. What is permafrost? It is a layer of permanently frozen subsoil.

28. What happens to the ground in tundra during the summer? It thaws to a depth of a few
centimeters and becomes soggy and wet.

29. Why are tundra plants small and stunted? The cycle of thawing and freezing of the ground
rips and crushes plant roots. Cold temperatures, high winds, the short growing season, and
humus-poor soils also limit plant height.

© Pearson Education, Inc., publishing as Pearson Prentice Hall.

Other Land Areas (page 105)

30. When are the polar regions cold? They are cold year-round.
_____

31. What plants and algae can be found in the polar ice regions? They include mosses and
lichens.

32. In the north polar region, what are the dominant animals? They include polar bears,
seals, insects, and mites.

33. The abiotic and biotic conditions of mountain ranges vary with _____elevation_____.

34. Number the sequence of conditions you would find as you moved from the base to the summit of a mountain. Number the conditions at the base *1*.

___4___ **a.** Stunted vegetation like that in tundra

___1___ **b.** Grassland

___3___ **c.** Forest of spruce and other conifers

___2___ **d.** Open woodland of pines

Reading Skill Practice

You can often increase your understanding of what you've read by making comparisons. A compare-and-contrast table helps you to do this. On a separate sheet of paper, make a table to compare the major land biomes you read about in Section 4–3. The characteristics that you might use to form the basis of your comparison could include a general description, abiotic factors, dominant plants, dominant wildlife, and geographic distribution. For more information about compare-and-contrast tables, see Organizing Information in Appendix A of your textbook.

Students' tables should include the basic information about the major land biomes discussed in the section.

Section 4–4 Aquatic Ecosystems (pages 106–112)

⊂▭⊃ **Key Concepts**
- What are the main factors that govern aquatic ecosystems?
- What are the two types of freshwater ecosystems?
- What are the characteristics of the different marine zones?

Introduction (page 106)

1. Aquatic ecosystems are primarily determined by what characteristics of the overlying water?

   a. _Depth_____

   b. _Flow_____

   c. _Temperature_____

   d. _Chemistry_____

2. What does the depth of the water determine? _It determines the amount of light that_ _organisms can receive._____

3. What does water chemistry primarily refer to? _It refers to the amount of dissolved_ _chemicals—especially salts, nutrients, and oxygen—on which life is dependent._____

Freshwater Ecosystems (pages 106–107)

4. What are the two main types of freshwater ecosystems?

   a. _Flowing-water ecosystems_____

   b. _Standing-water ecosystems_____

5. Where do flowing-water ecosystems originate? _They originate in mountains or hills, often_ _springing from an underground water source._____

6. How does the circulating water in a standing-water ecosystem affect the ecosystem? _The circulating water distributes heat, oxygen, and nutrients throughout the system._

7. What is plankton? _Plankton is a general term for the tiny, free-floating, weakly swimming_ _organisms that occur in both fresh water and salt water._____

8. Complete the table about kinds of plankton.

KINDS OF PLANKTON

Kind	Organisms	How Nutrition Obtained
Phytoplankton	Single-celled algae	Supported by nutrients in the water
Zooplankton	Planktonic animals	Feed on phytoplankton

9. What is a wetland? _It is an ecosystem in which water either covers the soil or is present at or_ _near the surface of the soil, at least part of the year._____

10. What is brackish water? It is a mixture of fresh and salt water._____

11. What are three main types of freshwater wetlands?

   a. Bogs_____ b. Marshes_____ c. Swamps_____

12. What distinguishes a marsh from a swamp? The presence of trees and shrubs in swamps
distinguishes marshes from swamps.

Estuaries (page 108)

13. What are estuaries? They are wetlands formed where rivers meet the sea._____

14. Tiny pieces of decaying plants and animals make up the _____detritus_____ that
provides food for organisms at the base of an estuary's food web.

15. Circle the letter of each sentence that is true about estuaries.

   a. Most primary production is consumed by herbivores.

   (b.) They contain a mixture of fresh water and salt water.

   c. Sunlight can't reach the bottom to power photosynthesis.

   (d.) They are affected by the rise and fall of ocean tides.

16. What are salt marshes? They are temperate-zone estuaries dominated by salt-tolerant
grasses above the low-tide line and by seagrasses under water.

17. What are mangrove swamps, and where are they found? They are coastal wetlands that
are widespread across tropical regions, including southern Florida and Hawaii.

Marine Ecosystems (pages 109–112)

18. What is the photic zone of the ocean? It is the well-lit upper layer._____

19. The permanently dark zone below the photic zone is called the
_____aphotic zone_____.

20. What are the three main vertical divisions of the ocean based on the depth and distance
from the shore?

   a. Intertidal zone

   b. Coastal ocean

   c. Open ocean

21. Circle the letter of each sentence that is true about the intertidal zone.

    (a.) Organisms there are exposed to extreme changes in their surroundings.

    (b.) The rocky intertidal zones exist in temperate regions.

    c. Organisms are battered by currents but not by waves.

    (d.) Competition among organisms often leads to zonation.

22. What is zonation? It is the prominent horizontal banding of organisms that live in a particular habitat.

23. What are the boundaries of the coastal ocean? It extends from the low-tide mark to the outer edge of the continental shelf.

24. Why is the coastal ocean often rich in plankton and many other organisms? The continental shelf is often shallow enough to fall mostly or entirely within the photic zone, where photosynthesis can occur.

25. A huge forest of giant brown algae in the coastal ocean is a(an) _____kelp forest_____.

26. Circle the letter of each sentence that is true about coral reefs.

    (a.) The coasts of Florida and Hawaii have coral reefs.

    (b.) The primary structure of coral reefs is made of the skeletons of coral animals.

    (c.) Almost all growth in a coral reef occurs within 40 meters of the surface.

    d. Only a few organisms are able to live near coral reefs.

27. What are the boundaries of the open ocean? It begins at the edge of the continental shelf and extends outward.

28. The benthic zone covers the ocean _____floor_____.

29. What are the boundaries of the benthic zone? It extends along the ocean floor from the coastal ocean through the open ocean.

30. Organisms that live attached to or near the bottom of the ocean are called _____benthos_____.

Name_____ Class_____ Date _____

Vocabulary Review

Multiple Choice   *In the space provided, write the letter of the answer that best completes each sentence.*

___b___ **1.** The situation in which atmospheric gases trap the sun's heat and keep Earth's surface warm is called
    a. weather.
    b. greenhouse effect.
    c. climate.
    d. primary succession.

___a___ **2.** Earth's three main climate zones are the result of
    a. latitude and angle of heating.
    b. precipitation and temperature.
    c. winds and ocean currents.
    d. air masses and mountains.

___d___ **3.** An example of a biotic factor is
    a. air temperature.
    b. availability of water.
    c. soil type.
    d. soil organisms.

___b___ **4.** The type of community interaction that involves one species living in or on another organism and harming the other organism is called
    a. commensalism.
    b. parasitism.
    c. competition.
    d. mutualism.

___c___ **5.** A group of communities on land that covers a large area and is characterized by certain soil and climate is referred to as a(an)
    a. niche.
    b. wetland.
    c. biome.
    d. habitat.

Completion   *Fill in the blanks with terms from Chapter 4.*

6. The average yearly condition of temperature and precipitation in a region is called ____climate____.

7. A physical factor that influences an ecosystem is called a(an) ____abiotic factor____.

8. When one organism captures and eats another it is referred to as ____predation____.

9. The first species to live in an area of primary succession are called ____pioneer species____.

10. The area where an organism lives is its ____habitat____.

11. The ability of organisms to survive and reproduce under less than optimal conditions is called ____tolerance____.

12. The well-lit upper layer of ocean water is known as the ____photic zone____.

13. Kelp forests are found in the ocean zone called ____coastal ocean____.

14. Organisms that live on the ocean floor are referred to as ____benthos____.

15. Zonation occurs in the ocean zone called the ____intertidal zone____.

Summary

5–1 How Populations Grow

Important characteristics of a population are its geographic distribution, density, growth rate, and age structure. Geographic distribution, or range, is the area a population inhabits. Density is the number of individuals per unit area, such as number of people per square kilometer.

Population growth rate refers to how quickly a population is increasing or decreasing in size. Growth rate depends on how many individuals are added to the population or removed from it. Individuals are added to a population through births and immigration, or movement of individuals into an area. Individuals are removed from a population through deaths and emigration, or movement of individuals out of an area.

If a population has unlimited resources and limited predators and disease, it will grow exponentially. Exponential growth is a pattern of growth represented by a J-shaped curve. Exponential growth occurs when the individuals in a population reproduce at a constant rate. As the population grows, the number of individuals who are reproducing keeps increasing. This causes the population to grow faster and faster.

Exponential growth does not continue in natural populations for very long. Resources eventually are used up, and population growth slows or stops. When population growth slows or stops following a period of exponential growth, the pattern of growth is called logistic growth. Logistic growth is represented by an S-shaped curve. The population size when the growth rate stops is called the carrying capacity. Carrying capacity is defined as the number of individuals of a particular species that a given environment can support.

5–2 Limits to Growth

A factor that causes population growth to decrease is referred to as a limiting factor. Limiting factors can be either density dependent or density independent.

Density-dependent limiting factors depend on population size. They operate most strongly when a population is large and dense. Density-dependent limiting factors include competition, predation, parasitism, and disease. When populations become crowded, organisms compete, or struggle, with one another for food, water, space, sunlight, and other life essentials. The more individuals in an area, the sooner they use up the available resources. In nature, populations are often controlled by predation. Just about every species serves as food for some other species. In a predator-prey relationship, a decrease in the prey population will be followed, sooner or later, by a decrease in the predator population. Parasites can also limit the size of a population because they live off their hosts, weakening them and causing disease. Like predators, parasites work most effectively if hosts are present in large numbers.

Density-independent limiting factors do not depend on population size. They include unusual weather, natural disasters, seasonal cycles, and human activities such as damming rivers. In response to such factors, many species have a rapid drop in population size.

5–3 Human Population Growth

Like the populations of many other organisms, the human population tends to increase with time. For most of human existence, the population grew slowly. Limiting factors such as scarce food kept population sizes low. About 500 years ago, the human population began growing faster. First agriculture and later industry increased the food supply and made life easier and safer. Improved sanitation and medicine reduced death rates. However, birthrates remained high in most places. This led to exponential growth of the human population. Exponential growth continues today in the human population as a whole.

The human population cannot keep growing exponentially forever, because Earth and its resources are limited. Factors such as war, starvation, and disease limit some human populations. Scientists also have identified a variety of social and economic factors that can affect human populations. The scientific study of human populations is called demography. Demographers study characteristics of human populations and try to predict how the populations will change over time.

Over the past century, population growth in the United States, Japan, and much of Europe slowed dramatically. Demographers call this shift in population growth rates the demographic transition. In the transition, first death rates fell, causing a temporary increase in population growth. Then, birthrates fell, causing population growth to slow. Most people live in countries that have not yet completed the demographic transition.

To help predict future population growth, demographers use models called age-structure diagrams. An age-structure diagram is a bar graph of the number of people in each age group in the population. To predict how the world's human population will grow, demographers also must consider factors such as the number of people with fatal diseases, including AIDS.

Section 5–1 How Populations Grow (pages 119–123)

🔑 Key Concepts

- What characteristics are used to describe a population?
- What factors affect population size?
- What are exponential growth and logistic growth?

Characteristics of Populations (page 119)

1. What are the four main characteristics of a population?

   a. Geographic distribution

   b. Density

   c. Growth rate

   d. Age structure

2. What is a population's geographic distribution? It is the area inhabited by the population.

3. Another term for geographic distribution is _____ range _____.

4. What is population density? It is the number of individuals per unit area.

Population Growth (page 120)

5. Circle the letter of each sentence that is true about populations.

   (a.) They can grow rapidly.

   (b.) They can decrease in size.

   (c.) They may stay the same size from year to year.

   d. They stay the same size until they disappear.

6. What three factors can affect population size?

   a. The number of births

   b. The number of deaths

   c. The number of individuals that enter or leave the population

7. If more individuals are born than die in any period of time, how will the population change? It will grow.

8. Complete the table about changes in population.

CHANGES IN POPULATION

Type of Change	Definition	Resulting Change in Size
Immigration	The movement of individuals into an area	The population grows
Emigration	The movement of individuals out of an area	The population decreases

9. What are two possible reasons individuals may immigrate into an area? Two possible reasons include searching for mates or searching for food.

Exponential Growth (page 121)

10. How will a population change if there is abundant space and food and if the population is protected from predators and disease? <u>The population will multiply, and the population size</u> <u>will increase.</u>

11. When does exponential growth occur? <u>It occurs when individuals in a population reproduce</u> <u>at a constant rate.</u>

12. What are three ways that a growth rate may be stated, or expressed? <u>It may be stated as a</u> <u>doubling time, a birthrate per female, or a percentage of growth per year.</u>

13. Under ideal conditions with unlimited resources, how will a population grow?
    <u>Such a population will grow exponentially.</u>

14. Complete the graph by drawing the characteristic shape of exponential population growth.

Exponential Growth of Bacterial Population

15. Is the following sentence true or false? Elephants never grow exponentially because their rate of reproduction is so slow. _____<u>false</u>_____

Logistic Growth (page 122)

16. Circle each sentence that is true about exponential growth.
    a. It continues until the organism covers the planet.
    b. It continues at the same rate as resources become less available.
    c. It does not continue in natural populations for very long.
    d. It continues in natural populations until the birthrate increases.

17. When resources become less available, how does population growth change?
    <u>It slows or stops.</u>

18. When does logistic growth occur? It occurs when a population's growth slows or stops
following a period of exponential growth.

_____

19. Circle the letter of each instance when a population's growth will slow down.

    a. The birthrate and death rate are the same.

    b. The birthrate is greater than the death rate.

    c. The rate of immigration is equal to the rate of emigration.

    d. The rate of emigration is less than the rate of immigration.

20. What is the carrying capacity of the environment for a particular species?
It is the largest number of individuals that the given environment can support.

_____

21. Complete the graph by drawing the characteristic shape of logistic population growth.

Logistic Growth of a Population

Name_____ Class_____ Date _____

Section 5–2 Limits to Growth (pages 124–127)

🔑 **Key Concept**
- What factors limit population growth?

Limiting Factors (pages 124–125)

1. What is a limiting factor? It is a factor that causes population growth to decrease._____
_____

2. A limiting nutrient is an example of a _____limiting factor_____.

Density-Dependent Factors (pages 125–126)

3. What is a density-dependent limiting factor? It is a limiting factor that depends on_____
population size._____

4. When do density-dependent factors become limiting? They become limiting only when_____
the population density reaches a certain level._____

5. When do density-dependent factors operate most strongly? They operate most strongly_____
when a population is large and dense._____

6. What are four density-dependent limiting factors?
   a. Competition_____   c. Parasitism_____
   b. Predation_____   d. Disease_____

7. When populations become crowded, what do organisms compete with one another for?
   They compete for food, water, space, sunlight, and other essentials of life._____
_____

8. The mechanism of population control in which a population is regulated by predation
   is called a(an) _____predator-prey relationship_____.

9. What are the prey and what are the predators in the predator-prey relationship on Isle
   Royale? The prey are moose, and the predators are wolves._____

10. Why does the wolf population on Isle Royale decline following a decline in the moose
    population? The wolf population declines because there is less for the wolves to feed upon._____
_____

11. How are parasites like predators? Like predators, parasites take nourishment at the expense_____
    of their hosts, often weakening them and causing disease or death._____
_____

Density-Independent Factors (page 127)

12. A limiting factor that affects all populations in similar ways, regardless of population size, is called a(an) _____density-independent limiting factor_____.

13. What are examples of density-independent limiting factors? Examples include unusual weather, natural disasters, seasonal cycles, and certain human activities, such as damming rivers and clear-cutting forests.

14. Circle the letter of each sentence that is true about changes caused by density-independent factors.

(a.) Most populations can adapt to a certain amount of change.

(b.) Periodic droughts can affect entire populations of grasses.

c. Populations never build up again after a crash in population size.

(d.) Major upsets in an ecosystem can lead to long-term declines in certain populations.

15. What is the characteristic response in the population size of many species to a density-independent limiting factor? The population size characteristically crashes.

Reading Skill Practice

A graph can help you understand comparisons of data at a glance. By looking carefully at a graph in a textbook, you can help yourself understand better what you have read. Look carefully at the graph in Figure 5–7 on page 126. What important concept does this graph communicate?

The graph shows that as the population of the predator increases, the population of the prey decreases, and vice versa. This cycle of predator and prey populations can be repeated indefinitely.

Section 5–3 Human Population Growth
(pages 129–132)

Key Concepts
- How has the size of the human population changed over time?
- Why do population growth rates differ in countries throughout the world?

Historical Overview (page 129)

1. How does the size of the human population change with time? It tends to increase with time.

2. Why did the population grow slowly for most of human existence? Life was harsh, and limiting factors kept population sizes low.

3. Circle the letter of each reason why the human population began to grow more rapidly about 500 years ago.
   - a. Improved sanitation and health care reduced the death rate.
   - b. Industry made life easier and safer.
   - c. The world's food supply became more reliable.
   - d. Birthrates in most places remained low.

Patterns of Population Growth (pages 130–131)

4. Why can't the human population keep growing exponentially forever? Earth and its resources are limited.

5. What is demography? It is the scientific study of human populations.

6. What factors help predict why the populations of some countries grow faster than others? Factors include birthrates, death rates, and the age structure of the populations.

7. The hypothesis that explains why population growth has slowed dramatically in the United States, Japan, and much of Europe is called the _____demographic transition_____.

8. Throughout much of human history, what have been the levels of birthrates and death rates in human societies? Human societies have had high birthrates and equally high death rates.

9. What factors lower the death rate? Advances in nutrition, sanitation, and medicine lower the death rate.

10. Is the following sentence true or false? Population growth depends, in part, on how many people of different ages make up a given population. _____true_____

11. Complete the flowchart about the demographic transition.

```
┌─────────────────────────────────────────────────────────────┐
│ Changes brought about by modernization lower the __death__ rate. │
└─────────────────────────────────────────────────────────────┘
                              ↓
┌─────────────────────────────────────────────────────────────┐
│ Births greatly exceed deaths, resulting in rapid population __increases__. │
└─────────────────────────────────────────────────────────────┘
                              ↓
┌─────────────────────────────────────────────────────────────┐
│ As modernization continues, the birthrate __falls__ and population growth __decreases__. │
└─────────────────────────────────────────────────────────────┘
                              ↓
┌─────────────────────────────────────────────────────────────┐
│ The birthrate falls to meet the death rate, and population growth __stops__. │
└─────────────────────────────────────────────────────────────┘
```

12. Circle the letter of each sentence that is true about human population growth.

a. The demographic transition is complete in China and India.

b. The worldwide human population is still growing exponentially.

c. Most people live in countries that have not yet completed the demographic transition.

d. The demographic transition has happened in the United States.

13. What do age-structure diagrams graph? They graph the numbers of individuals in different age groups in the population.

14. What do the age structures of the United States and of Rwanda predict about the population growth of each country? The age structure in the United States predicts a slow but steady growth rate for the near future. The age structure in Rwanda predicts a population that will double in about 30 years.

Future Population Growth (page 132)

15. What may cause the growth rate of the world population to level off or even slow down? That may happen if countries that are currently growing rapidly move toward the demographic transition.

16. What do many ecologists suggest will happen if the growth in human population does not slow down? There could be serious damage to the environment as well as to the global economy.

Chapter 5   Populations

Vocabulary Review

Labeling Diagrams   *Label the diagrams of population growth.*

Number of individuals at this time

3. ___carrying___
___capacity___

Pattern of Growth: 1. ___exponential___

Pattern of Growth: 2. ___logistic___

True or False   *Determine whether each statement is true or false. If it is true, write* true *in the space provided. If the statement is false, change the underlined word or words to make the statement true.*

___true___ **4.** <u>Population density</u> is the number of individuals per unit area.

___decrease___ **5.** Emigration causes population size to <u>increase</u>.

___emigration___ **6.** The movement of individuals out of an area is called <u>immigration</u>.

___limiting factor___ **7.** A(An) <u>population profile</u> is any factor that causes population growth to decrease.

___dependent___ **8.** Density-<u>independent</u> limiting factors include competition and parasitism.

___true___ **9.** A predator-prey relationship is a(an) <u>density-dependent</u> limiting factor.

___true___ **10.** The scientific study of human populations is called <u>demography</u>.

Answering Questions   *Write one or more sentences to answer each question.*

11. How do birth and death rates change when a population goes through the demographic transition? First, the death rate falls, causing the population growth rate to increase. Then, the birthrate falls, causing the population growth rate to decrease.

12. What do demographers try to predict using age-structure diagrams? Using age-structure diagrams, demographers try to predict future population growth.

13. What does the term *geographic distribution* mean? Geographic distribution means the area inhabited by a population.

14. When does exponential growth occur? Exponential growth occurs when a population has unlimited resources, limited predators and disease, and a constant rate of reproduction.

15. Which countries have completed the demographic transition? The United States, Japan, and much of Europe are countries that have completed the demographic transition.

| Chapter 6   Humans in the Biosphere |

Summary

6–1 A Changing Landscape

All organisms on Earth share limited resources. They also depend on ecological processes, such as the water cycle, that sustain the resources. To protect these resources and processes, we must know how humans interact with the biosphere. Humans have become the most important source of environmental change. They affect the biosphere through hunting and gathering, agriculture, industry, and urban development.

Prehistoric hunters and gatherers changed their environments by hunting some species of animals to extinction. When humans began the practice of farming, or agriculture, they could produce more food. More food enabled the development of cities, and cities produced wastes. Advances in agriculture occurred later. These advances included the development of pesticides and monoculture—the planting of large fields with the same crop year after year. Advances such as these dramatically increased the world's food supply, an event called the green revolution. Agricultural advances also created problems, such as pollution from pesticides. After the Industrial Revolution, machines and factories increased the human impact on the biosphere. Industry used more resources and produced more pollution than ever before.

6–2 Renewable and Nonrenewable Resources

Environmental resources may be renewable or nonrenewable. Renewable resources, such as forests or water, can regrow if they are alive or be replaced by biochemical cycles if they are nonliving. Nonrenewable resources, such as fossil fuels, cannot be replaced by natural processes. Environmental

resources are threatened by human activities. Sustainable development of renewable resources means using the resources without using them up.

Plowing removes roots that hold soil in place. This causes soil erosion. Soil erosion is the wearing away of surface soil by water and wind. In some areas, plowing and other factors have turned good soils into deserts. This process is called desertification. Sustainable development of soils includes contour plowing, which reduces soil erosion.

Forests provide wood, oxygen, and other important resources. Forests are being used up rapidly. Loss of forests is called deforestation. Sustainable development of forests includes planting trees to replace those that are cut down. Fish populations are declining because of overfishing. Aquaculture is the raising of aquatic animals for food. It is helping to sustain fish resources.

Smog is a mixture of chemicals that forms a gray-brown haze in the air. It is caused mostly by car exhausts and industrial emissions. Smog is considered a pollutant. A pollutant is a harmful material that can enter the biosphere through land, air, or water. Burning fossil fuels also releases compounds that combine with water vapor in air and produce acid rain. Acid rain kills plants and causes other damage. Emission controls have improved air quality and reduced acid rain.

Water supplies can be polluted by sewage or discarded chemicals. Sustainable development of water includes protecting the water cycle. Wetlands play an important role in the water cycle. Thus, protecting wetlands is one way to sustain water resources.

6–3 Biodiversity

Biological diversity, or biodiversity, is the sum of the genetically based variety of all organisms in the biosphere. Ecosystem diversity is the variety of habitats, communities, and ecological processes in ecosystems. Species diversity is the number of different species in the biosphere.

Genetic diversity refers to all the different forms of genetic information carried by all organisms living on Earth today. Biodiversity is one of Earth's greatest natural resources. Diverse species have provided humans with foods, industrial products, and medicines.

Humans reduce biodiversity by destroying habitats, hunting species to extinction, introducing toxic compounds into food webs, and introducing foreign species into new environments. Extinction occurs when a species disappears from all or part of its range. An endangered species is a species whose population size is declining in a way that places it in danger of extinction. As humans destroy habitats, the species that once lived in the habitats die out. Development often splits habitats into separate pieces. This process is called habitat fragmentation. The smaller the pieces of habitat, the less likely that their species will be able to survive.

Pollution can seriously threaten biodiversity. Toxic compounds build up in the tissues of organisms. Concentrations of toxins increase in organisms at higher trophic levels in a food chain or food web. This is called biological magnification.

Plants and animals introduced from other areas are an important threat to biodiversity. Introduced organisms often become invasive species. Invasive species increase rapidly because their new habitat lacks the parasites and predators that control their population "back home."

Conservation is the wise management of natural resources. Conservation focuses on protecting entire ecosystems as well as single species. Protecting entire ecosystems ensures that many species are preserved.

6–4 Charting a Course for the Future

The ozone layer is an area of relatively great concentration of ozone gas high in the atmosphere. The layer protects Earth from harmful radiation. The ozone layer has been damaged by compounds in certain products. The compounds have now been banned.

Global warming refers to the increase in average temperature of the biosphere. It is mainly due to humans burning fossil fuels. Burning adds gases to the atmosphere, causing the atmosphere to retain more heat. Continued global warming may lead to rising sea levels and coastal flooding, among other environmental changes.

People can help maintain the health of the biosphere by conserving resources. For example, they can avoid using more water than necessary. They can also reuse or recycle trash.

Section 6–1 A Changing Landscape (pages 139–143)

Key Concept
• What types of human activities can affect the biosphere?

Earth as an Island (page 139)

1. Increasing demands on what resources come with a growing human population?
   There are increasing demands on Earth's air, water, land, and living things.

Human Activities (page 140)

2. Is the following sentence true or false? Human activity uses as much energy as all of Earth's other multicellular species combined. _____true_____

3. What four human activities have transformed the biosphere?
   a. Hunting and gathering
   b. Agriculture
   c. Industry
   d. Urban development

Hunting and Gathering (page 140)

4. How did prehistoric hunters and gatherers change the environment? They may have caused major extinction of some animals.

Agriculture (pages 141–142)

5. What is agriculture? It is the practice of farming.

6. Why was the spread of agriculture an important event in human history?
   It provided people with one of their most basic needs, a dependable supply of food.

7. What social changes came with the cultivation of both plants and animals?
   Humans began to gather in large settlements, enabling the development of elements of civilization.

8. What changes in agriculture occurred in the 1800s as a result of advancements in science and technology? Irrigation, new crop varieties, and the invention of farm machines for plowing, planting, and harvesting helped farmers increase their yields tremendously.

_____

9. What was the green revolution? It was the effort in the 1950s by governments and scientists to increase food production through new, intensive farming practices that greatly increased yields of rice, wheat, and other crops.

_____

10. What is the farming method called monoculture? It calls for large fields to be cleared, plowed, and planted with a single crop year after year.

_____

11. Circle the letter of each benefit of the green revolution to human society.
   (a.) It helped prevent food shortages.
   b. China and India depleted water supplies.
   (c.) It increased food production.
   d. Global food production was cut in half.

Industrial Growth and Urban Development (page 143)

12. What occurred during the Industrial Revolution of the 1800s? It added machines and factories to civilization.

13. From what resources do we obtain most of the energy to produce and power the machines we use? We obtain most of it from fossil fuels, including coal, oil, and natural gas.

14. The continued spread of suburban communities across the American landscape is referred to as _____suburban growth_____.

15. How does suburban growth place stress on plant and animal populations? Growth consumes farmland and natural habitats.

Section 6–2 Renewable and Nonrenewable Resources (pages 144–149)

🔑 Key Concepts
- How are environmental resources classified?
- What effects do human activities have on natural resources?

Introduction (page 144)

1. How were the commons in an old English village destroyed? People added more and more cattle, and they would not remove cattle because they did not want to sacrifice profits. They kept adding cattle until, eventually, the commons were destroyed by overgrazing.

2. What is meant by the phrase the "tragedy of the commons"? This phrase expresses the idea that any resource that is open to everyone will eventually be destroyed because everyone can use the resource but no one is responsible for preserving it.

Classifying Resources (page 144)

3. Complete the table about types of environmental resources.

TYPES OF ENVIRONMENTAL RESOURCES

Type of Resource	Definition	Examples
Renewable resources	Resources that can regenerate and are therefore replaceable	Trees, fresh water
Nonrenewable resources	Resources that cannot be replenished by natural processes	Fossil fuels

Sustainable Development (page 145)

4. What is sustainable development? It is a way of using natural resources without depleting them.

5. How do human activities affect renewable resources? Human activities affect the supply and quality of renewable resources, including resources such as land, forests, fisheries, air, and water.

6. What are five characteristics of sustainable use?
   a. Stability
   b. Flexibility
   c. Appropriate technology
   d. Efficiency
   e. Productivity

Land Resources (page 145)

7. What is fertile soil? It is a mixture of humus, sand, clay, and rock particles.

8. The uppermost layer of soil is called _____topsoil_____.

9. What is soil erosion? It is the wearing away of surface soil by water and wind.

10. How does plowing the land increase the rate of soil erosion? It removes the roots of plants that hold soil in place.

11. The conversion of a previously soil-rich, productive area into a desert is called _____desertification_____.

12. What can cause desertification? It can be caused by a combination of farming, overgrazing, and drought.

Forest Resources (page 146)

13. Why have forests been called the "lungs of the Earth"? They remove carbon dioxide and produce oxygen.

14. Why are forests in Alaska and the Pacific Northwest called old-growth forests? They have never been cut.

15. What is deforestation, and how does it affect soil? Deforestation is the loss of forests. It can lead to severe erosion as soil is exposed to heavy rains.

Fishery Resources (page 147)

16. For what resources are Earth's oceans particularly valuable? They are particularly valuable for the food resources they contain.

17. The practice of harvesting fish faster than they can reproduce is called _____overfishing_____.

18. What is one approach to sustainable development of fisheries? One approach is to regulate the catch of fish populations stressed by overfishing.

19. What is aquaculture? It is the raising of aquatic animals for human consumption.

Air Resources (page 148)

20. What is smog? It is a mixture of chemicals that occurs as a gray-brown haze in the atmosphere.

21. What is a pollutant? It is a harmful material that can enter the biosphere through the land, air, or water.

© Pearson Education, Inc., publishing as Pearson Prentice Hall.

22. How does the burning of fossil fuels affect air quality? The burning of fossil fuels can
release pollutants that cause smog and other problems in the atmosphere.

_____

23. Microscopic particles of ash and dust in the air that can cause health problems are
called _____particulates_____.

24. What does acid rain contain that kills plants and harms soil? It contains nitric and
sulfuric acids.

25. Complete the illustration by writing the names of the processes that lead to the formation of acid rain.

Freshwater Resources (page 149)

26. Why are protecting water supplies from pollution and managing demand for water
major priorities? The total supply of fresh water is limited.

_____

27. What is domestic sewage, and how does it threaten water supplies? It is wastewater from
sinks and toilets. It encourages the growth of algae and bacteria in aquatic habitats. It also
contains microorganisms that can spread disease among humans and animals.

_____

28. How can protecting forests ensure sustainable use of water resources?
Forests help to purify water that seeps into the ground or runs off into rivers and lakes.

_____

29. Why can conservation in agriculture save large amounts of water? More than
three quarters of all the water consumed in this country is used in agriculture.

_____

Section 6–3 Biodiversity (pages 150–156)

🔑 **Key Concepts**
- What is the value of biodiversity?
- What are the current threats to biodiversity?
- What is the goal of conservation biology?

The Value of Biodiversity (page 150)

1. What is biodiversity? It is the sum total of the genetically based variety of all organisms in the biosphere.

2. Complete the table about diversity.

DIVERSITY IN THE BIOSPHERE

Type of Diversity	Definition
Ecosystem diversity	The variety of habitats, communities, and ecological processes in the living world
Species diversity	The number of different species in the biosphere
Genetic diversity	The sum total of all the different forms of genetic information carried by all organisms living on Earth today

3. Why is biodiversity one of Earth's greatest natural resources? Species of many kinds have provided us with foods, industrial products, and medicines, including painkillers, antibiotics, heart drugs, antidepressants, and anticancer drugs.

Threats to Biodiversity (page 151)

4. What are four ways that human activity can reduce biodiversity?
   a. Altering habitats
   b. Hunting species to extinction
   c. Introducing toxic compounds into food webs
   d. Introducing foreign species to new environments

5. When does extinction occur? It occurs when a species disappears from all or part of its range.

6. A species whose population size is declining in a way that places it in danger of extinction is called a(an) _____ endangered species _____.

7. Why does a declining population make a species more vulnerable to extinction? As populations decline, there is less genetic diversity. _____

_____

Habitat Alteration (page 151)

8. The process of splitting a habitat into small pieces is called _____ habitat fragmentation _____.

9. What is the relationship between biological "island" size and the number of species that can live there? The smaller the "island," the fewer species that can live there, the smaller their populations can be, and the more vulnerable they are to further disturbance or climate change. _____

_____

_____

Demand for Wildlife Products (page 151)

10. Why are species hunted? Some are hunted for meat, fur, or hides. Others are hunted because people think that the body parts have medical properties. _____

_____

Pollution (page 152)

11. What is DDT? It was one of the first widely used pesticides. _____

12. What two properties of DDT make it hazardous over the long term? First, it is nonbiodegradeable. Second, when DDT is picked up by organisms, they do not eliminate it from their bodies. _____

_____

13. What is biological magnification? It is the increase in concentration of a harmful substance in organisms at higher trophic levels in a food chain or food web. _____

_____

Introduced Species (page 153)

14. Plants and animals that have migrated to places where they are not native are called _____ invasive species _____.

15. Why do invasive species reproduce rapidly and increase their populations? Their new habitat lacks the parasites and predators that control their populations back home. _____

_____

Conserving Biodiversity (pages 154–156)

16. What is conservation? It is the wise management of natural resources, including the preservation of habitats and wildlife.

17. What is the purpose of conservation biology? It seeks to protect biodiversity.

18. What does protecting an ecosystem ensure? It ensures that the natural habitats and the interactions of many different species are preserved at the same time.

19. What are some of the challenges that conservationists face? Protecting resources requires people to change the way they earn their living. For example, restrictions on fishing impact fishers.

Reading Skill Practice

Writing a summary can help you remember the information you have read. When you write a summary, write only the important points. Write a summary of the information in Section 6–3. Your summary should be shorter than the text on which it is based.

Students' summaries will vary, though all should include descriptions of biodiversity and the major threats to biodiversity.

Section 6–4 Charting a Course for the Future
(pages 157–160)

⊂⊃ **Key Concept**
- What are two types of global change of concern to biologists?

Ozone Depletion (pages 157–158)

1. Where is ozone concentrated in the atmosphere? It is concentrated between 20 and 50 kilometers above Earth's surface.

2. What is causing the problem of ozone depletion? It is caused by compounds called chlorofluorocarbons, or CFCs, which were once widely used as propellants in aerosol cans, in the production of plastic foams, and as coolants in refrigerators, freezers, and air conditioners.

Global Climate Change (page 159)

3. What is global warming? It is the increase in the average temperature of the biosphere.

4. What is the most widely accepted hypothesis about the cause of global warming? Human activities have, at least in part, caused global warming by adding carbon dioxide and other greenhouse gases such as methane to the atmosphere.

5. If global warming continues at the current rate, how might sea level be affected? Sea level could rise enough to flood some low-lying coastal areas.

The Value of a Healthy Biosphere (page 160)

6. What goods and services does a healthy biosphere provide to us? Goods include the raw materials for foods, medicines, and many other products. Services include temperature control, water purification, and soil formation.

7. What is the first step in charting a course that will improve living conditions without harming the environment? The first step is understanding that humans are part of the ecosystems they inhabit.

Chapter 6   Humans in the Biosphere

Vocabulary Review

Matching   *In the space provided, write the letter of the definition that best matches each term.*

<u>c</u>   **1.** monoculture

<u>e</u>   **2.** green revolution

<u>g</u>   **3.** renewable resource

<u>a</u>   **4.** soil erosion

<u>h</u>   **5.** smog

<u>j</u>   **6.** acid rain

<u>b</u>   **7.** sustainable development

<u>i</u>   **8.** endangered species

<u>d</u>   **9.** habitat fragmentation

<u>f</u>   **10.** global warming

a. wearing away of surface soil by water and wind

b. way of using resources without using them up

c. practice in which large fields are planted with a single crop year after year

d. splitting of a habitat into pieces

e. dramatic increase in the world's food supply due to agricultural advances

f. increase in the average temperature of the biosphere

g. resource that can regenerate or be replenished

h. mixture of chemicals that occurs as a gray-brown haze in the atmosphere

i. species in danger of extinction

j. rain that forms from pollutants and kills plants

Completion   *Fill in the blanks with terms from Chapter 6.*

11. The raising of aquatic animals for human food is called _____aquaculture_____.

12. The loss of forests is referred to as _____deforestation_____.

13. A harmful material that can enter the biosphere through the land, air, or water is a(an) _____pollutant_____.

14. The process in which good soils are turned into deserts is called _____desertification_____.

15. When a species disappears from all or part of its range, _____extinction_____ has occurred.

16. The wise management of natural resources is called _____conservation_____.

Writing Descriptions   *Describe each type of diversity in the space provided.*

17. biological diversity ___Biological diversity, or biodiversity, is the sum of the genetically___ ___based variety of all organisms in the biosphere.___

18. ecosystem diversity ___Ecosystem diversity is the variety of habitats, communities, and___ ___ecological processes in ecosystems.___

19. species diversity ___Species diversity is the number of different species in the biosphere.___

20. genetic diversity ___Genetic diversity refers to all the different forms of genetic information carried___ ___by all organisms living on Earth today.___

Chapter 7   Cell Structure and Function

Summary

7–1 Life Is Cellular

Since the 1600s, scientists have made many discoveries that have showed how important cells are in living things. Such discoveries are summarized in the cell theory. The cell theory states:

- All living things are composed of cells.
- Cells are the basic units of structure and function in living things.
- New cells are produced from existing cells.

All cells have two characteristics in common. They are surrounded by a barrier called a cell membrane, and they contain the molecule that carries biological information—DNA.

Cells fall into two broad categories, depending on whether they contain a nucleus. The nucleus is a large membrane-enclosed structure that contains the cell's genetic material in the form of DNA. The nucleus controls many of the cell's activities. Prokaryotic cells have genetic material that is not contained in a nucleus. Bacteria are prokaryotes. Eukaryotic cells contain a nucleus in which their genetic material is separated from the rest of the cell. Plants, animals, fungi, and protists are eukaryotes.

7–2 Eukaryotic Cell Structure

Cell biologists divide the eukaryotic cell into two major parts: the nucleus and the cytoplasm. The cytoplasm is the portion of the cell outside the nucleus. Eukaryotic cells contain structures known as organelles.

The nucleus contains nearly all the cell's DNA and with it the coded instructions for making proteins. The nucleus is surrounded by a nuclear envelope composed of two membranes. Inside the nucleus is granular material called chromatin. Most nuclei also contain a small, dense region known as the nucleolus.

Ribosomes are small particles of RNA and protein found throughout the cytoplasm. Proteins are assembled on ribosomes. Eukaryotic cells contain an internal membrane system known as the endoplasmic reticulum, or ER. The ER is where lipid components of the cell membrane are assembled, along with proteins and other materials that are exported from the cell. The portion of the ER involved in the synthesis of proteins is called rough ER. Smooth ER, which does not contain ribosomes, is involved in the making of lipids. The function of the Golgi apparatus is to modify, sort, and package proteins and other materials from the ER for storage in the cell or secretion outside the cell.

Other organelles include lysosomes, vacuoles, mitochondria, and chloroplasts. Mitochondria are organelles that convert the chemical energy stored in food into compounds that are more convenient for the cell to use. Chloroplasts are organelles that capture the energy from sunlight and convert it into chemical energy.

Eukaryotic cells have a structure called the cytoskeleton that helps support the cell. The cytoskeleton is a network of protein filaments that helps the cell to maintain its shape. The cytoskeleton is also involved in movement.

7–3 Cell Boundaries

All cells are surrounded by a thin, flexible barrier known as the cell membrane. The cell membrane regulates what enters and leaves the cell and also provides protection and support. The composition of nearly all cell membranes is a double-layered sheet called a lipid bilayer. Many cells also produce a strong supporting layer around the membrane known as the cell wall. Cell walls are present in plants, algae, fungi, and many prokaryotes. The main function of the cell wall is to provide support and protection for the cell.

One of the most important functions of the cell membrane is to regulate the movement of dissolved molecules from the liquid on one side of the membrane to the liquid on the other side. The cytoplasm of a cell contains a solution of many different substances in water. The concentration of a solution is the mass of solute in a given volume of solution.

In a solution, particles move constantly. Particles tend to move from an area where they are more concentrated to an area where they are less concentrated, a process called diffusion. When the concentration of a solute is the same throughout a solution, the solution has reached equilibrium. Because diffusion depends upon random particle movements, substances diffuse across membranes without requiring the cell to use energy. Water passes quite easily across most membranes. Osmosis is the diffusion of water through a selectively permeable membrane. Many cell membranes have protein channels that allow certain molecules to cross the membranes. In such cases, the cell membrane protein is said to facilitate, or help, the diffusion of the molecules across the membrane. This process is called facilitated diffusion. It does not require use of the cell's energy.

Active transport does require the cell's energy. In active transport, cells move materials from one side of a membrane to the other side against the concentration difference. Types of active transport include endocytosis, phagocytosis, pinocytosis, and exocytosis.

7–4 The Diversity of Cellular Life

An organism that consists of a single cell is called a unicellular organism. Unicellular organisms carry out all the essential functions of life. Organisms that are made up of many cells are called multicellular organisms. Cells throughout a multicellular organism can develop in different ways to perform different tasks. This process is called cell specialization.

The levels of organization in a multicellular organism are individual cells, tissues, organs, and organ systems. Individual cells are the first level. Similar cells are grouped into units called tissues. A tissue is a group of cells that perform a particular function. Groups of tissues that work together form an organ. A group of organs that work together to perform a specific function is called an organ system.

Section 7–1 Life Is Cellular (pages 169–173)

🔑 Key Concepts
- What is the cell theory?
- What are the characteristics of prokaryotes and eukaryotes?

Introduction (page 169)

1. What is the structure that makes up every living thing? <u>The cell</u>

The Discovery of the Cell (pages 169–170)

2. What was Anton van Leeuwenhoek one of the first to see in the 1600s? <u>He saw</u>
   <u>tiny living organisms in a drop of water.</u>

3. What did a thin slice of cork seem like to Robert Hooke when he observed it
   through a microscope? <u>The cork seemed to be made of tiny empty chambers.</u>

4. What did the German botanist Matthias Schleiden conclude? <u>He concluded that all</u>
   <u>plants are made of cells.</u>

5. What did the German biologist Theodor Schwann conclude? <u>He concluded that animals</u>
   <u>were also made of cells.</u>

6. How did Rudolph Virchow summarize his years of work? <u>He stated that new cells</u>
   <u>could be produced only from the division of existing cells.</u>

7. What are the three concepts that make up the cell theory?
   a. <u>All living things are composed of cells.</u>
   b. <u>Cells are the basic units of structure and function in living things.</u>
   c. <u>New cells are produced from existing cells.</u>

Exploring the Cell (pages 170–172)

8. Why are electron microscopes capable of revealing details much smaller than those
   seen through light microscopes? <u>The wavelengths of electrons are much shorter than</u>
   <u>those of light.</u>

Prokaryotes and Eukaryotes (pages 172–173)

9. Circle the letter of each sentence that is true about prokaryotes.

   (a.) They grow and reproduce.

   b. Many are large, multicellular organisms.

   ç. They are more complex than cells of eukaryotes.

   (d.) They have cell membranes and cytoplasm.

10. Are all eukaryotes large, multicellular organisms? No, some live solitary lives as single-celled organisms.

   _____

11. Complete the table about the two categories of cells.

TWO CATEGORIES OF CELLS

Category	Definition	Examples
Prokaryotes	Organisms whose cells lack nuclei	Bacteria
Eukaryotes	Organisms whose cells contain nuclei	Plants, animals, fungi, protists

Name_____ Class_____ Date _____

Section 7–2 Eukaryotic Cell Structure
(pages 174–181)

🔑 Key Concept
- What are the functions of the major cell structures?

Comparing a Cell to a Factory (page 174)

1. What is an organelle? It is a structure in eukaryotic cells that acts as if it is a
specialized organ.

2. Label the structures on the illustrations of the plant and animal cells.

Nucleolus

Nucleus

Nuclear envelope

Cell membrane

Centrioles

Mitochondrion

Golgi apparatus

Nucleus

Nuclear envelope

Cell Wall

Cell membrane

Chloroplast

Golgi apparatus

Mitochondrion

Vacuole

© Pearson Education, Inc., publishing as Pearson Prentice Hall.

3. Circle the letter of each structure that animal cells contain.

   a. chloroplasts

   b. lysosomes

   c. mitochondria

   d. ER

4. Circle the letter of each structure that plant cells contain.

   a. cell wall

   b. ER

   c. lysosomes

   d. chloroplast

Nucleus (page 176)

5. What is the function of the nucleus? It is the control center of the cell.

   _____

6. What important molecules does the nucleus contain? It contains DNA.

   _____

7. The granular material visible within the nucleus is called _____ chromatin _____.

8. What does chromatin consist of? It consists of DNA bound to protein.

   _____

9. What are chromosomes? They are distinct, threadlike structures formed of condensed
   chromatin that contain genetic information that is passed from one generation of cells to the next.

   _____

   _____

10. Most nuclei contain a small, dense region known as the _____ nucleolus _____.

11. What occurs in the nucleolus? This is where the assembly of ribosomes begins.

    _____

12. What is the nuclear envelope? It is a double-membrane layer that surrounds the nucleus.

Ribosomes (page 177)

13. What are ribosomes? Ribosomes are small particles of RNA and protein found
    throughout the cytoplasm that are involved in protein synthesis.

    _____

Endoplasmic Reticulum (pages 177–178)

14. What is the difference between rough ER and smooth ER? Ribosomes are found on
the surface of rough ER. There are no ribosomes on smooth ER.

_____

Golgi Apparatus (page 178)

15. Using the cell as a factory analogy, describe the role of the Golgi apparatus in the cell.
The Golgi apparatus is like a customization shop, where the finishing touches are put on proteins
before they are ready to leave the cell "factory."

_____

Lysosomes (page 179)

16. Circle the letter of each sentence that is true about lysosomes.

   a. They contain enzymes that help synthesize lipids.

   (b.) They break down organelles that have outlived their usefulness.

   c. They produce proteins that are modified by the ER.

   (d.) They contain enzymes that break down lipids, carbohydrates, and proteins.

Vacuoles (page 179)

17. What are vacuoles? Vacuoles are saclike structures that store materials such as water, salts,
proteins, and carbohydrates.

_____

18. What is the role of the central vacuole in plants? When the central vacuole is filled with
liquid, the pressure within the vacuole supports the heavy structures of the plant, such as leaves
and flowers.

19. How does the contractile vacuole in a paramecium help maintain homeostasis?
By contracting rhythmically, the contractile vacuole pumps excess water out of the cell.

_____

Mitochondria and Chloroplasts (pages 179–180)

20. Is the following sentence true or false? Both chloroplasts and mitochondria are
enclosed by two membranes. _____ true _____

21. Chloroplasts and mitochondria contain their own genetic information in the form of
_____ small DNA molecules _____.

22. What are mitochondria? Mitochondria are organelles that convert the chemical energy stored in food into compounds that are more convenient for the cell to use.

_____

23. Are mitochondria found in plant cells, animal cells, or both? Mitochondria are found in both.

24. Where are chloroplasts found? Chloroplasts are found in plant cells and some other organisms but not in animal cells.

25. Biologist Lynn Margulis has suggested that mitochondria and chloroplasts are descendants of what kind of organisms? They are descendants of ancient prokaryotes.

_____

Cytoskeleton (page 181)

26. What is the cytoskeleton? It is a network of protein filaments that helps the cell to maintain its shape.

_____

27. Complete the table about structures that make up the cytoskeleton.

STRUCTURES OF THE CYTOSKELETON

Structure	Description	Functions
Microtubules	Hollow tubes of tubulins	Maintain cell shape, help build cilia and flagella, form centrioles in cell division
Microfilaments	Threadlike structures made of actin	Support the cell, help cells move

© Pearson Education, Inc., publishing as Pearson Prentice Hall.

Name_____ Class_____ Date _____

Match the organelle with its description.

Organelle	Description

Organelle

_f_ 28. Ribosome

_d_ 29. Endoplasmic reticulum

_b_ 30. Golgi apparatus

_g_ 31. Lysosome

_e_ 32. Vacuole

_a_ 33. Chloroplast

_c_ 34. Mitochondrion

Description

a. Uses energy from sunlight to make energy-rich food

b. Stack of membranes in which enzymes attach carbohydrates and lipids to proteins

c. Uses energy from food to make high-energy compounds

d. An internal membrane system in which components of cell membrane and some proteins are constructed

e. Saclike structure that stores materials

f. Small particle of RNA and protein that produces protein following instructions from nucleus

g. Filled with enzymes used to break down food into particles that can be used

Reading Skill Practice

A flowchart can help you remember the order in which events occur. On a separate sheet of paper, create a flowchart that describes the steps by which proteins are made in the cell. You will find that the steps of this process are explained on pages 176–178. For more information about flowcharts, see Organizing Information in Appendix A in your textbook.

Students' flowcharts should include RNA moving out of the nucleus, the production of proteins in ribosomes, modification in rough ER, proteins moving into the Golgi apparatus, proteins sent to their final destinations.

© Pearson Education, Inc., publishing as Pearson Prentice Hall.

Section 7–3 Cell Boundaries (pages 182–189)

Key Concepts
- What are the main functions of the cell membrane and the cell wall?
- What happens during diffusion?
- What is osmosis?

Cell Membrane (page 182)

1. What are the functions of the cell membrane? It regulates what enters and leaves the cell and also provides protection and support.

2. The core of nearly all cell membranes is a double-layered sheet called a(an) lipid bilayer .

3. What is the difference in the function of the proteins and the carbohydrates attached to a cell membrane? Some of the proteins form channels and pumps that help move materials across the membrane. Many of the carbohydrates act like chemical identification cards.

Cell Walls (page 183)

4. In what organisms are cell walls found? They are found in plants, algae, fungi, and many prokaryotes.

5. Is the following sentence true or false? The cell wall lies inside the cell membrane. false

6. What is the main function of the cell wall? It provides support and protection for the cell.

7. What are plant cell walls mostly made of? They are made mostly of cellulose.

Diffusion Through Cell Boundaries (pages 183–184)

8. What is the concentration of a solution? It is the mass of the solute in a given volume of solution, or mass/volume.

9. What is diffusion? It is the process by which molecules tend to move from an area where they are more concentrated to an area where they are less concentrated.

10. What is meant when a system has reached equilibrium? It means that the concentration of the solute is the same throughout the system.

11. The molecules of solute in the illustration are moving through the cell membrane from top to bottom. Indicate with labels which side of the membrane has a high concentration of solute and which has a low concentration.

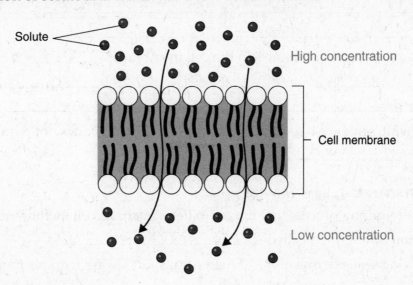

Osmosis (pages 185–186)

12. What does it mean that biological membranes are selectively permeable?
Some substances can pass across them and others cannot.

13. What is osmosis? It is the diffusion of water through a selectively permeable membrane.

14. Is the following sentence true or false? Water tends to diffuse from a region where it is less concentrated to a region where it is highly concentrated. _____ false _____

15. When will water stop moving across a membrane? It will move across the membrane until equilibrium is reached.

Match the situation to the description.

	Situation	Description
b	**16.** Two solutions are isotonic.	**a.** The solution is above strength in solute.
a	**17.** A solution is hypertonic.	**b.** The solutions are the same strength.
c	**18.** A solution is hypotonic.	**c.** The solution is below strength in solute.

19. On which side of a selectively permeable membrane does osmosis exert a pressure?
It exerts a pressure on the hypertonic side.

Facilitated Diffusion (page 187)

20. What happens during the process of facilitated diffusion? <u>Molecules such as glucose that</u>
    <u>cannot cross the cell membrane's lipid bilayer directly move through protein channels instead.</u>
    _____

21. What is the role of protein channels in the cell membrane? <u>Protein channels allow</u>
    <u>molecules (that are too large) to cross the membrane.</u>
    _____

22. Is the following sentence true or false? Facilitated diffusion does not require the cell to
    use energy. _____<u>true</u>_____

Active Transport (pages 188–189)

23. The energy-requiring process that moves material across a cell membrane against a
    concentration difference is called _____<u>active transport</u>_____.

24. Is the following sentence true or false? Active transport always requires transport proteins
    during the process. _____<u>false</u>_____

25. Complete the table about types of active transport.

TYPES OF ACTIVE TRANSPORT

Type	Description
Endocytosis	Process of taking materials into the cell by means of infoldings of the cell membrane
Phagocytosis	Process of taking large particles into the cell
Exocytosis	The release of large amounts of material from the cell

26. During endocytosis, what happens to the pocket in the cell membrane when it breaks
    loose from the membrane? <u>It forms a vacuole within the cytoplasm.</u>
    _____

Name_____ Class_____ Date _____

Section 7–4 The Diversity of Cellular Life
(pages 190–193)

👄 **Key Concepts**
- What is cell specialization?
- What are the four levels of organization in multicellular organisms?

Unicellular Organisms (page 190)

1. A single-celled organism is also called a(an) _____unicellular_____ organism.

Multicellular Organisms (pages 190–192)

2. What is cell specialization in a multicellular organism? It is the characteristic of having separate tasks for each type of cell.

3. Circle the letter of each sentence that is true about cell specialization.

   (a.) Specialized cells perform particular functions within the organism.

   b. Only unicellular organisms have specialized cells.

   (c.) The human body contains many different cell types.

   (d.) Some cells are specialized to enable movement.

Levels of Organization (pages 192–193)

4. What are four levels of organization in a multicellular organism?

   a. Individual cells

   b. Tissues

   c. Organs

   d. Organ systems

5. What is a tissue? It is a group of similar cells that perform a particular function.

6. What are the four main types of tissue in most animals?

   a. Muscle

   b. Epithelial

   c. Nervous

   d. Connective

7. Groups of tissues that work together to perform a specific function are called a(an) _____organ_____.

8. What kinds of tissues can be found within a muscle in your body? They include muscle tissue, nervous tissue, and connective tissue.

9. What is an organ system? It is a group of organs that work together to perform a specific function.

Reading and Study Workbook **83**

Vocabulary Review

Matching   *In the space provided, write the letter of the function that best matches each organelle.*

<u>e</u> **1.** mitochondrion	**a.** site where lipid components of the cell membrane are assembled
<u>d</u> **2.** ribosome	
<u>a</u> **3.** endoplasmic reticulum	**b.** captures energy from sunlight and converts it into chemical energy
<u>c</u> **4.** Golgi apparatus	**c.** modifies, sorts, and packages proteins
<u>f</u> **5.** lysosome	**d.** site where proteins are assembled
<u>b</u> **6.** chloroplast	**e.** converts chemical energy in food into compounds the cell can use
	f. acts as the cell's cleanup crew

Completion   *Fill in the blanks with terms from Chapter 7.*

7. Bacteria are examples of _____prokaryotes_____.

8. Cells that are larger and more complex than prokaryotes are _____eukaryotic_____ cells.

9. The _____cytoplasm_____ is the portion of the cell outside of the nucleus.

10. The supporting structure of the cell that is also involved in movement is the _____cytoskeleton_____.

11. All cells are surrounded by a flexible barrier known as the _____cell membrane_____.

12. The movement of particles from an area of greater concentration to an area of lower concentration is called _____diffusion_____.

13. When comparing two solutions, the solution with the greater concentration of solutes is called _____hypertonic_____, while the solution with the lower concentration of solutes is called _____hypotonic_____.

14. The process of taking material into the cell by means of infoldings of the cell membrane is called _____endocytosis_____.

15. Amoebas use the process of _____phagocytosis_____ to take in food and other materials.

16. _____Cell specialization_____ is the process by which cells in an organization develop in different ways to perform different tasks.

17. In the process of _____facilitated diffusion_____, a protein channel helps the diffusion of glucose across a membrane.

18. The diffusion of water through a selectively permeable membrane is called _____osmosis_____.

19. The process that moves materials through a membrane against a concentration difference is known as _____active transport_____.

Summary

8–1 Energy and Life

Plants and some other types of organisms are able to use light energy from the sun to produce food. Organisms that make their own food are called autotrophs. Other organisms cannot use the sun's energy directly. These organisms, called heterotrophs, obtain energy from the foods they consume.

One of the principal chemical compounds that cells use to store and release energy is adenosine triphosphate, or ATP. ATP consists of adenine, a 5-carbon sugar called ribose, and three phosphate groups. Adenosine diphosphate (ADP) is a similar compound that has only two phosphate groups instead of three. When a cell has energy available, it can store small amounts of energy by adding a third phosphate group to ADP, producing ATP. The energy stored in ATP can be released by breaking the bond between the second and third phosphate groups. Because a cell can subtract this third phosphate group, it can release energy as needed. The characteristics of ATP make it exceptionally useful as the basic energy source of all cells. Cells use energy from ATP to carry out many important activities, including active transport, synthesis of proteins and nucleic acids, and responses to chemical signals at the cell surface. Cells store a small amount of ATP because ATP is easy to regenerate from ADP. When ATP is needed, cells use the energy in foods such as glucose to produce ATP.

8–2 Photosynthesis: An Overview

Research into photosynthesis began centuries ago. In 1643, Jan van Helmont concluded that trees gain most of their mass from water. In 1771, Joseph Priestley determined that plants release oxygen, which can keep a candle burning.

In 1779, Jan Ingenhousz concluded that plants need sunlight to produce oxygen. The experiments performed by van Helmont, Priestley, and Ingenhousz led to work by other scientists who finally discovered that in the presence of light, plants transform carbon dioxide and water into carbohydrates and plants also release oxygen.

The overall equation for photosynthesis can be shown as follows:

$$6CO_2 + 6 H_2O \xrightarrow{light} C_6H_{12}O_6 + 6O_2$$

carbon dioxide + water $\xrightarrow{light}$ sugars + oxygen

Photosynthesis uses the energy of sunlight to convert water and carbon dioxide into high-energy sugars and oxygen. Plants use the sugars to produce complex carbohydrates such as starches. Plants obtain the carbon dioxide they need for photosynthesis from the air or from the water in which they grow.

In addition to water and carbon dioxide, photosynthesis requires light and chlorophyll. Plants gather the sun's energy with light-absorbing molecules called pigments. The plants' principal pigment is chlorophyll. There are two main types of chlorophyll: chlorophyll *a* and chlorophyll *b*.

The wavelengths of sunlight you can see make up the visible spectrum, which contains all the colors. Chlorophyll absorbs light in the blue-violet and red regions very well. But it does not absorb light in the green region well. Green light is reflected by leaves, which is why plants look green.

Any compound that absorbs light absorbs the energy in light. When chlorophyll absorbs sunlight, much of the energy of the light is transferred directly to the electrons in the chlorophyll molecule, raising the energy level of the electrons.

8–3 The Reactions of Photosynthesis

In plants and other photosynthetic prokaryotes, photosynthesis takes place inside the chloroplasts. Chloroplasts contain saclike photosynthetic membranes called thylakoids. Thylakoids are arranged in stacks called grana. Proteins in the thylakoid membrane organize chlorophyll and other pigments into clusters known as photosystems. These photosystems are the light-collecting units of chlorophyll. The reactions of photosynthesis occur in two parts: (1) the light-dependent reactions and (2) the light-independent reactions, which are also called the Calvin cycle. The light-dependent reactions take place within the thylakoid membranes. The Calvin cycle takes place in the stroma—the region outside of the thylakoid membranes.

When sunlight excites electrons in chlorophyll, the electrons gain a great deal of energy. A carrier molecule is a compound that can accept a pair of high-energy electrons and transfer them along with most of their energy to another molecule. One of these carrier molecules is $NADP^+$. In the process of photosynthesis, $NADP^+$ accepts and holds 2 high-energy electrons along with a hydrogen ion (H^+). This converts the $NADP^+$ into NADPH.

The light-dependent reactions require light. These reactions use energy from light to produce oxygen gas and convert ADP and $NADP^+$ into the energy carriers ATP and NADPH. Photosynthesis begins when pigments in photosystem II absorb light. A series of reactions follows. The reactants are water, ADP, and $NADP^+$. The products are oxygen gas, ATP, and NADPH. The oxygen gas produced by photosynthesis is the source of nearly all the oxygen in Earth's atmosphere.

The Calvin cycle does not require light. During the Calvin cycle, plants use the energy of ATP and NADPH—products of the light-dependent reactions—to produce high-energy sugars. The Calvin cycle uses carbon dioxide in its series of reactions. As photosynthesis proceeds, the Calvin cycle works steadily, removing carbon dioxide from the atmosphere and turning out energy-rich sugars. Six carbon dioxide molecules are needed to produce a single 6-carbon sugar.

Many factors affect the rate of photosynthesis. Such factors include availability of water, temperature, and intensity of light.

Chapter 8 Photosynthesis

Section 8–1 Energy and Life (pages 201–203)

🔑 Key Concepts
- Where do plants get the energy they need to produce food?
- What is the role of ATP in cellular activities?

Autotrophs and Heterotrophs (page 201)

1. Where does the energy of food originally come from? <u>Energy in most food comes from</u> <u>the sun.</u>

2. Complete the table describing the types of organisms.

TYPES OF ORGANISMS

Type	Description	Examples
Autotrophs	Organisms that make their own food	Plants
Heterotrophs	Organisms that obtain energy from the food they eat	Animals, mushrooms

Chemical Energy and ATP (page 202)

3. What is one of the principal chemical compounds that cells use to store energy?
<u>Adenosine triphosphate, or ATP</u>

4. How is ATP different from ADP? <u>ATP has three phosphate groups, whereas ADP has two</u> <u>phosphate groups.</u>

5. Label each part of the ATP molecule illustrated below.

6. When a cell has energy available, how can it store small amounts of that energy?
<u>It can add a phosphate group to ADP molecules, producing ATP molecules.</u>

7. When is the energy stored in ATP released? <u>It is released when the chemical bond between</u>
<u>the second and third phosphates is broken.</u>
_____

8. For what purpose do the characteristics of ATP make it exceptionally useful
to all types of cells? <u>All types of cells use ATP as their basic energy source.</u>
_____

9. What are two ways in which cells use the energy provided by ATP?

   a. <u>Active transport</u>

   b. <u>Movement within the cell</u>

Using Biochemical Energy (pages 202–203)

10. Why is it efficient for cells to keep only a small supply of ATP on hand?
<u>ATP is not very good for storing large amounts of energy over the long term. A single sugar</u>
<u>molecule stores more than 90 times the chemical energy of an ATP molecule.</u>
_____

11. Circle the letter of where cells get the energy to regenerate ATP.

   a. ADP

   b. phosphates

   c. foods like glucose

   d. organelles

Section 8–2 Photosynthesis: An Overview (pages 204–207)

⊂⊃ **Key Concepts**
- What did the experiments of van Helmont, Priestley, and Ingenhousz reveal about how plants grow?
- What is the overall equation for photosynthesis?
- What is the role of light and chlorophyll in photosynthesis?

Introduction (page 204)

1. What occurs in the process of photosynthesis? __Plants use the energy of sunlight to convert__ water and carbon dioxide into high-energy carbohydrates—sugars and starches—and oxygen.

Investigating Photosynthesis (pages 204–206)

2. What did Jan van Helmont conclude from his experiment? __He concluded that most of__ the mass a plant had gained had come from water, because that was the only thing he had added to the pot.

3. Circle the letter of the substance produced by the mint plant in Joseph Priestley's experiment.
    a. carbon dioxide
    b. water
    c. air
    (d.) oxygen

4. What did Jan Ingenhousz show? __He showed that light is necessary for plants to produce__ oxygen.

The Photosynthesis Equation (page 206)

5. Write the overall equation for photosynthesis using words.
    carbon dioxide + water $\xrightarrow{\text{light}}$ sugars + oxygen

6. Photosynthesis uses the energy of sunlight to convert water and carbon dioxide into oxygen and high-energy _____ sugars _____.

Light and Pigments (page 207)

7. What does photosynthesis require in addition to water and carbon dioxide?
    It requires light and chlorophyll, a molecule in chloroplasts.

© Pearson Education, Inc., publishing as Pearson Prentice Hall.

8. Plants gather the sun's energy with light-absorbing molecules called _____pigments_____.

9. What is the principal pigment of plants? _____It is chlorophyll._____

10. Circle the letters of the regions of the visible spectrum in which chlorophyll absorbs light very well.

   (a.) blue-violet region

   b. green region

   (c.) red region

   d. yellow region

Reading Skill Practice

By looking at illustrations in textbooks, you can help yourself remember better what you have read. Look carefully at Figure 8–4 on page 206. What important ideas does this illustration communicate? Do your work on a separate sheet of paper.

Photosynthesis uses light energy to convert carbon dioxide and water into sugars and oxygen. This takes place in chloroplasts.

Section 8–3 The Reactions of Photosynthesis
(pages 208–214)

🔑 **Key Concepts**
- What happens in the light-dependent reactions?
- What is the Calvin cycle?

Inside a Chloroplast (page 208)

1. Chloroplasts contain saclike photosynthetic membranes called _____thylakoids_____.

2. What is a granum? A granum is a stack of thylakoids.
_____

3. The region outside the thylakoid membranes in the chloroplasts is called the
_____stroma_____ .

4. What are the two stages of photosynthesis called?

   a. Light-dependent reactions _____

   b. Light-independent reactions, or Calvin cycle _____

5. Complete the illustration of the overview of photosynthesis by writing the products and the reactants of the process, as well as the energy source that excites the electrons.

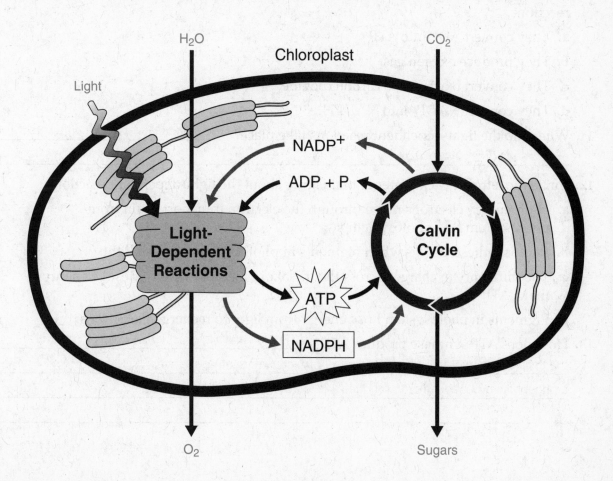

Electron Carriers (page 209)

6. When sunlight excites electrons in chlorophyll, how do the electrons change?
The electrons gain a great deal of energy.

7. What is a carrier molecule? A carrier molecule is a compound that can accept
a pair of high-energy electrons and transfer them along with most of their energy to another
molecule.

8. Circle the letter of the carrier molecule involved in photosynthesis.

   a. H_2O c. CO_2

   (b.) $NADP^+$ d. O_2

9. How does $NADP^+$ become NADPH? NADP+ becomes NADPH when it accepts a pair
of high-energy electrons along with a hydrogen ion (H+).

Light-Dependent Reactions (pages 210–211)

10. Circle the letter of each sentence that is true about the light-dependent reactions.

   (a.) They convert ADP into ATP.

   (b.) They produce oxygen gas.

   c. They convert oxygen into carbon dioxide.

   (d.) They convert $NADP^+$ into NADPH.

11. Where do the light-dependent reactions take place? They take place within the thylakoid
membranes of chloroplasts.

12. Circle the letter of each sentence that is true about the light-dependent reactions.

   (a.) High-energy electrons move through the electron transport chain from photosystem II to photosystem I.

   b. Photosynthesis begins when pigments in photosystem I absorb light.

   (c.) The difference in charges across the thylakoid membrane provides the energy to make ATP.

   d. Pigments in photosystem I use energy from light to reenergize electrons.

13. How does ATP synthase produce ATP? ATP synthase allows H+ ions to pass through
the thylakoid membrane. As the ions pass through, ATP synthase rotates, binding ADP and
a phosphate group together to produce ATP.

Name_____ Class_____ Date _____

The Calvin Cycle (pages 212–214)

14. What does the Calvin cycle use to produce high-energy sugars?

The Calvin cycle uses ATP and NADPH from the light-dependent reactions to produce

high-energy sugars.

15. Why are the reactions of the Calvin cycle also called the light-independent reactions?

The Calvin cycle does not require light.

16. Circle the letter of each statement that is true about the Calvin cycle.

   a. The main products of the Calvin cycle are six carbon dioxide molecules.

   (b.) Carbon dioxide molecules enter the Calvin cycle from the atmosphere.

   (c.) Energy from ATP and high-energy electrons from NADPH are used to convert 3-carbon molecules into higher-energy forms.

   (d.) The Calvin cycle uses six molecules of carbon dioxide to produce a single 6-carbon sugar molecule.

Factors Affecting Photosynthesis (page 214)

17. What are three factors that affect the rate at which photosynthesis occurs?

   a. Availability of water

   b. Temperature

   c. Intensity of light

18. Is the following sentence true or false? Increasing the intensity of light decreases the rate of photosynthesis. _____false_____

© Pearson Education, Inc., publishing as Pearson Prentice Hall.

Name_____ Class_____ Date _____

Vocabulary Review

Matching *In the space provided, write the letter of the definition that best matches each term.*

___d___ **1.** photosynthesis

___j___ **2.** chlorophyll

___f___ **3.** pigment

___g___ **4.** adenosine triphosphate

___i___ **5.** thylakoid

___a___ **6.** photosystems

___b___ **7.** stroma

___c___ **8.** NADP+

___e___ **9.** Calvin cycle

___h___ **10.** light-dependent reactions

a. clusters in the thylakoid membrane of chlorophyll and other pigments

b. the region of the chloroplast outside the thylakoid membranes

c. electron carrier

d. process in which plants use the energy of sunlight to make high-energy carbohydrates

e. reactions that use ATP and NADPH to produce high-energy sugars

f. light-absorbing molecules

g. the basic energy source of all cells

h. reactions that produce oxygen gas and convert ADP and NADP+ into the energy carriers ATP and NADPH

i. saclike photosynthetic membranes in chloroplasts

j. principal pigment of plants

Answering Questions *In the space provided, write an answer to each question.*

11. What is an organism that obtains energy from the food it consumes? _____Heterotroph_____

12. What is an organism that is able to make its own food? _____Autotroph_____

13. What is released when the chemical bond is broken between the second and third phosphates of an ATP molecule? _____Energy_____

14. What are the reactants of the equation for photosynthesis? ___Carbon dioxide and water___

15. What are the products of the equation for photosynthesis? _____Sugars and oxygen_____

Summary

9–1 Chemical Pathways

Food serves as the source of energy for cells. Quite a lot of energy is stored in food. For instance, 1 gram of the sugar glucose releases 3811 calories of heat energy when burned in the presence of oxygen. A calorie is the amount of energy needed to raise the temperature of 1 gram of water 1 degree Celsius. Cells don't burn glucose and other food compounds. They gradually release the energy. The process begins with a pathway called glycolysis. In the presence of oxygen, glycolysis is followed by the Krebs cycle and the electron transport chain. Together, these three pathways make up cellular respiration. Cellular respiration is the process that releases energy by breaking down glucose and other food molecules in the presence of oxygen. The equation for cellular respiration is:

$$6O_2 + C_6H_{12}O_6 \rightarrow 6CO_2 + 6H_2O + \text{Energy}$$

$$\text{oxygen} + \text{glucose} \rightarrow \begin{matrix}\text{carbon} \\ \text{dioxide}\end{matrix} + \text{water} + \text{energy}$$

There are three main stages of cellular respiration: (1) glycolysis, (2) the Krebs cycle, and (3) electron transport.

Glycolysis is the process in which one molecule of glucose is broken in half, producing two molecules of pyruvic acid, a 3-carbon compound. Through glycolysis, the cell gains 2 ATP molecules. In one of the reactions of glycolysis, the electron carrier NAD^+ accepts a pair of high-energy electrons, producing NADH. By doing this, NAD^+ helps pass energy from glucose to other pathways in the cell.

When oxygen is not present, glycolysis is followed by another pathway. This pathway is called fermentation. Fermentation releases energy from food molecules by producing ATP. Because fermentation does not require oxygen, it is said to be anaerobic.

During fermentation, cells convert NADH back into the electron carrier NAD^+, which is needed for glycolysis.

This action allows glycolysis to continue producing a steady supply of ATP. The two main types of fermentation are alcoholic fermentation and lactic acid fermentation. Yeasts and a few other microorganisms carry out alcoholic fermentation. The equation for alcoholic fermentation after glycolysis is:

$$\begin{matrix}\text{pyruvic} \\ \text{acid}\end{matrix} + \text{NADH} \rightarrow \text{alcohol} + CO_2 + NAD^+$$

Lactic acid fermentation occurs in your muscles during rapid exercise. The equation for lactic acid fermentation after glycolysis is:

$$\text{pyruvic acid} + \text{NADH} \rightarrow \text{lactic acid} + NAD^+$$

9–2 The Krebs Cycle and Electron Transport

When oxygen is available, glycolysis is followed by the Krebs cycle and the electron transport chain. The three pathways together make up the process of cellular respiration. Because the pathways of cellular respiration require oxygen, they are said to be aerobic.

The Krebs cycle is the second stage of cellular respiration. In eukaryotes, the Krebs cycle takes place in the mitochondrion. During the Krebs cycle, pyruvic acid is broken down into carbon dioxide in a series of energy-extracting reactions. The Krebs cycle is also known as the citric acid cycle, because citric acid is one of the first products.

The Krebs cycle begins when pyruvic acid produced by glycolysis enters the mitochondrion. One carbon atom from pyruvic acid becomes part of a molecule of carbon dioxide, which is eventually released into the air. The carbon dioxide released during the Krebs cycle is the source of much of the carbon dioxide in air. The other two carbon atoms from pyruvic acid are used in a series of reactions. During these reactions, two energy carriers accept high-energy electrons. NAD^+ is changed to NADH, and FAD is changed to $FADH_2$. These molecules carry the high-energy electrons to the electron transport chain.

Electron transport is the third stage of cellular respiration. The electron transport chain uses the high-energy electrons from the Krebs cycle to convert ADP into ATP. In eukaryotes, the electron transport chain is composed of a series of carrier proteins located in the inner membrane of the mitochondrion. In prokaryotes, the same chain is in the cell membrane. In this pathway, high-energy electrons move from one carrier protein to the next. Their energy is used to move hydrogen ions across the membrane through a protein sphere called ATP synthase. Each time an ATP synthase spins, a phosphate group is added to an ADP molecule, producing an ATP molecule.

In the absence of oxygen, all the energy that a cell can extract from a single molecule of glucose is 2 ATP molecules—the product of glycolysis.

In the presence of oxygen, though, the cell can extract many more ATP molecules. The Krebs cycle and the electron transport chain enable the cell to produce 34 more ATP molecules per glucose molecule. The total, then, for cellular respiration (glycolysis plus the Krebs cycle plus electron transport) is 36 ATP molecules per glucose molecule.

Human body cells normally contain small amounts of ATP produced during cellular respiration. When the body needs energy in a hurry, muscle cells produce ATP by lactic acid fermentation. For long-term energy needs, the body must use cellular respiration.

The energy flows in photosynthesis and cellular respiration take place in opposite directions. On a global level, photosynthesis and cellular respiration are also opposites. Photosynthesis removes carbon dioxide from the atmosphere and puts back oxygen. Cellular respiration removes oxygen from the atmosphere and puts back carbon dioxide.

Name_____ Class_____ Date _____

Chapter 9 Cellular Respiration

Section 9–1 Chemical Pathways (pages 221–225)

Key Concepts
- What is cellular respiration?
- What happens during the process of glycolysis?
- What are the two main types of fermentation?

Chemical Energy and Food (page 221)

1. What is a calorie? It is the amount of energy needed to raise the temperature of 1 gram of water 1 degree Celsius.

2. How many calories make up 1 Calorie? _____1000_____

3. Cellular respiration begins with a pathway called _____glycolysis_____.

4. Is the following sentence true or false? Glycolysis releases a great amount of energy. _____false_____

Overview of Cellular Respiration (page 222)

5. What is cellular respiration? It is the process that releases energy by breaking down food molecules in the presence of oxygen.

6. What is the equation for cellular respiration, using chemical formulas?
$6O_2 + C_6H_{12}O_6 \rightarrow 6CO_2 + 6H_2O + Energy$

7. Label the three main stages of cellular respiration on the illustration of the complete process.

Glucose → Glycolysis

Pyruvic acid

Electrons carried in NADH

Electrons carried in NADH and $FADH_2$

Krebs Cycle

Electron Transport Chain

Cytoplasm

Mitochondrion

ATP   ATP   ATP

Reading and Study Workbook 97

8. What would be the problem if cellular respiration took place in just one step? All the energy from glucose would be released at once, and most of it would be lost in the form of light and heat.

9. Where does glycolysis take place? It takes place in the cytoplasm.

10. Where do the Krebs cycle and electron transport take place? They take place inside the mitochondria.

Glycolysis (page 223)

11. What is glycolysis? It is the process in which one molecule of glucose is broken in half, producing two molecules of pyruvic acid, a 3-carbon compound.

12. How does the cell get glycolysis going? It uses the energy of 2 molecules of ATP.

13. If the cell uses 2 ATP molecules at the beginning of glycolysis, how does it end up with a net gain of 2 ATP molecules? When glycolysis is complete, 4 ATP molecules have been produced.

14. What is NAD^+? It is the electron carrier nicotinamide adenine dinucleotide.

15. What is the function of NAD^+ in glycolysis? One of the reactions of glycolysis removes 4 high-energy electrons and passes them to NAD^+, which becomes NADH and holds the electrons until they can be transferred to other molecules.

16. Why can glycolysis supply energy to cells when oxygen is not available? It does not require oxygen.

17. What problem does a cell have when it generates large amounts of ATP from glycolysis? In just a few seconds, all of the cell's available NAD^+ are filled with electrons.

Fermentation (pages 224–225)

18. What is fermentation? It is a process that releases energy from food molecules by producing ATP in the absence of oxygen.

19. How does fermentation allow glycolysis to continue? <u>Fermentation produces a steady</u>
<u>supply of ATP.</u>

20. Because fermentation does not require oxygen, it is said to be _____<u>anaerobic</u>_____.

21. What are the two main types of fermentation?

a. <u>Alcoholic fermentation</u>

b. <u>Lactic acid fermentation</u>

22. What organisms use alcoholic fermentation? <u>Yeasts and a few other microorganisms use it.</u>

23. What is the equation for alcoholic fermentation after glycolysis?
Pyruvic acid + NADH → alcohol + CO_2 + NAD^+

24. What happens to the small amount of alcohol produced in alcoholic fermentation during the baking of bread? <u>It evaporates.</u>

25. What does lactic acid fermentation convert into lactic acid? <u>It converts glucose into</u>
<u>lactic acid.</u>

26. What is the equation for lactic acid fermentation after glycolysis?
Pyruvic acid + NADH → lactic acid + NAD^+

27. During rapid exercise, how do your muscle cells produce ATP? <u>After they use up the</u>
<u>ATP produced from cellular respiration, they produce it by lactic acid fermentation.</u>

Reading Skill Practice

When you read about complex topics, writing an outline can help you organize and understand the material. Outline Section 9–1 by using the headings and subheadings as topics and subtopics and then writing the most important details under each topic. Do your work on a separate sheet of paper.

Students' outlines should have four major topics, matching the four blue headings of the section. Details should include the highlighted, boldface vocabulary terms as well as the important concepts discussed under each heading.

Name_____ Class_____ Date _____

Section 9–2 The Krebs Cycle and Electron Transport (pages 226–232)

🔑 Key Concepts
- What happens during the Krebs cycle?
- How are high-energy electrons used by the electron transport chain?

Introduction (page 226)

1. At the end of glycolysis, how much of the chemical energy in glucose is still unused?
   About 90 percent is still unused.

2. Because the final stages of cellular respiration require oxygen, they are said to be
   _____aerobic_____.

The Krebs Cycle (pages 226–227)

3. In the presence of oxygen, how is the pyruvic acid produced in glycolysis used?
   It passes to the second stage of cellular respiration, the Krebs cycle.

4. What happens to pyruvic acid during the Krebs cycle? It is broken down into carbon
   dioxide in a series of energy-extracting reactions.

5. Why is the Krebs cycle also known as the citric acid cycle? Citric acid is the first
   compound formed in this series of reactions.

6. When does the Krebs cycle begin? It begins when pyruvic acid produced by glycolysis enters
   the mitochondrion.

7. What happens to each of the 3 carbon atoms in pyruvic acid when it is broken down?
   One carbon atom becomes part of a molecule of carbon dioxide. Two of the carbon atoms are
   joined to a compound called coenzyme A to form acetyl-CoA.

8. What happens to the carbon dioxide produced in breaking down pyruvic acid?
   It is released into the air.

9. How is citric acid produced? Acetyl-CoA adds the 2-carbon acetyl group to a 4-carbon
   molecule, producing a 6-carbon molecule called citric acid.

10. During the energy extraction part of the Krebs cycle, how many molecules of CO_2 are
    released? Two molecules are released.

11. What is the energy tally from 1 molecule of pyruvic acid during the Krebs cycle?
    It is 4 NADH molecules, 1 $FADH_2$ molecule, and 1 ATP molecule.

100 Chapter 9

© Pearson Education, Inc., publishing as Pearson Prentice Hall.

12. When electrons join NAD⁺ and FAD during the Krebs cycle, what do they form? They form NADH and FADH₂.

13. Why is the 4-carbon compound generated in the breakdown of citric acid the only permanent compound in the Krebs cycle? It is regenerated at the end of each complete turn of the cycle.

Electron Transport (pages 228–229)

14. What is the electron transport chain? It is a series of proteins in the inner membrane of mitochondria.

15. What does the electron transport chain use the high-energy electrons from the Krebs cycle for? The chain uses the electrons to convert ADP into ATP.

16. How does the location of the electron transport chain differ in eukaryotes and prokaryotes? In eukaryotes, the chain is composed of a series of proteins located in the inner membrane of the mitochondrion. In prokaryotes, the chain is in the cell membrane.

17. Where does the electron transport chain get the high-energy electrons that are passed down the chain? It gets the electrons from NADH and FADH₂, which are produced in the Krebs cycle.

18. Is the following sentence true or false? Hydrogen serves as the final electron acceptor of the electron transport chain. false

19. What is the energy of the high-energy electrons used for every time 2 high-energy electrons move down the electron transport chain? Their energy is used to transport hydrogen ions across the membrane.

20. What causes the H⁺ ions in the intermembrane space to move through the channels in the membrane and out into the matrix? During electron transport, H⁺ ions build up in the intermembrane space, making it positively charged. The other side of the membrane, from which those H⁺ ions have been taken, is now negatively charged. The charge differences that build up cause the ions to move.

21. On average, how many ATP molecules are produced as each pair of high-energy electrons moves down the electron transport chain? Three ATP molecules are produced.

22. Complete the flowchart about electron transport. (Review Figure 9–7 on page 228 of your textbook.)

> High-energy electrons from NADH and FADH$_2$ are passed into and along the
> _____electron transport chain_____ .

$\downarrow$

> The energy from the electrons moving down the chain is used to move H$^+$ ions across the
> _____inner membrane_____ .

$\downarrow$

> H$^+$ ions build up in the _____intermembrane_____ space, making it
> _____positively_____ charged and making the matrix negatively charged.

$\downarrow$

> H$^+$ ions move through channels of _____ATP synthase_____ in the inner membrane.

$\downarrow$

> The ATP synthase uses the energy from the moving ions to combine ADP and phosphate,
> forming high-energy _____ATP_____ .

The Totals (page 229)

23. How many ATP molecules are formed during cellular respiration? _____36_____

24. Why is more ATP generated from glucose in the presence of oxygen?
When oxygen is not available, the Krebs cycle and electron transport cannot proceed, and
glycolysis produces just 2 ATP molecules per glucose molecule. Under aerobic conditions, the
Krebs cycle and electron transport enable the cell to produce 34 more ATP molecules per glucose
molecule.

25. What happens to the energy of glucose that is not used to make ATP molecules?
It is released as heat.

26. What are the final waste products of cellular respiration? They are water and carbon dioxide.

Energy and Exercise (pages 230–231)

27. What are three sources of ATP a human body uses at the beginning of a race?
Three sources are ATP already in the muscles, new ATP made by lactic acid fermentation,
and cellular respiration.

_____

28. When a runner needs quick energy for a short race, what source can supply enough ATP for about 90 seconds? Lactic acid fermentation can supply the ATP.

29. Why does a sprinter have an oxygen debt to repay after the race is over? Lactic acid fermentation produces lactic acid as a byproduct. The only way to get rid of the lactic acid is in a chemical pathway that requires extra oxygen.

30. A runner needs more energy for a longer race. How does the body generate the necessary ATP? Cellular respiration is the only way to generate a continuing supply of ATP.

31. Why are aerobic forms of exercise so beneficial for weight control? Stores of glycogen used in cellular respiration usually last for 15 to 20 minutes. After that, the body begins to break down other stored molecules, including fats, for energy.

Comparing Photosynthesis and Cellular Respiration (page 232)

32. If photosynthesis is the process that "deposits" energy in a "savings account," then what is cellular respiration? It is the process that "withdraws" energy.

33. How are photosynthesis and cellular respiration opposite in terms of carbon dioxide? Photosynthesis removes carbon dioxide from the atmosphere, and cellular respiration puts it back.

34. How are photosynthesis and cellular respiration opposite in terms of oxygen? Photosynthesis releases oxygen into the atmosphere, and cellular respiration uses the oxygen to release energy from food.

Chapter 9   Cellular Respiration

Vocabulary Review

Matching   *In the space provided, write the letter of the definition that best matches each term.*

<u>f</u>   **1.** calorie

<u>d</u>   **2.** glycolysis

<u>g</u>   **3.** cellular respiration

<u>a</u>   **4.** NAD$^+$

<u>b</u>   **5.** fermentation

<u>e</u>   **6.** anaerobic

<u>c</u>   **7.** aerobic

a. electron carrier

b. pathway that releases energy from food in the absence of oxygen

c. requires oxygen

d. process in which one molecule of glucose is broken in half, producing two molecules of pyruvic acid

e. does not require oxygen

f. amount of energy needed to raise 1 gram of water 1 degree Celsius

g. process that releases energy by breaking down food molecules in the presence of oxygen

Answering Questions   *In the space provided, write an answer to each question.*

8. What is the first stage of cellular respiration? _____Glycolysis_____

_____

9. What is the second stage of cellular respiration? _____Krebs cycle_____

_____

10. What is the third stage of cellular respiration? _____Electron transport_____

_____

11. How many ATP molecules can the cell produce from a single molecule of glucose through glycolysis? _____2_____

12. How many ATP molecules can the cell produce from a single molecule of glucose through the complete process of cellular respiration? _____36_____

Completion   *Write an equation for each of the pathways below.*

13. lactic acid fermentation after glycolysis _____pyruvic acid + NADH → lactic acid + NAD$^+$_____

_____

14. alcoholic fermentation after glycolysis _____pyruvic acid + NADH → alcohol + CO$_2$ + NAD$^+$_____

_____

15. cellular respiration _____oxygen + glucose → carbon dioxide + water + energy_____

_____

Chapter 10   Cell Growth and Division

Summary

10–1 Cell Growth

The larger a cell becomes, the more demands the cell places on its DNA. As a cell increases in size, it usually does not make copies of DNA. If a cell were to grow without limit, an "information crisis" would occur. In addition, as a cell increases in size, the more trouble it has moving enough nutrients (food) and wastes across its cell membrane. The rate at which materials move through the cell membrane depends on the surface area of the cell—the total area of its cell membrane. However, the rate at which food and oxygen are used up and waste products are produced depends on the volume of the cell.

If a cell were a cube, you could determine surface area by multiplying length × width × number of sides. You could determine volume by multiplying length × width × height. You then could determine the cell's ratio of surface area to volume by dividing the surface area by the volume. As a cell grows, its volume increases more rapidly than its surface area. That is, as a cell becomes larger, its ratio of surface area to volume decreases.

Before a cell becomes too large, a growing cell divides, forming two "daughter" cells. The process by which a cell divides into two new daughter cells is called cell division.

10–2 Cell Division

Each cell has only one set of genetic information. For that reason, a cell must first copy its genetic information before cell division begins. Each daughter cell then gets a complete copy of that information. In most prokaryotes, cell division is a simple matter of separating the contents of the cell into two parts. In eukaryotes, cell division occurs in two main stages. The first stage is division of the nucleus, called mitosis. The second stage is division of the cytoplasm, called cytokinesis.

In eukaryotes, genetic information is passed on by chromosomes. Well before cell division, each chromosome is replicated (copied). When copying occurs, each chromosome consists of two identical "sister" chromatids. Each pair of chromatids is attached at an area called a centromere.

The cell cycle is a series of events that cells go through as they grow and divide. During the cell cycle, a cell grows, prepares for division, and divides to form two daughter cells, each of which then begins the cycle again. The cell cycle consists of four phases. The M phase includes mitosis and cytokinesis. The other three phases are sometimes grouped together and called interphase. Interphase is divided into three phases: G_1, S, and G_2. During the G_1 phase, cells increase in size and make new proteins and organelles. During the next phase, the S phase, the replication (copying) of chromosomes takes place. When the S phase is complete, the cell enters the G_2 phase. During the G_2 phase, many of the organelles and molecules required for cell division are produced.

Mitosis consists of four phases: prophase, metaphase, anaphase, and telophase. The first and longest phase is prophase. During prophase, the chromosomes condense and become visible. The centrioles separate and take up positions on opposite sides of the nucleus. Centrioles are two tiny structures located in the cytoplasm near the nuclear envelope. The centrioles lie in a region called the centrosome that helps to organize the spindle, a fanlike microtubule structure that helps separate the chromosomes.

During the second phase, called metaphase, chromosomes line up across the center of the cell. During the third phase, called anaphase, the centromeres that join the sister chromatids split and the sister chromatids become individual chromosomes. The two sets of chromosomes move apart. During the fourth and final phase, called telophase, the chromosomes gather at opposite ends of the cell and lose their distinct shapes. Two new nuclear envelopes form.

Cytokinesis usually occurs at the same time as telophase. In most animal cells, the cell membrane is drawn inward until the cytoplasm is pinched into two nearly equal parts. In plant cells, a structure known as a cell plate forms midway between the divided nuclei. A cell wall then begins to appear in the cell plate.

10–3 Regulating the Cell Cycle

In a multicellular organism, cell growth and cell division are carefully controlled. For instance, when an injury such as a cut in the skin occurs, cells at the edge of the cut will divide rapidly. When the healing process nears completion, the rate of cell division slows down and then returns to normal.

Cyclins—a group of proteins—regulate the timing of the cell cycle in eukaryotic cells. There are two types of these regulatory proteins: internal regulators and external regulators.

Internal regulators are proteins that respond to events inside the cell. They allow the cell cycle to proceed only when certain processes have happened inside the cell. External regulators are proteins that respond to events outside the cell. They direct cells to speed up or slow down the cell cycle. Growth factors are important external regulators. Growth factors stimulate growth and division of cells, such as during the development of the embryo or when a wound is healing.

Cancer is a disorder in which some of the body's own cells lose the ability to control growth. Cancer cells do not respond to the signals that regulate the growth of most cells. As a result, they divide uncontrollably and form masses of cells called tumors. Cancer cells may break lose from tumors and spread throughout the body. Cancer cells damage tissues and disrupt normal activities, causing serious medical problems or even death.

Chapter 10 Cell Growth and Division

Section 10–1 Cell Growth (pages 241–243)

🔑 **Key Concept**
- What problems does growth cause for cells?

Limits to Cell Growth (pages 241–243)

1. What are two reasons why cells divide rather than continue to grow indefinitely?

   a. The larger a cell becomes, the more demands the cell places on its DNA.

   b. The larger a cell becomes, the more trouble the cell has moving nutrients and wastes across the cell membrane.

2. Is the following sentence true or false? As a cell increases in size, it usually makes extra copies of its DNA. _____false_____

3. Circle the letter of what determines the rate at which food and oxygen in a cell are used up and waste products produced.

   a. The cell's organelles   **c.** The cell's location

   (b.) The cell's volume   **d.** The cell's DNA

4. How can you obtain a cell's ratio of surface area to volume? Divide the surface area by the volume.

5. If a cell's surface area is 6 cm^3 and its volume is 1 cm^3, then what is its ratio of surface area to volume? ____6 / 1 or 6 : 1____

6. Is the following sentence true or false? As a cell grows in size, its volume increases much more rapidly than its surface area. _____true_____

7. Circle the letter of what happens to a cell's ratio of surface area to volume as the cell's volume increases more rapidly than its surface area.

   (a.) The ratio decreases.   **c.** The ratio remains the same.

   b. The ratio increases.   **d.** The ratio disappears.

Division of the Cell (page 243)

8. What is cell division? Cell division is the process by which a cell divides into two new daughter cells.

9. How does cell division solve the problem of increasing size? Cell division reduces cell volume.

Section 10–2 Cell Division (pages 244–249)

⊂⊐ **Key Concepts**
- What are the main events of the cell cycle?
- What are the four phases of mitosis?

Chromosomes (pages 244–245)

1. In eukaryotic cells, what are the two main stages of cell division? They are mitosis
   and cytokinesis.

2. When chromosomes become visible at the beginning of cell division, what does each
   chromosome consist of? Each chromosome consists of two identical sister chromatids.

_____

3. Each pair of chromatids is attached at an area called the _____centromere_____.

The Cell Cycle (page 245)

4. The period of growth in between cell divisions is called _____interphase_____.

5. What is the cell cycle? The cell cycle is the series of events that cells go through as they grow
   and divide.

_____

6. Complete the diagram of the cell cycle by writing the names of each
   of the four phases.

© Pearson Education, Inc., publishing as Pearson Prentice Hall.

7. The division of the cell nucleus during the M phase of the cell cycle is called
   _____mitosis_____.

Events of the Cell Cycle (page 245)

8. Interphase is divided into what three phases?

   a. G_1 _____   b. S _____   c. G_2 _____

9. What happens during the G_1 phase? Cells do most of their growing, increasing in size and
   synthesizing new proteins and organelles.

   _____

10. What happens during the S phase? Chromosomes are replicated, and the synthesis of DNA
    molecules takes place. Also, key proteins associated with the chromosomes are synthesized.

    _____

11. What happens during the G_2 phase? Many of the organelles and molecules required for cell
    division are produced.

    _____

Mitosis (pages 246–248)

12. What are the four phases of mitosis?

    a. Prophase _____   c. Anaphase _____

    b. Metaphase _____   d. Telophase _____

13. What are the two tiny structures located in the cytoplasm near the nuclear envelope at
    the beginning of prophase? They are centrioles.

14. What is the spindle? The spindle is a fanlike microtubule structure that helps separate the
    chromosomes.

*Match the description of the event with the phase of mitosis it is in. Each
phase may be used more than once.*

	Event	Phase
c	15. The chromosomes move until they form two groups near the poles of the spindle.	a. Prophase
		b. Metaphase
a	16. The chromosomes become visible. The centrioles take up positions on opposite sides of the nucleus.	c. Anaphase
		d. Telophase
d	17. A nuclear envelope re-forms around each cluster of chromosomes. The nucleolus becomes visible in each daughter nucleus.	
b	18. The chromosomes line up across the center of the cell.	

Name_____ Class_____ Date _____

19. Identify each of the four phases of mitosis pictured below.

a. _Anaphase_____

c. _Telophase_____

b. _Prophase_____

d. _Metaphase_____

Cytokinesis (page 248)

20. What is cytokinesis? _Cytokinesis is the division of the cytoplasm itself._____

21. How does cytokinesis occur in most animal cells? _The cell membrane is drawn inward until_ _the cytoplasm is pinched into two nearly equal parts._____

22. What forms midway between the divided nucleus during cytokinesis in plant cells?
_The cell plate forms._____

Reading Skill Practice

You may sometimes forget the meanings of the vocabulary terms that were introduced earlier in the textbook. When this happens, you can check the meanings of the terms in the Glossary, which you can find at the end of the book, preceding the Index. Use the Glossary to review the meanings of all the vocabulary terms listed on page 244. Write their definitions on a separate sheet of paper.

The wording of the definitions in the Glossary is often slightly different from how the terms are defined in the flow of the text. Students should write the Glossary definition of each term.

Section 10–3 Regulating the Cell Cycle

(pages 250–252)

🔑 **Key Concepts**
- How is the cell cycle regulated?
- How are cancer cells different from other cells?

Controls on Cell Division (page 250)

1. What happens to the cells at the edges of an injury when a cut in the skin or a break in a bone occurs? The cells at the edges of the injury are stimulated to divide rapidly.

2. What happens to the rapidly dividing cells when the healing process nears completion? The rate of cell division slows down, controls on growth are restored, and everything returns to normal.

Cell Cycle Regulators (page 251)

3. What do cyclins regulate? Cyclins regulate the timing of the cell cycle in eukaryotic cells.

4. What are internal regulators? They are proteins that respond to events inside the cell.

5. Circle the letter of each sentence that is true about external regulators.

   a. They direct cells to speed up or slow down the cell cycle.

   b. They prevent the cell from entering anaphase until all its chromosomes are attached to the mitotic spindle.

   c. They include growth factors.

   d. They prevent excessive cell growth and keep the tissues of the body from disrupting one another.

Uncontrolled Cell Growth (page 252)

6. What is cancer? Cancer is a disorder in which some of the body's own cells lose the ability to control growth.

7. Complete the flowchart about cancer.

   > Cancer cells don't respond to signals that regulate _____growth_____.

   ↓

   > Cancer cells form masses of cells called _____tumors_____.

   ↓

   > Cancer cells break loose and spread throughout the _____body_____.

8. Is the following sentence true or false? Cancer is a disease of the cell cycle. _____true_____

Name_____ Class_____ Date _____

Vocabulary Review

Completion   *Fill in the blanks with terms from Chapter 10.*

1. The division of a cell's cytoplasm is called _____cytokinesis_____.

2. The final phase of mitosis is _____telophase_____.

3. The phase of mitosis in which microtubules connect the centromere of each chromosome to the poles of the spindle is _____metaphase_____.

4. At the beginning of cell division, each chromosome consists of two sister _____chromatids_____.

5. The longest phase of mitosis is _____prophase_____.

6. The phase of mitosis that ends when the chromosomes stop moving is _____anaphase_____.

7. The process by which a cell divides into two new daughter cells is called _____cell division_____.

8. A tiny structure located in the cytoplasm near the nuclear envelope is a(an) _____centriole_____.

9. A disorder in which some of the body's cells lose the ability to control growth is called _____cancer_____.

10. The area where a pair of chromatids is attached is the _____centromere_____.

11. The division of the cell nucleus is called _____mitosis_____.

12. A protein that regulates the timing of the cell cycle in eukaryotic cells is _____cyclin_____.

13. The series of events that cells go through as they grow and divide is known as the _____cell cycle_____.

14. A fanlike microtubule structure that helps separate the chromosomes is a(an) _____spindle_____.

15. The time period between cell divisions is called _____interphase_____.

Summary

11–1 The Work of Gregor Mendel

The scientific study of heredity is called genetics. Gregor Mendel used purebred pea plants in a series of experiments to understand inheritance.

Pea flowers have both male and female parts. Normally, pollen from the male part of the pea flower fertilizes the female egg cells of the same flower. This is called self-pollination. Seeds that come from self-pollination inherit all their characteristics from just one parent.

To carry out his experiments, Mendel had to prevent self-pollination. He did this by cutting away the pollen-bearing male parts and then dusting pollen from another plant on the flower. This process is called cross-pollination. The seeds that come from cross-pollination are the offspring of two different parents.

Mendel decided to study just a few traits, or characteristics, of the pea plants. He studied seven traits: seed shape, seed color, seed coat color, pod shape, pod color, flower position, and plant height.

First, Mendel crossed two plants with different characters, or forms, for the same trait. For example, one plant was tall and the other was short. Mendel used the seeds produced by this cross to grow plants. These plants were hybrids. Hybrids are the offspring of crosses between parents with different traits.

To Mendel's surprise, the hybrid plants looked like only one of the parents. He concluded that each trait was controlled by one gene that occurred in two different forms. The different forms of a gene are called alleles. Mendel formed the theory of dominance. He concluded that some alleles are dominant, while others are recessive. Whenever a living thing inherits a dominant allele, that trait is visible. The effects of a recessive allele are not seen if the dominant allele is present.

Mendel wanted to know what happened to the recessive allele. He allowed his hybrid plants to self-pollinate. Some of the plants that were produced showed the recessive trait. The alleles responsible for the recessive characters had not disappeared. Before, the dominant allele had masked the recessive allele, so it was not visible. Mendel concluded that the alleles for the same trait can be separated. He called this segregation. Alleles segregate when gametes are formed. Each gamete carries only one copy of each gene.

11–2 Probability and Punnett Squares

Mendel used the principles of probability to explain his results. Probability is the likelihood that a particular event will occur. Probability can be used to predict the outcome of genetic crosses because alleles segregate randomly. The gene combinations that might result from a genetic cross can be determined by drawing a Punnett square.

In a Punnett square, alleles are represented by letters. A capital letter represents the dominant allele, and a lowercase letter represents the recessive allele. Organisms that have two identical alleles for a particular trait are called homozygous. Homozygous organisms are true-breeding for a particular trait. Organisms that have two different alleles for a particular trait are called heterozygous. Heterozygous organisms are hybrid for a particular trait.

The physical traits of an organism make up its phenotype (for example, height). The genetic makeup of an organism is its genotype (for example, TT or Tt).

One important rule of probability is that probabilities predict the average outcome of a large number of events. They cannot predict what will happen in a single event. The more organisms examined, the closer the numbers will get to the expected values.

11–3 Exploring Mendelian Genetics

Mendel wondered whether genes that determine one trait have anything to do with genes that determine another trait. He wanted to know, for example, whether the gene that determines seed shape affects the gene for seed color. To answer this question, he did an experiment. He crossed plants and recorded two traits—seed shape and seed color.

Mendel found that the gene controlling seed shape did not affect the gene controlling seed color. Mendel concluded that genes can segregate independently, or undergo independent assortment, during gamete formation.

Not all genes show simple patterns of dominant and recessive alleles. In incomplete dominance, one allele is not completely dominant over another. In codominance, both alleles contribute to the phenotype. Many genes have more than two alleles and are said to have multiple alleles. Polygenic traits are traits controlled by two or more genes.

The characteristics of any organism are not caused only by its genes. Instead, characteristics are determined by the interaction between the genes and the environment.

11–4 Meiosis

According to Mendel, living things inherit a single copy of each gene from each of their parents. When gametes are formed, these two copies are separated.

Gametes are made during meiosis. In a complex process, the number of chromosomes in each cell is cut in half. The chromosomes are different from one another and from the parent cell.

There are two stages in meiosis. During the first stage, the DNA in special cells in the reproductive organs is copied. The cells then divide. Two cells are formed. These cells are different from each other and different from the parent cell. In the second stage of meiosis, the cells divide again. This time, their DNA is not copied first. Four daughter cells are produced. Each cell contains half the number of chromosomes of the original parent cell.

In male animals, the gametes produced by meiosis are called sperm. Some plants also have sperm cells. In females, meiosis produces one large reproductive cell and three smaller cells. In animals, the larger reproductive cell is called an egg. In some plants, it is called an egg cell. The three smaller cells produced during meiosis are called polar bodies. They do not participate in reproduction.

Meiosis is very different from mitosis. Mitosis makes two cells that are exactly alike. The cells are also exactly like the parent cell. Meiosis, however, produces four cells. Each of the cells has only half the number of chromosomes of the parent cell. The cells are genetically different from one another.

11–5 Linkage and Gene Maps

Some genes are almost always inherited together. These genes belong to the same linkage group. A chromosome is a group of linked genes. It is actually the chromosomes that assort independently during gamete formation, not single genes.

The location of genes can be mapped to a chromosome. The rate of crossover events is used to find the distance between genes on a chromosome. The farther apart two genes are, the more likely they will be separated by a crossover event.

Section 11–1 The Work of Gregor Mendel
(pages 263–266)

👁 Key Concepts
- What is the principle of dominance?
- What happens during segregation?

Gregor Mendel's Peas (pages 263–264)

1. The scientific study of heredity is called _____genetics_____.

2. Circle the letter of each sentence that is true about Gregor Mendel's peas.

    a. The male parts of pea flowers produce eggs.

    (**b.**) When pollen fertilizes an egg cell, a seed for a new plant is formed.

    (**c.**) Pea plants normally reproduce by self-pollination.

    d. Seeds that are produced by self-pollination inherit their characteristics from two different plants.

3. What does it mean when pea plants are described as being true-breeding?
   If the plants are allowed to self-pollinate, they will produce offspring identical to themselves.

4. To perform his experiments, how did Mendel prevent pea flowers from self-pollinating and control their cross-pollination? He cut away the pollen-bearing male parts of a flower and dusted that flower with pollen from another plant.

Genes and Dominance (pages 264–265)

Match the term with its definition.

Terms		Definitions
c	**5.** genes	**a.** Specific characteristics that vary from one individual to another
b	**6.** hybrids	**b.** The offspring of crosses between parents with different traits
a	**7.** traits	**c.** Chemical factors that determine traits
d	**8.** alleles	**d.** The different forms of a gene

9. State the principle of dominance. Some alleles are dominant and others are recessive.

10. Is the following sentence true or false? An organism with a recessive allele for a particular form of a trait will always exhibit that form. _____false_____

11. Circle the letters of the traits controlled by dominant alleles in Mendel's pea plants.

    (**a.**) tall   **b.** short   (**c.**) yellow   **d.** green

Segregation (pages 265–266)

12. How did Mendel find out whether the recessive alleles were still present in the F₁ plants? _He allowed the F₁ plants to produce an F₂ generation by self-pollination._

_____

_____

13. About one fourth of the F₂ plants from Mendel's F₁ crosses showed the trait controlled by the _____recessive_____ allele.

14. Circle the letter of each sentence that is true about Mendel's explanation of the results from his F₁ cross.

   (a.) Mendel assumed that a dominant allele had masked the corresponding recessive allele in the F₁ generation.

   b. The trait controlled by the recessive allele never showed up in any F₂ plants.

   c. The allele for shortness was always inherited with the allele for tallness.

   (d.) At some point, the allele for shortness was segregated, or separated, from the allele for tallness.

15. What are gametes? _They are the sex cells._

_____

16. Complete the following diagram to show how alleles segregate during the formation of gametes.

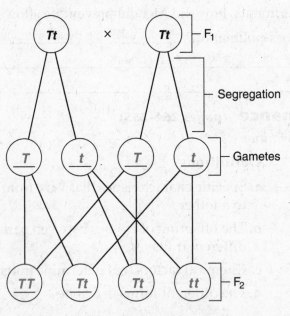

17. In the diagram above, the dominant allele is represented by _____T_____ and the recessive allele is represented by _____t_____.

Section 11–2 Probability and Punnett Squares
(pages 267–269)

👉 **Key Concepts**
- How do geneticists use the principles of probability?
- How do geneticists use Punnett squares?

Genetics and Probability (page 267)

1. The likelihood that a particular event will occur is called ____probability____.
2. Circle the letter of the probability that a single coin flip will come up heads.

   a. 100 percent   **b.** 75 percent   (**c.**) 50 percent   **d.** 25 percent

3. Is the following sentence true or false? The past outcomes of coin flips greatly affect the outcomes of future coin flips. ____false____

4. Why can the principles of probability be used to predict the outcomes of genetic crosses? The way in which the alleles segregate is completely random, like a coin flip.

Punnett Squares (page 268)

5. How do geneticists use Punnett squares? Punnett squares can be used to predict and compare the genetic variations that will result from a cross.

6. Complete the Punnett square to show the possible gene combinations for the F₂ offspring.

PUNNETT SQUARE FOR Tt × Tt

	T	t
T	TT	Tt
t	Tt	tt

Match the terms with the definitions.

Terms	Definitions
d 7. genotype	**a.** Organisms that have two identical alleles for a particular trait (*TT* or *tt*)
a 8. homozygous	**b.** Organisms that have two different alleles for the same trait (*Tt*)
c 9. phenotype	**c.** Physical characteristic of an organism (tall)
b 10. heterozygous	**d.** Genetic makeup of an organism (*Tt*)

Name_____ Class_____ Date _____

11. Is the following sentence true or false? Homozygous organisms are true-breeding for a particular trait. _____true_____

12. Is the following sentence true or false? Plants with the same phenotype always have the same genotype. _____false_____

Probability and Segregation (page 269)

13. Circle the letter of each sentence that is true about probability and segregation.

   a. In an F₁ cross between two hybrid tall pea plants (*Tt*), ½ of the F₂ plants will have two alleles for tallness (*TT*).

   b. The F₂ ratio of tall plants to short plants produced in a cross between two hybrid tall pea plants (*Tt*) is 3 tall plants for every 1 short plant.

   c. Mendel observed that about ¾ of the F₂ offspring showed the dominant trait.

   d. Segregation occurs according to Mendel's model.

14. In Mendel's model of segregation, what was the ratio of tall plants to short plants in the F₂ generation? The ratio was 3 : 1.

Probabilities Predict Averages (page 269)

15. Is the following sentence true or false? Probabilities predict the precise outcome of an individual event. _____false_____

16. How can you be sure of getting the expected 50 : 50 ratio from flipping a coin?
You must flip the coin many times.

17. The _____larger_____ the number of offspring from a genetic cross, the closer the resulting numbers will get to expected values.

18. Is the following sentence true or false? The ratios of an F₁ generation are more likely to match Mendelian predicted ratios if the F₁ generation contains hundreds or thousands of individuals. _____true_____

Reading Skill Practice

Taking notes helps the reader focus on the main ideas and the vocabulary of the reading. Take notes while rereading Section 11–2. Note the main ideas and the highlighted, boldface terms in the order in which they are presented. You may copy the ideas word for word or summarize them using your own words. Do your work on a separate sheet of paper.

Notes should be based on the key concepts and vocabulary from Section 11–2 on pages 267–269.

Section 11–3 Exploring Mendelian Genetics
(pages 270–274)

Key Concepts
- What is the principle of independent assortment?
- What inheritance patterns exist aside from simple dominance?

Independent Assortment (pages 270–271)

1. In a two-factor cross, Mendel followed _____ two _____ different genes as they passed from one generation to the next.

2. Write the genotypes of the true-breeding plants that Mendel used in his two-factor cross.

Phenotype	Genotype
a. round yellow peas	RRYY
b. wrinkled green peas	rryy

3. Circle the letter that best describes the F₁ offspring of Mendel's two-factor cross.
   - **a.** Homozygous dominant with round yellow peas
   - **b.** Homozygous recessive with wrinkled green peas
   - **(c.)** Heterozygous dominant with round yellow peas
   - **d.** Heterozygous recessive with wrinkled green peas

4. Is the following sentence true or false? The genotypes of the F₁ offspring indicated to Mendel that genes assort independently. _____ false _____

5. How did Mendel produce the F₂ offspring? He crossed F₁ plants with each other.

6. Circle the letter of the phenotypes that Mendel would expect to see if genes segregated independently.
   - **a.** round and yellow
   - **b.** wrinkled and green
   - **(c.)** round and green
   - **(d.)** wrinkled and yellow

7. What did Mendel observe in the F₂ offspring that showed him that the alleles for seed shape segregate independently of those for seed color? He observed F₂ offspring that had combinations of phenotypes—and therefore combinations of alleles—not found in either parent.

8. What were the phenotypes of the F₂ generation that Mendel observed? He observed seeds that were round and yellow, wrinkled and green, round and green, and wrinkled and yellow.

9. What was the ratio of Mendel's F$_2$ generation for the two-factor cross? __9 : 3 : 3 : 1__

_____

10. Complete the Punnett square below to show the predicted results of Mendel's two-factor cross.

MENDEL'S TWO-FACTOR CROSS
RrYy × *RrYy*

	RY	Ry	rY	ry
RY	RRYY	RRYy	RrYY	RrYy
Ry	RRYy	RRyy	RrYy	Rryy
rY	RrYY	RrYy	rrYY	rrYy
ry	RrYy	Rryy	rrYy	rryy

11. State Mendel's principle of independent assortment. Genes for different traits can
segregate independently during the formation of gametes.

_____

A Summary of Mendel's Principles (page 272)

12. Circle the letter of each sentence that is true about Mendel's principles.

(a.) The inheritance of biological characteristics is determined by genes that are passed from parents to their offspring.

b. Two or more forms of the gene for a single trait can never exist.

(c.) The copies of genes are segregated from each other when gametes are formed.

(d.) The alleles for different genes usually segregate independently of one another.

13. When two or more forms of the gene for a single trait exist, some forms of the gene

may be ____dominant____ and others may be ____recessive____.

Beyond Dominant and Recessive Alleles (pages 272–273)

14. Is the following sentence true or false? All genes show simple patterns of dominant

and recessive alleles. ____false____

15. Complete the table of the different patterns of inheritance.

PATTERNS OF INHERITANCE

Type	Description	Examples
Incomplete Dominance	One allele is not completely dominant over another. The heterozygous phenotype is somewhere in between the two homozygous phenotypes.	Flower color in four o'clock plants
Codominance	Both alleles contribute to the phenotype of the organism.	Black and white feather color in certain varieties of chickens
Multiple Alleles	Genes have more than two alleles.	Coat color in rabbits, blood type in humans, eye color in humans
Polygenic Traits	Two or more genes control a trait.	Eye color in fruit flies, skin color in humans

Applying Mendel's Principles (page 274)

16. List three criteria Thomas Hunt Morgan was looking for in a model organism for genetic studies.

a. Small in size _____

b. Easy to keep in the laboratory _____

c. Able to produce large numbers of offspring in a short time _____

17. Is the following sentence true or false? Mendel's principles apply not just to pea plants but to other organisms as well. _____true_____

Genetics and the Environment (page 274)

18. Characteristics are determined by interaction between genes and the _____environment_____.

© Pearson Education, Inc., publishing as Pearson Prentice Hall.

Section 11–4 Meiosis (pages 275–278)

Key Concepts
- What happens during the process of meiosis?
- How is meiosis different from mitosis?

Introduction (page 275)

1. List the two things that Mendel's principles of genetics required in order to be true.

   a. Each organism must inherit a single copy of every gene from both its parents.

   _____

   b. When an organism produces its own gametes, those two sets of genes must be separated from

   each other.

   _____

Chromosome Number (page 275)

2. What does it mean when two sets of chromosomes are homologous? Each of the

   chromosomes in the set from the male parent has a corresponding chromosome from the

   female parent.

   _____

3. Circle the letter of each way to describe a diploid cell.

   (a.) 2N

   (b.) Contains two sets of homologous chromosomes

   c. Contains a single set of homologous chromosomes

   d. A gamete

4. Circle the letter of the number of chromosomes in a haploid *Drosophila* cell.

   a. 8   (b.) 4   c. 2   d. 0

Phases of Meiosis (pages 276–277)

5. Draw the chromosomes in the diagrams below to show the correct phase of meiosis.

Prophase I   Metaphase I   Anaphase II

© Pearson Education, Inc., publishing as Pearson Prentice Hall.

6. Identify which phase of meiosis is shown in the diagrams below.

__Interphase I__   __Telophase II and Cytokinesis__

7. Why is meiosis described as a process of reduction division? The number of
chromosomes per cell is cut in half through the separation of homologous chromosomes in a
diploid cell.

_____

8. What are the two distinct divisions of meiosis?
   a. Meiosis I   **b.** Meiosis II

9. Is the following sentence true or false? The diploid cell that enters meiosis becomes
   4 haploid cells at the end of meiosis. _____true_____

10. How does a tetrad form in prophase I of meiosis? A tetrad forms when each chromosome
pairs with its corresponding homologous chromosome.

_____

11. Circle the number of chromatids in a tetrad.
   a. 8   **b.** 6   (**c.**) 4   **d.** 2

12. What results from the process of crossing-over during prophase I? When homologous
chromosomes in tetrads exchange portions of their chromatids, alleles are exchanged between the
homologous chromosomes to produce new combinations of alleles.

_____

13. Circle the letter of each sentence that is true about meiosis.

　(a.) During meiosis I, homologous chromosomes separate.

　b. The two daughter cells produced by meiosis I still have the two complete sets of chromosomes, as does a diploid cell.

　(c.) During anaphase II, the paired chromatids separate.

　d. After meiosis II, the four daughter cells contain the diploid number of chromosomes.

Gamete Formation (page 278)

Match the products of meiosis with the descriptions.

Product of Meiosis		Description
_b_	**14.** eggs	**a.** Haploid gametes produced in males
_a_	**15.** sperm	**b.** Haploid gametes produced in females
_c_	**16.** polar bodies	**c.** Cells produced in females that do not participate in reproduction

Comparing Mitosis and Meiosis (page 278)

17. Circle the letter of each sentence that is true about mitosis and meiosis.

　a. Mitosis produces four genetically different haploid cells.

　b. Meiosis produces two genetically identical diploid cells.

　(c.) Mitosis begins with a diploid cell.

　(d.) Meiosis begins with a diploid cell.

Reading Skill Practice

You can often increase your understanding of what you've read by making comparisons. A compare-and-contrast table helps you to do this. On a separate sheet of paper, make a table to compare the processes of mitosis and meiosis. For more information about compare-and-contrast tables, see Organizing Information in Appendix A.

Students' tables should include the basic information about mitosis and meiosis. You may wish to suggest that students review Section 10–2 in their textbooks before starting this exercise.

© Pearson Education, Inc., publishing as Pearson Prentice Hall.

Section 11–5 Linkage and Gene Maps
(pages 279–280)

🔑 **Key Concept**
- What structures actually assort independently?

Gene Linkage (page 279)

1. Is the following sentence true or false? Thomas Hunt Morgan discovered that some genes violated the principle of independent assortment. _____ true _____

2. Morgan grouped the *Drosophila* genes that were inherited together into four _____ linkage _____ groups.

3. List the two conclusions that Morgan made about genes and chromosomes.

   a. Each chromosome is a group of linked genes.

   b. Chromosomes assort independently, not individual genes.

4. Why didn't Mendel observe gene linkage? Six of the seven genes he studied are on different chromosomes. The two genes on the same chromosome are so far apart that they also assort independently.

Gene Maps (pages 279–280)

5. Explain why two genes found on the same chromosome are not always linked forever.
Crossing-over during meiosis sometimes separates genes that had been on the same chromosome onto homologous chromosomes.

6. The new combinations of alleles produced by crossover events help to generate genetic _____ diversity _____ .

7. Is the following sentence true or false? Genes that are closer together are more likely to be separated by a crossover event in meiosis. _____ false _____

8. What is a gene map? It shows the relative locations of each gene on a chromosome.

9. How is a gene map constructed? It is constructed by using recombination rates, which measure the frequencies of crossing-over between genes.

Vocabulary Review

Labeling Diagrams   *Use the words listed below to label the Punnett square. Some words may be used twice.*

heterozygous parent   homozygous offspring
dominant allele   heterozygous offspring
recessive allele

1. ___heterozygous parent___

6. ___homozygous offspring___

5. ___dominant allele___

4. ___recessive allele___

2. ___heterozygous offspring___

3. ___homozygous offspring___

	H	h
H	HH	Hh
h	Hh	hh

Matching   *In the space provided, write the letter of the definition that best matches each term.*

__c__	**7.** phenotype	**a.** likelihood that something will happen
__e__	**8.** gamete	**b.** shows the relative locations of genes on a chromosome
__h__	**9.** genetics	**c.** physical characteristics of an organism
__a__	**10.** probability	**d.** containing one set of chromosomes
__d__	**11.** haploid	**e.** sex cell
__b__	**12.** gene map	**f.** chemical factor that determines traits
__f__	**13.** gene	**g.** specific characteristic
__i__	**14.** multiple alleles	**h.** scientific study of heredity
__g__	**15.** trait	**i.** gene with more than two alleles

Completion   *Fill in the blanks with terms from Chapter 11.*

16. The process in which two genes segregate independently is called
___independent assortment___.

17. Plants that, if left to self-pollinate, produce offspring identical to themselves are called
___true-breeding___.

18. The offspring of crosses between parents with different traits are called
___hybrids___.

19. The process during sexual reproduction in which male and female sex cells join is called
___fertilization___.

20. The process of reduction division in which the number of chromosomes per cell is cut
in half is called ___meiosis___.

© Pearson Education, Inc., publishing as Pearson Prentice Hall.

Summary

12–1 DNA

To understand genetics, biologists had to learn the chemical structure of the gene. Frederick Griffith first learned that some factor from dead, disease-causing bacteria turned harmless bacteria into disease-causing ones. Griffith called this process transformation. Griffith thought that the transforming factor might be a gene. Oswald Avery and his research group later found that DNA was the transforming factor. Alfred Hershey and Martha Chase also showed that genes are made of DNA.

Scientists began studying the structure of DNA to learn how it can carry information, determine an organism's traits, and replicate itself. DNA is a long molecule made up of units called nucleotides. Each nucleotide is made up of a 5-carbon sugar, a phosphate group, and a nitrogen-containing base. There are four kinds of bases: adenine, guanine, cytosine, and thymine.

James Watson and Francis Crick discovered that DNA is shaped like a double helix, or a twisted ladder, in which two strands are wound around each other. The two strands are held together by hydrogen bonds between adenine and thymine and between guanine and cytosine. The sugar phosphate backbone makes up the sides of the ladder.

12–2 Chromosomes and DNA Replication

Single-celled organisms without a nucleus have DNA in the cytoplasm. Most have one circular DNA molecule. In organisms with a nucleus, DNA is in the nucleus. The DNA is organized into different numbers of chromosomes, depending on the organism.

DNA molecules are very long. To fit inside cells, they must be tightly folded. The DNA in a chromosome is wound around proteins, called histones. The DNA and histones wind together to form nucleosomes.

Before a cell divides, it copies its DNA in a process called replication. The DNA molecule separates into two strands. Then, two new strands form, following the rules of base pairing. Each strand of the DNA molecule serves as a template, or model, for the new strand.

Many enzymes carry out DNA replication. One enzyme, called DNA polymerase, joins individual nucleotides to produce the DNA molecule. It also checks that the correct nucleotide is added.

12–3 RNA and Protein Synthesis

In order for a gene to work, the genetic instructions in the DNA molecule must be decoded. The first step is to copy the DNA sequence into RNA. RNA makes it possible for a single gene in a DNA molecule to make hundreds of copies.

RNA has a structure like DNA, except for three differences: (1) The sugar in RNA is ribose instead of deoxyribose; (2) RNA is single-stranded; and (3) RNA has uracil in place of thymine.

Three kinds of RNA molecules work together to make proteins. Messenger RNA has the instructions to put together amino acids to make a protein. Proteins are put together on ribosomes. Ribosomes are made up of proteins and ribosomal RNA. Transfer RNA carries each amino acid to the ribosome according to the coded message in messenger RNA.

RNA is copied from DNA in a process called transcription. The enzyme RNA polymerase binds to DNA and separates the two strands. Then, RNA polymerase builds a strand of RNA using one strand of DNA as the template. The sequence of DNA that signals RNA polymerase where to bind and start making RNA is called the promoter.

The instructions for making proteins are found in the order of the four nitrogenous bases. This code is read three letters, or nucleotides, at a time. Each codon, or group of three nucleotides, specifies a certain amino acid that makes up a protein. In the genetic code, some amino acids are specified by more than one codon. One codon is a start signal for translation. Three codons signal the end of translation.

Translation is the process in which the genetic code in RNA is used to make proteins. Translation takes place on ribosomes. Before translation can begin, messenger RNA is transcribed from DNA. Then, the messenger RNA moves into the cytoplasm and attaches to a ribosome. As each codon of the messenger RNA moves through the ribosome, the proper amino acid is brought into the ribosome by transfer RNA. The ribosome joins together each amino acid. In this way, the protein chain grows. When the ribosome reaches a stop codon, it falls away from the protein chain and the messenger RNA molecule. Transcription has ended.

12–4 Mutations

Mutations are changes in the sequence of DNA. Gene mutations are changes in a single gene. Chromosomal mutations cause changes in whole chromosomes. Gene mutations that occur at a single point in the DNA sequence are called point mutations. When a point mutation causes one base to replace another, only one amino acid is affected. If a nucleotide is added or taken away, it causes a frameshift mutation. All the groupings of three nucleotides, or codons, are changed. This can cause the gene to produce a completely different protein.

In a chromosomal mutation, there is a change in the number or the structure of chromosomes. There are four kinds of chromosomal mutations: deletions, duplications, inversions, and translocations.

12–5 Gene Regulation

Genes can be turned on and off when proteins are needed. In prokaryotes, some genes are turned on and off by a section of a chromosome called an operon. An operon is a group of genes that work together. Two sequences of DNA in the operon that control when genes are turned on and off are the operator and the promoter. When the cell needs a certain protein, RNA polymerase attaches to the promoter and produces a messenger RNA that is translated into the needed protein.

When the cell no longer needs the protein, it makes another special protein called the repressor. The repressor attaches to the operator, blocking the promoter so that RNA polymerase cannot attach to it. This turns the genes of the operon off.

In eukaryotes, there are several ways of turning genes on and off. One system uses a protein that binds directly to DNA. This either starts or increases the transcription of certain genes.

Chapter 12 DNA and RNA

Section 12–1 DNA (pages 287–294)

⟜ Key Concepts
- What did scientists discover about the relationship between genes and DNA?
- What is the overall structure of the DNA molecule?

Griffith and Transformation (pages 287–289)

1. What did Frederick Griffith want to learn about bacteria? <u>He wanted to learn how certain</u>
<u>types of bacteria produce pneumonia.</u>

_____

2. The strain of bacteria that caused pneumonia grew into _____<u>smooth</u>_____ colonies
on culture plates; harmless bacteria produced colonies with _____<u>rough</u>_____ edges.

3. Circle the letter of each sentence that is true about Griffith's experiment.

   (**a.**) Mice injected with bacteria from smooth colonies died.

   b. Mice injected with bacteria from rough colonies died.

   c. Mice injected with heat-killed bacteria from smooth colonies died.

   (**d.**) Mice injected with a mixture of bacteria from heat-killed smooth colonies and live
rough colonies died.

4. What result from Griffith's experiment suggested that the cause of pneumonia was not a
chemical poison released by the disease-causing bacteria? <u>The mice survived after being</u>
<u>injected with heat-killed disease-causing bacteria.</u>

_____

5. What is transformation? <u>It is the process by which one strain of bacteria changes into another.</u>

_____

6. What hypothesis did Griffith form from the results of his experiments? <u>Some factor,</u>
<u>which might be a gene, was transferred from the heat-killed bacteria cells into the live cells.</u>

_____

Avery and DNA (page 289)

7. Is the following sentence true or false? Avery and his colleagues thought that the
molecule required in transformation might also be the molecule of the gene.
_____<u>true</u>_____

8. Briefly describe how Avery and his group determined which molecule was most
important for transformation. <u>They treated the extract of heat-killed bacteria with enzymes</u>
<u>that destroyed proteins, lipids, carbohydrates, and other molecules, including RNA and DNA.</u>

_____

Name_____ Class_____ Date _____

9. Transformation did not occur when _____DNA_____ was destroyed.
10. What was the conclusion from Avery's experiments? _DNA was the transforming factor._
_____

The Hershey-Chase Experiment (pages 289–290)

11. What is a bacteriophage? _It is a virus that infects bacteria._
_____

12. Circle the letter of each part that makes up a bacteriophage.
   a. lipid coat   c. carbohydrate core
   (b.) protein coat   (d.) DNA core

13. What happens when a bacteriophage infects a bacterial cell? _The bacteriophage injects_
   its DNA into the cell. The viral genes act to produce many new bacteriophages, which burst out
   when the cell splits open.

14. How would Hershey and Chase learn whether genes were made of protein or DNA?
   If they could determine which part of the virus entered the infected cell, they would learn whether
   genes were made of protein or DNA.
   _____

15. What results did Hershey and Chase observe? _Nearly all of the radioactivity in the bacteria_
   was from phosphorus, the marker found in DNA.
   _____

16. Hershey and Chase concluded that the genetic material of the bacteriophage was
   _____DNA_____.

The Components and Structure of DNA (pages 291–294)

17. List the three critical things that genes were known to do.
   a. Genes had to carry information from one generation to the next.
   _____

   b. Genes had to determine the heritable characteristics of organisms.
   _____

   c. Genes had to be easily copied.
   _____

18. What is the makeup of a nucleotide? _It is a five-carbon sugar, a phosphate group, and a_
   nitrogenous base.

19. Adenine, guanine, cytosine, and thymine are four kinds of ____nitrogenous____ bases
   in DNA.

Name_____ Class_____ Date _____

20. Identify the components of a nucleotide in the diagram below. Label the bases as purines or pyrimidines.

21. Is the following sentence true or false? Adenine and guanine are larger molecules than cytosine and thymine because they have two rings in their structure. _____true_____

22. What forms the backbone of a DNA chain? It is formed by the sugar and phosphate groups of each nucleotide.

23. Is the following sentence true or false? The nucleotides must be joined together in a specific order. _____false_____

24. According to Chargaff's rules, the percentages of _____adenine_____ are equal to those of thymine and the percentages of _____cytosine_____ are equal to those of guanine in the DNA molecule.

25. Rosalind Franklin's work with X-ray diffraction showed that the DNA molecule is shaped like a(an) _____helix_____ and contains _____two_____ strands.

26. How did Francis Crick and James Watson try to understand the structure of DNA? They built three-dimensional models of the DNA molecule from cardboard and wire.

27. How did Watson and Crick describe the structure of DNA? DNA was a double helix, in which two strands were wound around each other.

28. Is the following sentence true or false? According to the principle of base pairing, hydrogen bonds could form only between adenine and cytosine. _____false_____

Section 12–2 Chromosomes and DNA Replication (pages 295–299)

🔑 **Key Concept**

- What happens during DNA replication?

DNA and Chromosomes (pages 295–297)

1. Circle the letter of the location of DNA in prokaryotic cells.

   a. nucleus   **b.** mitochondria   (**c.**) cytoplasm   **d.** vacuole

2. Is the following sentence true or false? Most prokaryotes contain a single, circular DNA molecule. _____true_____

3. Eukaryotic DNA is generally located in the cell _____nucleus_____ in the form of a number of chromosomes.

4. Is the following sentence true or false? All organisms have the same number of chromosomes. _____false_____

5. Is the following sentence true or false? The *E. coli* chromosome is longer than the diameter of an individual *E. coli* bacterium. _____true_____

6. Circle the letter of each sentence that is true about chromosome structure.

   a. The DNA in eukaryotic cells is very loosely packed.

   b. Prokaryotic cells contain more DNA than eukaryotic cells.

   (**c.**) A human cell contains more than 1 meter of DNA.

   (**d.**) The DNA of the smallest human chromosome is nearly 10 times as long as many bacterial chromosomes.

7. Eukaryotic chromosomes contain both DNA and protein, packed together to form _____chromatin_____ .

8. What are histones? _Histones are proteins around which DNA is tightly coiled._

9. Why are individual chromosomes visible only during mitosis? _The fibers formed from nucleosomes packing together are dispersed in the nucleus during most of the cell cycle._

10. Is the following sentence true or false? Changes in chromatin structure and histone-DNA binding are associated with changes in gene activity. _____true_____

11. What do nucleosomes do? _They fold enormous lengths of DNA into the cell nucleus._

© Pearson Education, Inc., publishing as Pearson Prentice Hall.

DNA Replication (pages 297–299)

12. What occurs during the process of replication? <u>The cell duplicates its DNA in a copying</u> process.

13. Complete the flowchart to describe the process of DNA replication.

> The DNA molecule _____separates_____, or unzips, into two strands.

> Each strand serves as a(an) _____template_____, or model, to produce the new strands.

> Two new _____complementary_____ strands are produced, following the rules of _____base pairing_____.

14. Is the following sentence true or false? In eukaryotic chromosomes, DNA replication begins at a single point in the chromosome and proceeds in two directions. _____false_____

15. The sites where DNA replication and separation occur are called _____replication forks_____.

16. What occurs when a molecule of DNA is "unzipped"? <u>The hydrogen bonds between the</u> base pairs are broken, and the two strands of the molecule unwind.

17. What is the complementary strand of bases for a strand with the bases TACGTT? The complementary strand is ATGCAA.

18. Is the following sentence true or false? Each DNA molecule resulting from replication has one original strand and one new strand. _____true_____

19. List two major roles of DNA polymerase in the process of DNA replication.
a. It polymerizes individual nucleotides to produce DNA.
b. It "proofreads" each new DNA strand.

Reading Skill Practice

The illustrations in textbooks can help you better understand a difficult concept. Look at Figure 12–10 on page 297. List in order, beginning with DNA, the levels of organization of eukaryotic DNA to form chromosomes. Do your work on a separate sheet of paper.

DNA, histones, nucleosomes, coils, supercoils, chromosome

Name_____ Class_____ Date _____

Section 12–3 RNA and Protein Synthesis
(pages 300–306)

Key Concepts
- What are the three main types of RNA?
- What is transcription?
- What is translation?

The Structure of RNA (page 300)

1. List the three main differences between RNA and DNA.

   a. RNA has ribose sugar instead of deoxyribose.

   b. RNA is generally single-stranded, instead of double-stranded.

   c. RNA contains uracil in place of thymine.

2. What is the importance of the cell's ability to copy a single DNA sequence into RNA?
   It makes it possible for a single gene to produce large numbers of RNA molecules.

Types of RNA (pages 300–301)

3. What is the one job in which most RNA molecules are involved? Most are involved in protein synthesis.

4. Complete the table about the types of RNA.

TYPES OF RNA

Type	Function
Messenger RNA	Carries copies of the instructions for assembling amino acids from DNA to the rest of the cell
Ribosomal RNA	Is a part of ribosomes
Transfer RNA	Transfers each amino acid to the ribosome to help assemble proteins

Transcription (page 301)

5. Circle the letter of each sentence that is true about transcription.

   a. During transcription, DNA polymerase binds to RNA and separates the DNA strands.

   b. RNA polymerase uses one strand of DNA as a template to assemble nucleotides into a strand of RNA.

   c. RNA polymerase binds only to DNA promoters, which have specific base sequences.

   d. Promoters are signals in RNA that indicate to RNA polymerase when to begin transcription.

134 Chapter 12

© Pearson Education, Inc., publishing as Pearson Prentice Hall.

RNA Editing (page 302)

6. Many RNA molecules from eukaryotic genes have sections, called _____introns_____, edited out of them before they become functional. The remaining pieces, called _____exons_____, are spliced together.

7. Is the following sentence true or false? RNA editing occurs in the cytoplasm of the cell. _____false_____

8. What are two explanations for why some RNA molecules are cut and spliced?

   a. It makes it possible for a single gene to produce several different forms of RNA.

   b. It may play a role in evolution, making it possible for small changes in DNA to have dramatic effects in gene expression.

The Genetic Code (pages 302–303)

9. Proteins are made by joining _____amino acids_____ into long chains called polypeptides.

10. How can only four bases in RNA carry instructions for 20 different amino acids? The genetic code is read three letters at a time, so that each "word" of the coded message is three bases long.

11. What is a codon? It consists of three consecutive nucleotides that specify a single amino acid that is to be added to a polypeptide.

12. Circle the letter of the number of possible three-base codons.

    a. 4   b. 12   (c.) 64   d. 128

13. Is the following sentence true or false? All amino acids are specified by only one codon. _____false_____

14. Circle the letter of the codon that serves as the "start" codon for protein synthesis.

    a. UGA   b. UAA   c. UAG   (d.) AUG

Translation (pages 303–305)

15. What occurs during the process of translation? The cell uses information from messenger RNA to produce proteins.

16. Where does translation take place? Translation takes place on the ribosomes.

17. Circle the letter of each sentence that is true about translation.

(a.) Before translation occurs, messenger RNA is transcribed from DNA in the nucleus.

b. Translation occurs in the nucleus.

(c.) It is the job of transfer RNA to bring the proper amino acid into the ribosome to be attached to the growing peptide chain.

(d.) When the ribosome reaches a stop codon, it releases the newly formed polypeptide and the mRNA molecule.

18. What is an anticodon? The three bases on a tRNA molecule that are complementary to one of the mRNA codons.

The Roles of RNA and DNA (page 306)

Match the roles with the molecules. Molecules may be used more than once.

	Roles	Molecules
a	**19.** Master plan	**a.** DNA
b	**20.** Goes to the ribosomes in the cytoplasm	**b.** RNA
b	**21.** Blueprint	
a	**22.** Remains in the nucleus	

Genes and Proteins (page 306)

23. Many proteins are ___enzymes___, which catalyze and regulate chemical reactions.

24. Is the following sentence true or false? Genes are the keys to almost everything that living cells do. ___false___

Reading Skill Practice

A flowchart is useful for organizing the steps in a process. Make a flowchart that shows the steps in the process of translation. Look at Figure 12–18 on pages 304–305 for help. For more information about flowcharts, see Appendix A. Do your work on a separate sheet of paper.

Flowcharts should at least show the four major steps in translation as described in Figure 12–18 on pages 304–305.

Section 12–4 Mutations (pages 307–308)

 Key Concept
- What are mutations?

Introduction (page 307)

1. What are mutations? <u>Mutations are changes in the DNA sequence that affect genetic information.</u>

2. Is the following sentence true or false? Chromosomal mutations result from changes in a single gene. _____<u>false</u>_____

Kinds of Mutations (pages 307–308)

3. Mutations that occur at a single point in the DNA sequence are _____<u>point</u>_____ mutations.

4. A mutation involving the insertion or deletion of a nucleotide is a(an) _____<u>frameshift</u>_____ mutation.

5. Complete the table of types of chromosomal mutations.

CHROMOSOMAL MUTATIONS

Type	Description	Examples
Deletion	The loss of all or part of a chromosome	ABC•DEF → AC•DÉF
Duplication	A segment of a chromosome is repeated	ABC•DEF → ABBC•DEF
Inversion	Part of a chromosome becomes oriented in the reverse of its usual direction	ABC•DEF → AED•CBF
Translocation	Part of one chromosome breaks off and attaches to another chromosome	ABC•DEF → ABC•JKL GH•IJKL → GH•IDEF

6. Circle the letter of each sentence that is true about gene mutations.

   (a.) Point mutations affect just one nucleotide.

   b. The substitution of one nucleotide for another in the gene never affects the function of the protein.

   (c.) Point mutations that involve the insertion or deletion of a nucleotide change the reading frame of the genetic message.

   (d.) Frameshift mutations affect every amino acid that follows the point of the mutation.

Significance of Mutations (page 308)

7. Mutations that cause dramatic changes in protein structure are often _____harmful_____.

8. Mutations are a source of ___genetic variability___ in a species.

9. What is polyploidy? ___Polyploidy is a condition in which an organism has extra sets of___ chromosomes.

_____

Section 12–5 Gene Regulation (pages 309–312)

🗝 Key Concepts
- How are *lac* genes turned off and on?
- How are most eukaryotic genes controlled?

Introduction (page 309)

1. Label the parts of a typical gene in the diagram below.

2. Where does RNA polymerase bind? <u>It binds to the promoter.</u>

3. Is the following sentence true or false? The actions of DNA-binding proteins help to determine whether a gene is turned on or turned off. _____<u>true</u>_____

Gene Regulation: An Example (pages 309–310)

4. What is an operon? <u>It is a group of genes that operate together.</u>

5. What is the function of the genes in the *lac* operon? <u>They must be expressed for *E. coli* to</u> <u>use lactose as a food.</u>

6. Circle the letter of each sentence that is true about lactose.

   a. Lactose is a simple sugar.

   (b.) To use lactose for food, *E. coli* must take lactose across its cell membrane.

   (c.) The bond between glucose and galactose must be broken in order for *E. coli* to use lactose for food.

   d. Proteins encoded by the genes of the *lac* operon are needed only when *E. coli* is grown on a medium containing glucose.

7. What turns the *lac* operon off and on? <u>The *lac* genes are turned off by repressors and</u> <u>turned on by the presence of lactose.</u>

8. Complete the concept map to show how the *lac* operon is regulated.

9. How does the repressor protein prevent transcription? It prevents RNA polymerase from
binding to the operator.

_____

10. How does lactose cause the *lac* operon to turn on? Lactose molecules bind to the
repressor protein, causing it to change shape so that the repressor releases the operator. This
allows RNA polymerase to bind to the promoter and transcribe the genes of the operon.

_____

11. Circle the letter of each sentence that is true about gene regulation in prokaryotic genes.

  a. The *lac* operon is the only example of genes regulated by repressor proteins.

  (**b.**) Many other genes are regulated by repressor proteins.

  (**c.**) Some genes are regulated by proteins that enhance the rate of transcription.

  d. Cells cannot turn their genes on and off as needed.

Eukaryotic Gene Regulation (page 311)

12. Is the following sentence true or false? Operons are frequently found in eukaryotes.
_____false_____

13. How are eukaryotic genes usually controlled? Most are controlled individually and have
regulatory sequences that are much more complex than those of the *lac* operon.

_____

_____

Name_____ Class_____ Date _____

14. What is the function of the TATA box? It seems to help position RNA polymerase by
marking a point just before the point where transcription begins.

15. Eukaryotic promoters are usually found just _____before_____ the TATA box, and
they consist of a series of short _____DNA_____ sequences.

16. List three ways in which proteins that bind to enhancer sequences of a gene can work to
regulate gene expression.

a. They open up tightly packed chromatin.

b. They help to attract RNA polymerase.

c. They block access to genes.

17. Why is gene regulation in eukaryotes more complex than in prokaryotes? All of the
cells in a multicellular organism carry the complete genetic code in their nucleus, but only a few of
the available genes can be expressed in the appropriate cells of different tissues. Complex
regulation allows for this specificity.

Development and Differentiation (page 312)

18. What role do the hox genes play in the development of an organism? They control the
differentiation of cells and tissues in the embryo.

19. Circle the letter of each sentence that is true about hox genes.

a. A mutation in a hox gene has no effect on the organs that develop in specific parts of
the body.

b. In fruit flies, a mutation affecting the hox genes can replace a fly's antennae with a
pair of legs.

c. The function of the hox genes in humans seems to be almost the same as it is in fruit
flies.

d. A copy of the gene that controls eye growth in mice does not function in fruit flies.

20. Why do common patterns of genetic control for development exist among animals?
All the genes that control development have descended from the genes of common ancestors.

Chapter 12 DNA and RNA

Vocabulary Review

Matching *In the space provided, write the letter of the definition that best matches each term.*

_c_	**1.** base pairing	**a.** making a protein using messenger RNA
_g_	**2.** nucleotide	**b.** having extra sets of chromosomes
_l_	**3.** histone	**c.** hydrogen bonding between adenine and thymine
_h_	**4.** transcription	**d.** sequence in messenger RNA that is cut out
_d_	**5.** intron	**e.** cells specializing in structure and function
_a_	**6.** translation	**f.** carries amino acids to the ribosome during protein synthesis
_f_	**7.** transfer RNA	**g.** unit of DNA
_k_	**8.** promoter	**h.** copying part of DNA into RNA
_i_	**9.** mutation	**i.** change in the genetic material
_b_	**10.** polyploidy	**j.** group of genes that work together
_j_	**11.** operon	**k.** DNA sequence that binds RNA polymerase
_e_	**12.** differentiation	**l.** protein that binds DNA into tight coils

Completion *Fill in the blanks with terms from Chapter 12.*

13. A ____bacteriophage____ is a type of virus that infects bacteria.

14. Eukaryotic chromosomes contain both DNA and protein, tightly packed together to form a substance called ____chromatin____.

15. The duplication of DNA is called ____replication____.

16. The principal enzyme involved in DNA replication is ____DNA polymerase____ because it joins individual nucleotides to produce a DNA molecule.

17. DNA sequences that code for proteins are called ____exons____.

18. A ____codon____ consists of three consecutive nucleotides that specify a single amino acid.

19. Gene mutations, known as ____point mutations____, occur at a single point in the DNA sequence.

20. Differentiation of cells and tissues in the embryo is controlled by ____hox genes____.

Chapter 13   Genetic Engineering

Summary

13–1 Changing the Living World

For thousands of years, people have chosen to breed only the animals and plants with the desired traits. This technique is called selective breeding. Selective breeding takes advantage of naturally occurring genetic variation in a group of living things.

One tool used by selective breeders is hybridization. In hybridization, individuals with different traits are crossed. Hopefully, the offspring will have the best traits of both parents. The offspring of these crosses, called hybrids, are often hardier than the parents.

Once breeders have a group of plants or animals with the desired traits, they want to keep the traits. To do so, breeders use another tool called inbreeding. In inbreeding, individuals with similar characteristics are crossed. Inbreeding helps to ensure that the characteristics that make each breed unique will be preserved. Inbreeding does have the risk of bringing together two recessive alleles for a genetic defect.

Selective breeding would be nearly impossible without large amounts of variation in traits. Breeders can increase the variation in a group of organisms by causing mutations. Mutations are inheritable changes in DNA. Mutations do occur naturally. However, breeders can increase the rate of mutation by using radiation and chemicals. Many mutations are harmful. However with luck, breeders can produce useful mutations.

The use of mutations is particularly helpful with bacteria. Their small size enables millions of organisms to be treated with radiation or chemicals at the same time. Using this technique, scientists have been able to develop hundreds of beneficial bacteria strains, including bacteria that can digest the oil from oil spills.

New varieties of plants have also been developed using mutants. If chromosomes fail to separate, extra sets of chromosomes result. This is called polyploidy. In animals, polyploidy is usually fatal. In plants, however, the new species that result are larger and stronger than their diploid relatives.

13–2 Manipulating DNA

To increase variation, scientists can also make changes directly to the DNA molecule. In this group of techniques, called genetic engineering, scientists can change an organism's DNA.

Scientists can easily remove DNA from a cell and separate it from the other cell parts. Scientists can also cut DNA into smaller pieces using enzymes called restriction enzymes. Each restriction enzyme cuts DNA at a specific sequence of nucleotides. These DNA fragments can be separated and analyzed in a process called gel electrophoresis.

Scientists can also read the order of nucleotide bases in a DNA fragment. They use a technique in which a single strand of DNA is copied. However, the copy is made with colored nucleotides inserted at random places. Reading the order of colored bands in a gel gives the nucleotide sequence of the DNA fragment.

Scientists can change DNA sequences in many different ways. Short sequences of DNA made in the laboratory can be joined to the DNA molecule of an organism. DNA from one organism can be attached to the DNA of another organism. These DNA molecules are called recombinant DNA because they are made by combining DNA from different sources.

Scientists often need many copies of a certain gene to study it. A technique called polymerase chain reaction (PCR) allows scientists to do that. PCR is a chain reaction in which DNA copies become templates to make more DNA copies.

13–3 Cell Transformation

DNA fragments cannot work by themselves. They must be part of the DNA molecule in an organism. DNA fragments become part of a cell's DNA during the process of transformation. This is the same process that Griffith observed in his experiments.

To add DNA fragments to bacteria, a fragment is joined to a small, circular piece of DNA called a plasmid. Plasmids are found naturally in some bacteria. Scientists join the fragment to the plasmid by cutting both with the same restriction enzymes. The cut pieces join together because their ends match up.

When scientists transform bacteria, not all bacteria take in the plasmid. Scientists can identify those bacteria that carry the plasmid because the plasmid also carries a genetic marker. Usually, the genetic marker is a gene that gives the bacteria resistance to a certain antibiotic.

Plant cells can also be transformed. Scientists insert the DNA fragment into a plasmid. This plasmid is transformed into a bacterium that naturally infects plants. Plant cells in a culture that have had their cell walls removed will also take up DNA on their own. Scientists can also inject DNA directly into some plant cells.

Animal cells can be transformed in ways similar to those used for plant cells. Many egg cells are large enough that DNA can be directly injected into the nucleus. Once inside, the repair enzymes may help insert the DNA fragment into the chromosomes of the injected cell.

13–4 Applications of Genetic Engineering

Scientists wondered whether genes from one organism would work in a different organism. Some scientists isolated the gene from fireflies that allows them to glow. Then, they inserted this gene into the DNA of a plant. These plants glowed in the dark. This showed that plants and animals use the same process to translate DNA into proteins. The glowing plant is transgenic because it has a gene from another species.

Human genes have been added to bacteria. These transgenic bacteria are used to produce human proteins such as insulin, human growth hormone, and clotting factor.

Scientists have produced transgenic animals to study the function of genes and to improve the food supply. Transgenic animals might also be used to supply us with human proteins that can be collected in the animal's milk.

Transgenic plants have been produced that can make their own insecticide. Others are resistant to weed killers. Some have even been engineered to contain vitamins needed for human health.

A clone is a member of a population of genetically identical cells that were produced from a single cell. Clones are useful because it is one way to make copies of transgenic organisms. It is easy to produce cloned bacteria and plants.

Animals are very difficult to clone. However, scientists in Scotland successfully cloned a sheep, named Dolly. Animal cloning has risks. Studies suggest that cloned animals may have genetic defects and other health problems.

Chapter 13   Genetic Engineering

Section 13–1 Changing the Living World
(pages 319–321)

🔑 Key Concepts
- What is the purpose of selective breeding?
- Why might breeders try to induce mutations?

Selective Breeding (pages 319–320)

1. What is meant by selective breeding? _Breeders allow only animals and plants with desired_ characteristics to produce the next generation._____

2. Circle the letter of each organism that has been produced by selective breeding.
   (a.) horses   (b.) dogs   (c.) cats   (d.) potatoes

3. Who was Luther Burbank? _He was a botanist who developed disease-resistant potatoes to_ help fight potato blight in Ireland, as well as more than 800 varieties of other plants.___

4. Complete the table describing the types of selective breeding.

SELECTIVE BREEDING

Type	Description	Examples
Hybridization	Crossing dissimilar individuals to bring together the best of both organisms	Disease-resistant Burbank potato
Inbreeding	The continued breeding of individuals with similar characteristics	Maintaining dog breeds

5. Is the following sentence true or false? Hybrids are often hardier than either of the parents. ___true___.

6. What two plant traits did Luther Burbank try to combine in his crosses?
   a. _Disease resistance_____
   b. _Food-producing capacity_____

7. Is the following sentence true or false? To maintain the desired characteristics of a line of organisms, breeders often use hybridization. ___false_____

8. Most members of a breed are genetically ___similar_____.

9. What are the risks of inbreeding? _There is always a chance that a cross between two_ individuals will bring together two recessive alleles for a genetic defect._____

Increasing Variation (pages 320–321)

10. Why are biologists interested in preserving the diversity of plants and animals in the wild? <u>Selective breeding would be nearly impossible without the wide variation found in</u> <u>natural populations.</u>

_____

11. Is the following sentence true or false? The genetic variation that exists in nature is enough to satisfy the needs of breeders. _____<u>false</u>_____

12. Breeders can increase the genetic variation by inducing _____<u>mutations</u>_____, which are the ultimate source of genetic variability.

13. Circle the letter of an inheritable change in DNA.

a. variation   **b.** trait   **c.** mutation   **d.** genotype

14. Is the following sentence true or false? Mutations cannot occur spontaneously. _____<u>false</u>_____

15. Name two methods used by breeders to increase the rate of mutation.

a. <u>Radiation</u>   **b.** <u>Chemicals</u>

16. Is it easy for breeders to produce mutants with desirable mutations? Explain. <u>No, many mutations are harmful, and it requires luck and perseverance to produce a few mutants</u> <u>with desirable characteristics that are not found in the original population.</u>

_____

17. Why are radiation and chemicals useful techniques for producing mutant bacteria? <u>The small size of bacteria enables millions of organisms to be treated at the same time, thus</u> <u>increasing the chances of producing a useful mutant.</u>

_____

18. Is the following sentence true or false? Scientists have produced bacteria that can digest oil. _____<u>true</u>_____

19. What technique do scientists use to produce mutant plants? <u>Scientists use drugs that</u> <u>prevent chromosomal separation during meiosis.</u>

_____

20. Circle the letter of each sentence that is true about polyploidy.

a. Polyploid plants have many sets of chromosomes.

b. Polyploidy is usually fatal in animals.

c. Polyploidy produces new species of plants that are weaker and smaller than their diploid relatives.

d. Bananas and some citrus fruits are polyploid.

Section 13–2 Manipulating DNA (pages 322–326)

 Key Concept
- How do scientists make changes to DNA?

The Tools of Molecular Biology (pages 322–323)

1. What is genetic engineering? <u>Genetic engineering is making changes in the DNA code of a</u> <u>living organism.</u>

2. Is the following sentence true or false? Making changes to the DNA code is similar to changing the code of a computer program. _____true_____

3. Scientists use their knowledge of the _____structure_____ of DNA and its _____chemical_____ properties to study and change DNA molecules.

4. List four steps that molecular biologists use to study and change DNA molecules.

   a. <u>Extract DNA from cells</u>

   b. <u>Cut DNA into smaller pieces</u>

   c. <u>Identify the sequence of bases in a DNA molecule</u>

   d. <u>Make unlimited copies of DNA</u>

5. Explain how biologists get DNA out of a cell. <u>The cells are opened, and the DNA is</u> <u>separated from the other cell parts.</u>

6. Biologists use _____restriction enzymes_____ to cut DNA molecules at a specific sequence of nucleotides to make smaller fragments.

7. Circle the letter of the process by which DNA fragments are separated and analyzed.

   (a.) gel electrophoresis   c. transformation

   b. extraction   d. restriction

8. In the diagram below, label the positive and negative ends of the gel and identify the location of longer and shorter fragments.

9. Circle the letter of each sentence that is true about gel electrophoresis.

a. An electric voltage applied to the gel separates the DNA fragments.

b. DNA molecules are positively charged.

c. Gel electrophoresis is used to compare the genomes of different organisms.

d. Gel electrophoresis can be used to locate and identify one particular gene in an individual's genome.

Using the DNA Sequence (pages 323–326)

10. Complete the concept map to show how researchers use the DNA sequence of an organism.

11. List four "ingredients" added to a test tube to produce tagged DNA fragments that can be used to read a sequence of DNA.

a. Small, single-stranded pieces of DNA

b. DNA polymerase

c. Supply of the four nucleotide bases in DNA

d. One base labeled with a fluorescent dye

12. What does the reaction in the test tube generate when complementary DNA is made for reading DNA? The reaction generates a series of tiny DNA fragments that are color-coded according to the fluorescent base that has been added at the very end.

13. Is the following sentence true or false? The pattern of colored bands on a gel tells the exact sequence of bases in DNA. true

14. Enzymes that splice DNA together can also be used to join synthetic DNA sequences to natural DNA sequences.

15. How is recombinant DNA produced? It is produced by combining DNA from different sources.

16. What is polymerase chain reaction (PCR)? <u>It is a technique that allows biologists to make</u>
<u>many copies of a particular gene.</u>

_____

_____

17. What is the role of the primers in PCR? <u>The primers are short pieces of complementary</u>
<u>DNA sequences that provide a place for DNA polymerase to start working.</u>

_____

_____

18. Circle the letter of the first step in the polymerase chain reaction.

   a. The copies become templates to make more copies.

   b. The DNA is cooled to allow the primers to bind to the single-stranded DNA.

   (c.) The DNA is heated to separate its two strands.

   d. DNA polymerase makes copies of the region between the primers.

Reading Skill Practice

A flowchart is useful for organizing the steps in a process. Make a flowchart that
shows the steps molecular biologists use to determine the order of bases in a
segment of a DNA molecule.

Flowcharts should show in order the steps involved in the process of reading a DNA sequence as
described in this section.

Name_____ Class_____ Date _____

Section 13–3 Cell Transformation (pages 327–329)

⊂**▪ Key Concepts**
- What happens during cell transformation?
- How can you tell if a transformation experiment has been successful?

Introduction (page 327)

1. What occurs during transformation? <u>A cell takes in DNA from outside the cell. This external</u>
<u>DNA becomes a component of the cell's DNA.</u>

2. Is the following sentence true or false? Griffith's extract of heat-killed bacteria contained
DNA fragments. _____true_____

Transforming Bacteria (pages 327–328)

3. Complete the flowchart to show the steps in transforming bacteria.

┌──┐
│ Foreign DNA is joined to a(an) _____plasmid_____, which is a small, │
│ circular DNA molecule found naturally in some bacteria. │
└──┘
                              ↓
┌──┐
│ Recombinant plasmids are mixed with bacterial cells. Some bacterial cells take │
│ in the recombinant DNA by the process of _____transformation_____. │
└──┘
                              ↓
┌──┐
│ The culture is treated with a(an) ____antibiotic____, a compound that │
│ kills bacteria. │
└──┘
                              ↓
┌──┐
│ Only cells that have been transformed survive, because only they carry a(an) │
│ ____gene____ for antibiotic resistance. │
└──┘

4. Give two reasons why a plasmid is useful for DNA transfer.
   a. <u>It has a DNA sequence that helps promote plasmid replication, ensuring that the foreign DNA</u>
   <u>will be replicated.</u>
   b. <u>It has a genetic marker—a gene that makes it possible to distinguish bacteria that carry the</u>
   <u>plasmid from those that don't.</u>

Transforming Plant Cells (pages 328–329)

5. When researchers transform plant cells using a bacterium that causes plant tumors, how
do researchers prevent plant tumors from forming in the transformed cells?
<u>Researchers inactivate the tumor-producing gene.</u>

6. Circle the letter of each sentence that is true about transforming plant cells.

(**a.**) Many plant cells can be transformed by using a bacterium that will, in nature, insert a tumor-producing plasmid into plant cells.

(**b.**) Sometimes plant cells in culture will take up DNA on their own when their cell walls are removed.

c. It is impossible to inject DNA directly into plant cells.

d. Plant cells that are transformed cannot develop into adult plants.

7. Describe what occurs in a successful transformation of cells. The recombinant DNA is integrated into one of the chromosomes of the cell.

Transforming Animal Cells (page 329)

8. Describe how animal cells can be transformed by directly injecting DNA.
DNA can be directly injected into many egg cells. Once inside the nucleus, DNA repair enzymes may help to insert the foreign DNA into the chromosomes.

9. Is the following sentence true or false? The DNA molecules used for transformation of animal cells do not require marker genes. _____false_____

10. How is a DNA molecule constructed so that it will eliminate a particular gene?
The DNA molecule is constructed with two ends that will sometimes recombine with specific sequences in the host chromosome.

11. Is the following sentence true or false? Gene replacement has made it possible to identify the specific functions of genes in many organisms. _____true_____

Reading Skill Practice

When you read about related concepts, a compare-and-contrast table can help you focus on their similarities and differences. Construct a table to compare and contrast transformation in bacteria, plants, and animals. Look in Appendix A for more information about compare-and-contrast tables. Do your work on a separate sheet of paper.

In their tables, students should compare and contrast methods of transformation and how transformed cells are identified.

Section 13–4 Applications of Genetic Engineering (pages 331–333)

🔑 **Key Concept**
- How are transgenic organisms useful to human beings?

Introduction (page 331)

1. How do scientists know that plants and animals share the same basic mechanisms of gene expression? _A gene for luciferase, an animal enzyme, can specify a trait in a plant._

_____

Transgenic Organisms (pages 331–333)

2. What is a transgenic organism? _It is an organism that contains genes from other species._

_____

_____

3. Describe how to make a transgenic organism. _Using basic techniques of genetic_
engineering, a gene from one organism can be inserted into cells from another organism.

_____

_____

_____

4. Genetic engineering has spurred the growth of _____biotechnology_____, a new industry that is changing the way we interact with the living world.

5. Circle the letter of each sentence that is true about transgenic microorganisms.

   a. Transgenic bacteria will never produce useful substances for health and industry.

   (b.) Transgenic bacteria produce human proteins cheaply and in great abundance.

   (c.) People with insulin-dependent diabetes are now treated with pure human insulin.

   (d.) In the future, transgenic organisms may produce the raw materials for plastics.

6. List four ways in which transgenic animals have been used.

   a. _To study genes_

   b. _To improve the food supply_

   c. _To study the effects of diseases on the human immune system_

   d. _To produce human proteins_

7. Many transgenic plants contain genes that produce a natural _____insecticide_____, so the crops do not have to be sprayed with pesticides.

© Pearson Education, Inc., publishing as Pearson Prentice Hall.

8. Circle the letter of each item that might soon be produced by transgenic plants.
   (a.) human antibodies
   (c.) rot-resistant foods
   (b.) plastics
   (d.) vitamin A-enriched rice

Cloning (page 333)

9. What is a clone? It is a member of a population of genetically identical cells produced from a single cell.

10. Is the following sentence true or false? For years, many scientists thought that it was impossible to clone bacteria. _____false_____

11. Complete the sentences in the diagram below to show the steps in cloning a sheep.

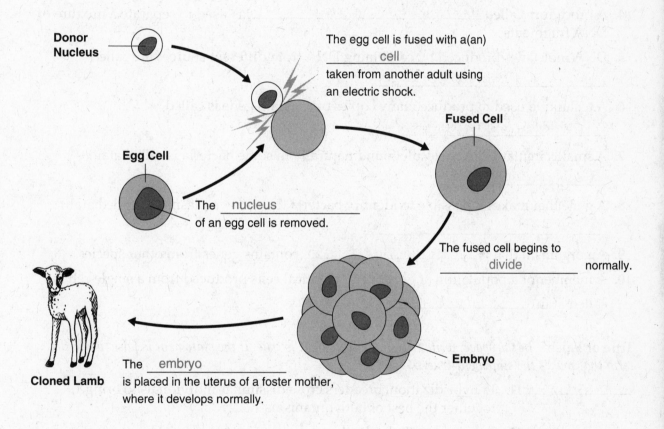

Donor Nucleus

The egg cell is fused with a(an) ___cell___ taken from another adult using an electric shock.

Egg Cell

The ___nucleus___ of an egg cell is removed.

Fused Cell

The fused cell begins to ___divide___ normally.

Embryo

Cloned Lamb

The ___embryo___ is placed in the uterus of a foster mother, where it develops normally.

12. Is the following sentence true or false? All cloned animals are also transgenic. _____false_____

13. What kinds of mammals have been cloned in recent years? Sheep, cows, pigs, mice, and other mammals have been cloned.

Name_____ Class_____ Date _____

Chapter 13   Genetic Engineering

Vocabulary Review

Completion   *Fill in the blanks with terms from Chapter 13.*

1. In the process of _____selective breeding_____, only those animals with desired characteristics are allowed to produce the next generation.

2. The continued breeding of individuals with similar characteristics is _____inbreeding_____.

3. Through the use of techniques in _____genetic engineering_____, which is the process of making changes in the DNA code of a living organism, scientists have produced bacteria that can make human proteins.

4. A procedure called _____gel electrophoresis_____ is used to separate a mixture of DNA fragments.

5. DNA molecules produced by combining DNA from different sources are called _____recombinant DNA_____.

6. A technique used to produce many copies of a certain gene is called _____polymerase chain reaction (PCR)_____.

7. A small, circular DNA molecule found naturally in some bacteria is called a(an) _____plasmid_____.

8. A gene that makes it possible to identify bacteria that carry a plasmid is called a(an) _____genetic marker_____.

9. An organism that is _____transgenic_____ contains genes from other species.

10. A member of a population of genetically identical cells produced from a single cell is called a(an) _____clone_____.

True or False   *In the space, write* true *if the statement is true. If the statement is false, write the term that makes the statement true.*

_____true_____ 11. In <u>hybridization</u>, breeders cross dissimilar individuals to bring together the best of both organisms.

_____inbreeding_____ 12. Breeders use <u>hybridization</u> to maintain a dog breed.

_____restriction enzymes_____ 13. Scientists use <u>gel electrophoresis</u> to cut DNA at a specific nucleotide sequence.

_____true_____ 14. A plant that glows in the dark is an example of a <u>transgenic</u> organism.

_____clone_____ 15. Dolly the sheep is an example of a <u>plasmid</u>.

© Pearson Education, Inc., publishing as Pearson Prentice Hall.

Chapter 14   The Human Genome

Summary

14–1 Human Heredity

Biologists can analyze human chromosomes by looking at a karyotype. A karyotype is a picture of the chromosomes from a cell arranged in homologous pairs.

Humans have 46 chromosomes. Two of these chromosomes, X and Y, are the sex chromosomes. Females have two X chromosomes (XX). Males have one X and one Y chromosome (XY). The other 44 chromosomes are called autosomes.

Human genes are inherited according to the same principles of genetics described by Mendel. To study the inheritance of human traits, biologists use a pedigree chart. A pedigree shows the relationships within a family. The inheritance of a certain trait in a family can be traced using a pedigree. From this, biologists can infer the genotypes of family members.

It is difficult to associate an observed human trait with a specific gene. Many human traits are polygenic, meaning that they are controlled by many genes. The environment also influences many traits.

Some of the first human genes to be identified were those that control blood type. Red blood cells can carry two different antigens, called A and B. Antigens are molecules that can be recognized by the immune system. The presence or absence of the A and B antigens produces four possible blood types: A, B, AB, and O. The ABO blood types are determined by a single gene with three alleles.

In addition to the ABO antigens, there is another antigen on red blood cells called the Rh antigen. People who have the Rh antigen are Rh positive. People without it are Rh negative. A single gene with two alleles determines the Rh blood group.

There are several human genetic disorders, including phenylketonuria (PKU), Huntington's disease, and sickle cell disease. PKU is caused by a recessive allele. It is expressed only in individuals who have inherited a recessive allele from each parent. Huntington's disease is caused by a dominant allele. It is expressed in any person who has that allele. Sickle cell disease is caused by a codominant allele.

Scientists are beginning to understand which changes in the DNA sequence cause certain genetic disorders. Cystic fibrosis is caused by the deletion of three bases in the middle of the sequence for a protein. This deletion inactivates the protein, which causes the symptoms of this disorder. Only one DNA base is changed in the allele that causes sickle cell disease. This base change produces a blood protein that is less soluble than normal.

14–2 Human Chromosomes

The two smallest human chromosomes, chromosomes 21 and 22, were the first chromosomes to have their DNA sequences identified. Both have many genes important for health. Both have regions of DNA that do not code for proteins.

Genes located on the X and Y chromosomes, the sex chromosomes, are said to be sex-linked. They are inherited in a different pattern than genes located on autosomes. For example, all alleles linked to the X chromosome, including those responsible for colorblindness, hemophilia, and Duchenne muscular dystrophy, are expressed in males even if they are recessive alleles. However, in order for these recessive alleles to be expressed in females, there must be two copies of them.

Females have two X chromosomes. Males have only one. To account for this difference, one X chromosome in females is randomly turned off. The turned-off chromosome forms a dense region in the nucleus known as a Barr body. Barr bodies are not found in males because their single X chromosome must be active.

The most common error during meiosis is nondisjunction. Nondisjunction is the failure of chromosomes to separate properly during meiosis. It causes abnormal numbers of chromosomes to find their way into gametes. This may result in a disorder of chromosome number. An example of autosomal nondisjunction is Down syndrome, in which there is an extra copy of chromosome 21. Nondisjunction can also occur in sex chromosomes. In Turner's syndrome, a female has only one X chromosome. In Klinefelter's syndrome, there are extra X chromosomes.

14–3 Human Molecular Genetics

Biologists can use techniques in molecular biology to read, analyze, and even change the DNA code of human genes. Genetic tests are available to test parents for the presence of recessive alleles for genetic disorders.

In a process called DNA fingerprinting, individuals can be identified by analyzing sections of DNA that have little or no known function. These sections of DNA vary widely from one person to the next.

In 1990, scientists around the world began the Human Genome Project. The goal was to identify the DNA sequence for the entire DNA in a human cell. In 2000, the human genome was sequenced. Now the project goal is to analyze these sequences. One way scientists are analyzing the DNA is by looking for genes. To do this, they look for promoter sequences. These are sequences that bind RNA polymerase.

Information about the human genome can be used to cure genetic disorders by gene therapy. In one method of gene therapy, a virus is used to deliver the normal gene into cells to correct the genetic defects. The virus is changed so that it cannot cause disease. The normal gene is attached to the DNA of the virus. The inserted gene can make proteins that correct the genetic defect.

There are risks and problems with gene therapy. Having the power to manipulate human DNA doesn't necessarily make it right. People in a society are responsible for making sure that the tools made available by science are used wisely.

Chapter 14   The Human Genome

Section 14–1 Human Heredity (pages 341–348)

⊂► **Key Concepts**
- How is sex determined?
- How do small changes in DNA cause genetic disorders?

Human Chromosomes (pages 341–342)

1. How do biologists make a karyotype? _They photograph cells in mitosis, cut out the_ _chromosomes from the photographs, and then group the chromosomes together in pairs._

_____

_____

2. Circle the letter of each sentence that is true about human chromosomes.

   (a.) The X and Y chromosomes are known as sex chromosomes because they determine an individual's sex.

   b. Males have two X chromosomes.

   (c.) All the chromosomes except the sex chromosomes are autosomes.

   d. Biologists would write 46,XY to indicate a human female.

3. Complete the Punnett square below to show how the sex chromosomes segregate during meiosis.

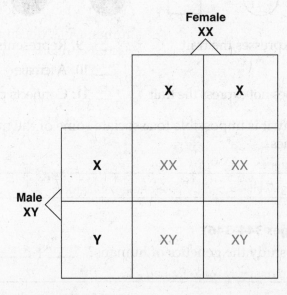

4. Why is there the chance that half of the zygotes will be female and half will be male?

   All the egg cells have a single X chromosome. However, half of all sperm cells carry an X _chromosome and half carry a Y chromosome._

_____

Name_____ Class_____ Date_____

Human Traits (pages 342–343)

5. What does a pedigree chart show? It shows the relationships within a family.

Match the labels to the parts of the pedigree chart shown below. Some of the parts of the pedigree chart may be used more than once.

Pedigree Chart

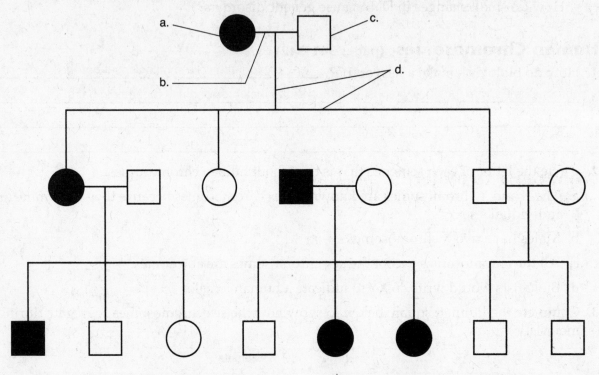

_a_ **6.** A person who expresses the trait   _b_ **9.** Represents a marriage

_c_ **7.** A male   _a_ **10.** A female

_c_ **8.** A person who does not express the trait _d_ **11.** Connects parents to their children

12. Give two reasons why it is impossible to associate some of the most obvious human traits with single genes.

   a. Many traits are polygenic.

   b. Many traits are strongly influenced by environmental factors.

Human Genes (pages 344–346)

13. Why is it difficult to study the genetics of humans? Humans have long generation times, a complex life cycle, and relatively few offspring.

14. Circle the letter of each sentence that is true about human blood group genes.

   (a.) The Rh blood group is determined by a single gene.

   b. The negative allele (Rh⁻) is the dominant allele.

   c. All of the alleles for the ABO blood group gene are codominant.

   (d.) Individuals with type O blood are homozygous for the *i* allele (*ii*) and produce no antigen on the surface of red blood cells.

15. Is the following sentence true or false? Many human genes have become known through the study of genetic disorders. _____true_____

Match the genetic disorder with its description.

Genetic Disorder	Description
__c__ **16.** Phenylketonuria (PKU)	**a.** Nervous system breakdown caused by an autosomal recessive allele
__a__ **17.** Tay-Sachs disease	**b.** A form of dwarfism caused by an autosomal dominant allele
__b__ **18.** Achondroplasia	**c.** A buildup of phenylalanine caused by an autosomal recessive allele
__d__ **19.** Huntington's disease	**d.** A progressive loss of muscle control and mental function caused by an autosomal dominant allele

From Gene to Molecule (pages 346–348)

20. What is the normal function of the protein that is affected in cystic fibrosis?

The protein allows chloride ions to pass across biological membranes.
_____

21. A change in just one DNA base for the gene that codes for the protein ____hemoglobin____ causes sickle-shaped red blood cells.

22. What is the advantage of being heterozygous for the sickle cell allele?

People who are heterozygous are generally healthy and are resistant to malaria.
_____

23. What makes an allele dominant, recessive, or codominant? __It depends on the nature of__

the gene's protein product and its role in the cell.
_____

© Pearson Education, Inc., publishing as Pearson Prentice Hall.

Section 14–2 Human Chromosomes (pages 349–353)

🔑 **Key Concepts**

- Why are sex-linked disorders more common in males than in females?
- What is nondisjunction, and what problems does it cause?

Human Genes and Chromosomes (page 349)

1. Circle the letter of each sentence that is true about human genes and chromosomes.

   a. Chromosomes 21 and 22 are the largest human chromosomes.

   (b.) Chromosome 22 contains long stretches of repetitive DNA that do not code for proteins.

   c. Biologists know everything about how the arrangements of genes on chromosomes affect gene expression.

   (d.) Human genes located close together on the same chromosome tend to be inherited together.

Sex-Linked Genes (pages 350–351)

2. What are sex-linked genes? _They are genes that are located on the X or Y chromosomes._

_____

3. Is the following sentence true or false? The Y chromosome does not contain any genes at all. _____false_____

4. Complete the table describing sex-linked disorders.

SEX-LINKED DISORDERS IN HUMANS

Disorder	Description	Cause
Colorblindness	Inability to distinguish certain colors	Defective version of any one of three genes associated with color vision
Hemophilia	Blood does not clot normally	A recessive allele in either of two genes resulting in a missing protein required for normal blood clotting
Duchenne Muscular Dystrophy	Progressive weakening and loss of skeletal muscle	A defective version of the gene that codes for a muscle protein

5. Is the following sentence true or false? All X-linked alleles are expressed in males, even if they are recessive. _____true_____

6. Complete the Punnett square to show how colorblindness is inherited.

	X^cY	
	X^c	Y
X^c	X^cX^c	X^cY
X^c	X^cX^c	X^cY

(left labels: X^cX^c)

X-Chromosome Inactivation (page 352)

7. How does the cell "adjust" to the extra X chromosome in female cells? In female cells, one X chromosome is switched off.

8. What is a Barr body? It is a dense region in the nucleus that is formed by the turned-off X chromosome.

9. Is the following sentence true or false? Barr bodies are found only in males. false

10. If you see a white cat with orange and black spots, is it most likely a male or a female? Explain. It's probably a female. In cells in some parts of the body, one X chromosome that has the allele for orange spots is switched off, whereas in cells in other parts of the body, the other X chromosome with the allele for black spots is switched off.

Chromosomal Disorders (pages 352–353)

11. What occurs during nondisjunction? Homologous chromosomes fail to separate during meiosis.

12. Is the following sentence true or false? If nondisjunction occurs, gametes may have abnormal numbers of chromosomes. true

13. The condition in which an individual has three copies of a chromosome is known as _____trisomy_____, which means "three bodies."

14. Is the following sentence true or false? Down syndrome occurs when an individual has two copies of chromosome 21. _____false_____

15. Circle the letter of the characteristic of Down syndrome.

a. dwarfism

c. colorblindness

(b.) mental retardation

d. muscle loss

16. Why does an extra copy of one chromosome cause so much trouble? Scientists do not know for sure.
_____

17. Circle the letter of each sentence that is true about sex chromosome disorders.

(a.) A female with the karyotype 45,X has inherited only one X chromosome and is sterile.

b. Females with the karyotype 47,XXY have Klinefelter's syndrome.

c. Babies have been born without an X chromosome.

(d.) The Y chromosome contains a sex-determining region that is necessary for male sexual development.

Reading Skill Practice

Writing an outline is a useful way to organize the important facts in a section. Write an outline of Section 14–2. Use the section headings as the headings in your outline. Include only the important facts and main ideas in your outline. Be sure to include the vocabulary terms. Do your work on a separate sheet of paper.

Outlines should be based on the information on pages 349–353.

Section 14–3 Human Molecular Genetics
(pages 355–360)

🔑 **Key Concepts**
- What is the goal of the Human Genome Project?
- What is gene therapy?

Human DNA Analysis (pages 355–357)

1. Biologists search the volumes of the human genome using __sequences of DNA bases__.

2. Why might prospective parents decide to have genetic testing? __Genetic tests can__ __determine whether prospective parents risk passing alleles for genetic disorders to their children.__
_____

3. Circle the letter of each sentence that is true about genetic testing.

   a. It is impossible to test parents to find out if they are carriers for cystic fibrosis or Tay-Sachs disease.

   b. Labeled DNA probes can be used to detect specific sequences found in disease-causing alleles.

   c. Some genetic tests use changes in restriction enzyme cutting sites to identify disease-causing alleles.

   d. DNA testing makes it possible to develop more effective therapy and treatment for individuals affected by genetic disease.

4. What is DNA fingerprinting? __It is the identification of individuals by a method that analyzes__ __sections of DNA that have little or no known function but vary widely from one individual to another.__
_____

5. Complete the flowchart to show the steps in DNA fingerprinting.

> Small sample of DNA is cut with a(an) _____restriction_____ enzyme.

⬇

> The fragments are separated by size using _____gel electrophoresis_____.

⬇

> Fragments with highly variable regions are detected with a(an) _____DNA probe_____, revealing a series of DNA bands of various sizes.

⬇

> The pattern of bands produced is the _____DNA fingerprint_____, which can be distinguished statistically from the pattern of any other individual in the world.

6. Circle the letter of each source for a DNA sample from an individual.

(a.) blood   c. clothing

(b.) sperm   (d.) hair with tissue at the base

7. Is the following sentence true or false? DNA evidence is not reliable enough to be used to convict criminals. _____false_____

The Human Genome Project (pages 357–358)

8. What is the Human Genome Project? It is an ongoing effort to analyze the human DNA sequence.

_____

9. Circle the letter of each sentence that is true about the Human Genome Project.

a. The human genome is the first genome entirely sequenced.

b. The human genome is about the same size as the genome of *E. coli*.

(c.) Researchers completed the genomes of yeast and fruit flies during the same time they sequenced the human genome.

(d.) A working copy of the human genome was completed in June 2000.

10. What were the three major steps in the process of sequencing the human genome?

a. Widely separated regions of DNA on each chromosome were sequenced.

b. Random fragments of DNA were sequenced.

c. Computers found overlapping regions between the fragments and positioned them relative to the known markers.

11. What is an open reading frame, and what is it used for? It is a series of DNA bases that will produce an mRNA sequence. Scientists use it to locate genes.

12. The mRNA coding regions of most genes are interrupted by _____introns_____.

13. List three other parts of the gene that researchers look for.

a. Promoter

b. "Start" site for transcription

c. "Stop" site for transcription

14. Why are biotechnology companies interested in genetic information? They are trying to use this information to develop new drugs and treatments for diseases.

_____

15. Is the following sentence true or false? Human genome data are top secret and can be accessed only by certain people. _____false_____

Gene Therapy (pages 359–360)

16. What is gene therapy? Gene therapy is the process of changing the gene that causes a genetic disorder.

17. Circle the letter of each sentence that is true about gene therapy.

(a.) When the normal copy of the gene is inserted, the body can make the correct protein, which eliminates the disorder.

b. So far, no one has been successfully cured of a genetic disorder using gene therapy.

(c.) Viruses are often used to carry the normal genes into cells.

d. Viruses used in gene therapy often cause disease in the patients.

18. Is the following sentence true or false? All gene therapy experiments have been successful. _____false_____

Ethical Issues in Human Genetics (page 360)

19. What other changes could be made to the human genome by manipulating human cells? Biologists could try to engineer taller people or change eye color, hair texture, sex, blood group, or appearance. They could even clone human beings.

20. What is the responsibility of society in biology? Society will have to learn to use wisely the tools that science has given it. It will have to develop an ethical consensus of what should and should not be done with the human genome.

21. Is the following true or false? Scientists should be expected to make all ethical decisions regarding advances in human genetics. _____false_____

Vocabulary Review

Labeling Diagrams   *Use the words listed below to label the diagram.*

autosome   sex chromosome   karyotype

2. _____autosome_____

1. _____karyotype_____

3. _____sex chromosome_____

Matching   *In the space provided, write the letter of the definition that best matches each term.*

___c___ **4.** karyotype

___e___ **5.** sex chromosomes

___g___ **6.** autosomes

___a___ **7.** pedigree

___f___ **8.** sex-linked gene

___b___ **9.** nondisjunction

___d___ **10.** DNA fingerprinting

a. chart that shows the relationships within a family

b. failure of homologous chromosomes to separate in meiosis

c. picture of chromosomes arranged in pairs

d. test used to identify individuals by analyzing sections of DNA

e. chromosomes that determine an individual's sex

f. gene located on the X or Y chromosome

g. chromosomes that do not determine sex

Summary

15–1 The Puzzle of Life's Diversity

The theory of evolution can explain the diversity of life on Earth. Evolution, or change over time, is the process by which modern organisms have descended from ancient organisms. A scientific theory is an explanation of natural events that is supported by evidence and can be tested with new evidence.

Charles Darwin contributed more than any other scientist to our understanding of evolution. During his trip on the *Beagle*, Darwin made many observations and collected a great deal of evidence. He observed tremendous diversity of organisms. He also noticed that many plants and animals were very well suited to their environment. Darwin collected fossils, or the preserved remains of ancient organisms. Some of the fossils were unlike any creatures he had ever seen. He wondered why the species represented by the fossils had disappeared.

Darwin's observations on the Galápagos Islands influenced him the most. The islands are close together but have different climates. Darwin noticed that the traits of many organisms—such as the shell shapes of tortoises—varied from island to island. Darwin wondered if animals living on different islands had once been members of the same species.

15–2 Ideas That Shaped Darwin's Thinking

In Darwin's day, most Europeans believed that Earth and all its life forms had been created just a few thousand years earlier. They also believed that species did not change through time. Several scientists who lived around the same time as Darwin began to challenge these ideas. These scientists had an important influence on the development of Darwin's theory of evolution.

Geologists James Hutton and Charles Lyell argued that Earth is many millions of years old. They also argued that the processes that changed Earth in the past were the same as the processes that are still changing Earth in the present. Knowing that Earth could change over time helped Darwin realize that life might change as well. Knowing that Earth was very old convinced Darwin that there had been enough time for life to evolve.

Jean-Baptiste Lamarck was one of the first scientists to recognize that evolution has occurred and that organisms are adapted to their environment. To explain evolution, Lamarck hypothesized that an organism could gain or lose traits during its lifetime by using or not using organs. He also hypothesized that these changes could be passed on to the organism's offspring and eventually change the species. Scientists now know that some of Lamarck's hypotheses about evolution are incorrect. However, his general ideas about evolution and adaptation are correct, and they influenced Darwin.

Another important influence on Darwin was the economist Thomas Malthus. Malthus thought that if the human population continued to grow unchecked, it would run out of living space and food. Darwin realized that this was true of all organisms and not just humans.

15–3 Darwin Presents His Case

Darwin was reluctant to publish his ideas because they were so radical. When he realized that another scientist, Alfred Russel Wallace, had the same ideas, Darwin finally published *On the Origin of Species* in 1859. In the book, Darwin provided evidence that evolution has occurred. He also explained his theory for how evolution comes about.

Darwin's theory was based on artificial selection. In artificial selection, animal breeders select for breeding only animals with the desired traits. For example, they select only the largest hogs or only the cows that produce the most milk. These traits are then passed on to the next generation.

Darwin thought that a process similar to artificial selection occurs in nature. He called this process natural selection. Darwin's theory of evolution by natural selection can be summed up as follows: Individuals differ, and some of the differences can be passed on to their offspring. More offspring are produced than can survive and reproduce. There is competition for limited resources, or a struggle for existence. Individuals best suited to their environment survive and reproduce most successfully. In other words, there is survival of the fittest. Fitness is the ability to survive and reproduce in a specific environment. It results from adaptations, or inherited characteristics that increase an organism's chance of survival. Only the fittest organisms pass on their traits. Because of this, species change over time.

Darwin argued that species alive today are descended, with modification, from ancestral species that lived in the past. Darwin also introduced the principle of common descent. According to this principle, all species come from common ancestors. The principle of common descent links all organisms on Earth into a single tree of life.

Darwin presented four types of evidence in support of evolution: the fossil record, the geographical distribution of living species, homologous structures of living organisms, and similarities in early development, or embryology. Comparing fossils from older and younger rock layers documents the fact that evolution has occurred. The presence of similar but unrelated organisms in similar environments suggests the operation of natural selection. Homologous structures have different mature forms but develop from the same embryonic tissues. They provide strong evidence that organisms have descended, with modifications, from common ancestors. Some homologous structures no longer serve important functions in descendants. If the structures are greatly reduced in size, they are called vestigial organs. The early stages, or embryos, of many animals are very similar. These similarities also provide evidence that the animals share common ancestors.

Scientific advances have supported most of Darwin's hypotheses. Today, evolutionary theory is called the "grand unifying theory of the life sciences." It gives insights to all biological and biomedical sciences.

Section 15–1 The Puzzle of Life's Diversity
(pages 369–372)

🔑 **Key Concepts**
- What was Charles Darwin's contribution to science?
- What pattern did Darwin observe among organisms of the Galápagos Islands?

Introduction (page 369)

1. The process by which modern organisms have descended from ancient organisms is called _____evolution_____.

2. A well-supported explanation of phenomena that have occurred in the natural world is a(an) _____theory_____.

Voyage of the *Beagle* (pages 369–370)

3. Circle the letter of each sentence that is true about Charles Darwin.

   (a.) He was born in 1809.

   (b.) He was an English naturalist.

   c. He was 42 when he began the voyage on the *Beagle*.

   (d.) The voyage lasted five years and took him around the world.

4. Label the Galápagos Islands on the map below.

5. Is the following sentence true or false? Darwin was looking for a scientific explanation for the diversity of life on Earth. _____true_____

Darwin's Observations (pages 370–372)

6. Circle the letter of each observation that Darwin made.

   a. An enormous number of species inhabit Earth.

   b. Many organisms seem to be poorly suited to their environment.

   c. The same sorts of animals are always found in the same ecosystems in different parts of the world.

   d. Some species that lived in the past no longer live on Earth.

7. The preserved remains of ancient organisms are called _____fossils_____.

8. As Darwin studied fossils, what new questions arose? __He wondered why so many__ species had disappeared and how they were related to living species.

9. How did Darwin explain differences in shell shape of tortoises from Hood Island and Isabela Island? __Darwin thought that Hood Island tortoises had curved shells to allow them to__ reach the sparse vegetation on their island, whereas Isabela Island tortoises had dome-shaped shells because vegetation on their island was more abundant and closer to the ground.

10. Darwin observed that small brown birds on the Galápagos Islands differed in the shape of their _____beaks_____.

The Journey Home (page 372)

11. What did Darwin think about on his journey home to England? __Darwin thought about__ how the characteristics of many animals and plants, including mockingbirds and tortoises, varied noticeably among the different islands of the Galápagos.

12. After he returned to England, what hypothesis did Darwin develop to explain his findings? __Separate species evolved from a common ancestor after becoming isolated from__ one another on different islands of the Galápagos.

Reading Skill Practice

You can focus on the most important points in a section by turning the headings into questions and then trying to find the answers as you read. For each heading in Section 15–1, first write the heading as a *how, what,* or *why* question. Then, find and write the answer to your question. Do your work on a separate sheet of paper.

A sample question for the heading Voyage of the *Beagle* might be "What was the voyage of the *Beagle*?" The answer might be: "The voyage of the *Beagle* was a 5-year trip around the world that was made in the 1830s by the English naturalist Charles Darwin."

Section 15–2 Ideas That Shaped Darwin's Thinking (pages 373–377)

Key Concepts
- How did Hutton and Lyell describe geological change?
- According to Lamarck, how did species evolve?
- What was Malthus's theory of population growth?

An Ancient, Changing Earth (pages 374–375)

1. Two scientists who helped Darwin and others recognize how old Earth is were _____James Hutton_____ and _____Charles Lyell_____.

2. Circle the letter of each idea that was proposed by James Hutton.
   a. Earth is a few thousand years old.
   (b.) Layers of rock are moved by forces beneath Earth's surface.
   (c.) Most geological processes operate extremely slowly.
   d. The processes that changed Earth in the past are different from the processes that operate in the present.

3. Circle the letter of each sentence that is true about Lyell's work.
   a. His book, *Principles of Geology*, was published after Darwin returned from his voyage.
   (b.) His work explained how awesome geological features could be built up or torn down over long periods of time.
   (c.) His publications helped Darwin appreciate the significance of the geological phenomena that he had observed.
   (d.) He stressed that scientists must explain past events in terms of processes that they can actually observe.

4. In what two ways did an understanding of geology influence Darwin? _____Knowing that_____ Earth could change over time helped Darwin believe that life might change as well. Knowing that Earth was very old assured Darwin that there had been enough time for life to change.

Lamarck's Evolution Hyphotheses (page 376)

5. Is the following sentence true or false? Lamarck was among the first scientists to recognize that living things have changed over time. _____true_____

6. Is the following sentence true or false? Lamarck proposed that all organisms have an innate tendency toward complexity and perfection. _____true_____

Name_____ Class_____ Date _____

7. How did Lamarck propose that species change over time? _Lamarck proposed that by_ _selective use or disuse of organs, organisms acquired or lost certain traits during their lifetime._ _These traits could then be passed on to their offspring. Over time, this process led to change in a_ _species._

8. How did Lamarck pave the way for the work of later biologists? _Lamarck was one of_ _the first to develop scientific hypotheses of evolution and to realize that organisms are adapted to_ _their environments._

9. Which step in the diagram below shows the inheritance of acquired traits as proposed by Lamarck? _Step 3 shows the inheritance of acquired traits._

1.
2.
3.

Population Growth (page 377)

10. Circle the letter of each sentence that is true about Thomas Malthus.

   a. He was an important influence on Darwin.

   b. He was an English naturalist.

   c. He believed that war, famine, and disease limit the growth of populations.

   d. His views were influenced by conditions in twentieth-century England.

11. Is the following sentence true or false? The overwhelming majority of a species' offspring survive. _____false_____

Name_____ Class_____ Date _____

7. How did Lamarck propose that species change over time? _Lamarck proposed that by_ _selective use or disuse of organs, organisms acquired or lost certain traits during their lifetime._ _These traits could then be passed on to their offspring. Over time, this process led to change in a_ _species._

8. How did Lamarck pave the way for the work of later biologists? _Lamarck was one of_ _the first to develop scientific hypotheses of evolution and to realize that organisms are adapted to_ _their environments._

9. Which step in the diagram below shows the inheritance of acquired traits as proposed by Lamarck? _Step 3 shows the inheritance of acquired traits._

1.
2.
3.

Population Growth (page 377)

10. Circle the letter of each sentence that is true about Thomas Malthus.

   a. He was an important influence on Darwin.

   b. He was an English naturalist.

   c. He believed that war, famine, and disease limit the growth of populations.

   d. His views were influenced by conditions in twentieth-century England.

11. Is the following sentence true or false? The overwhelming majority of a species' offspring survive. _____false_____

172 Chapter 15

Section 15–3 Darwin Presents His Case
(pages 378–386)

🔑 **Key Concepts**
- How is natural variation used in artificial selection?
- How is natural selection related to a species' fitness?
- What evidence of evolution did Darwin present?

Publication of *On the Origin of Species* (pages 378–379)

1. Is the following sentence true or false? When Darwin returned to England, he rushed to publish his thoughts about evolution. _____false_____

2. The naturalist whose essay gave Darwin an incentive to publish his own work was ___Alfred Russel Wallace___.

3. Circle the letter of each sentence that is true about Darwin's book *On the Origin of Species*.
   a. It was published in 1869.
   b. It was ignored when it was first published.
   (c.) It contained evidence for evolution.
   (d.) It described natural selection.

Inherited Variation and Artificial Selection (page 379)

4. Differences among individuals of a species are referred to as ___variation___.

5. Is the following sentence true or false? Genetic variation is found only in wild organisms in nature. _____false_____

6. Circle the letter of each sentence that is true about artificial selection.
   (a.) It is also called selective breeding.
   (b.) It occurs when humans select natural variations they find useful.
   (c.) It produces organisms that look very different from their ancestors.
   d. It is no longer used today.

Evolution by Natural Selection (pages 380–382)

7. What was Darwin's greatest contribution? His greatest contribution was developing a scientific hypothesis to explain how evolution occurs.

Match each term with its definition.

Terms		Definitions
c	8. fitness	a. Any inherited characteristic that increases an organism's chance of survival
a	9. adaptation	b. Survival of the fittest
b	10. natural selection	c. The ability of an individual to survive and reproduce in its specific environment

11. What does the phrase *struggle for existence* mean? <u>It means that members of each</u>
<u>species compete regularly to obtain food, living space, and other necessities of life.</u>

12. Is the following sentence true or false? Adaptations can be physical characteristics but
not more complex features such as behavior. <u>false</u>

13. Explain what Darwin meant by the phrase *survival of the fittest*. <u>Individuals that are</u>
<u>better suited to their environment survive and reproduce most successfully.</u>
_____

14. Circle the letter of each sentence that is true about natural selection.

(a.) It selects traits that increase fitness.

(b.) It takes place without human control.

c. It can be observed directly in nature.

d. It leads to an increase in a species' fitness.

15. The principle that living species descend, with changes, from other species over time is
referred to as <u>descent with modification</u>.

16. The principle that all species were derived from common ancestors is known as
<u>common descent</u>.

Evidence of Evolution (pages 382–385)

17. Is the following sentence true or false? Darwin argued that living things have been
evolving on Earth for thousands of years. <u>false</u>

18. Complete the concept map.

19. How do fossils that formed in different rock layers provide evidence of evolution?
<u>They document the fact that life on Earth has changed over time.</u>
_____
_____

20. Circle the letter of the way Darwin explained the distribution of finch species on the Galápagos Islands.

(a.) They had descended with modification from a common mainland ancestor.

b. They had descended with modification from several different mainland ancestors.

c. They had remained unchanged since arriving on the Galápagos from the mainland.

d. They had become more similar to one another after arriving on the Galápagos.

21. How did Darwin explain the existence of similar but unrelated species?
Darwin thought that such species evolved features in common because they were

exposed to similar pressures of natural selection.

_____

22. Structures that have different mature forms but develop from the same embryonic tissues are called _____homologous structures_____.

23. Is the following sentence true or false? Homologous structures provide strong evidence that all four-limbed vertebrates have descended, with modifications, from common ancestors. _____true_____

24. Organs that are so reduced in size that they are just vestiges, or traces, of homologous organs in other species are called _____vestigial organs_____.

Summary of Darwin's Theory (page 386)

25. Circle the letter of each idea that is part of Darwin's theory of evolution.

(a.) There is variation in nature.

b. Fewer organisms are produced than can survive.

(c.) There is a struggle for existence.

(d.) Species change over time.

26. According to Darwin's theory, what happens to individuals whose characteristics are not well suited to their environment? Such individuals die or leave fewer offspring.

_____

27. Darwin believed that all organisms on Earth are united into a single tree of life by
_____descent with modification_____.

Strengths and Weaknesses of Evolutionary Theory (page 386)

28. What is the status of Darwin's hypotheses today? They have been confirmed and
expanded by scientific advances in biology, geology, and physics.

_____

Chapter 15   Darwin's Theory of Evolution

Vocabulary Review

Crossword Puzzle   *Complete the puzzle by entering the term that matches each numbered description.*

Across

1. scientist whose ideas about evolution and adaptation influenced Darwin
3. ship on which Darwin traveled
7. change over time
10. explanation of natural events that is supported by evidence and can be tested with new evidence
12. economist whose ideas about human population influenced Darwin
14. remains of ancient life
15. homologous structure that is greatly reduced in size

Down

1. geologist who influenced Darwin
2. inherited characteristic that increases an organism's chance of survival
4. type of selection in which humans select the variations
5. islands where Darwin observed variation in tortoises
6. ability of an individual to survive and reproduce in its specific environment
8. type of selection Darwin referred to as survival of the fittest
9. structures that have different mature forms but develop from the same embryonic tissues
11. scientist whose ideas about evolution were the same as Darwin's
13. geologist who influenced Darwin

Summary

16–1 Genes and Variation

Darwin's original ideas can now be understood in genetic terms. Beginning with variation, we now know that traits are controlled by genes and that many genes have at least two forms, or alleles. We also know that individuals of all species are heterozygous for many genes.

To understand evolution, genetic variation is studied in populations. A population is defined as a group of individuals of the same species that interbreed. Members of a population share a common group of genes, called a gene pool. A gene pool consists of all the genes, including all the different alleles, that are present in the population. In genetic terms, evolution is any change in the relative frequency of alleles in a population. The relative frequency of an allele is the number of times the allele occurs in a gene pool, compared with the number of times other alleles for the same gene occur.

The two main sources of genetic variation are mutations and gene shuffling. A mutation is any change in a sequence of DNA. Gene shuffling occurs during the production of gametes in sexual reproduction. It can result in millions of different combinations of genes. Mutation and gene shuffling do not change relative allele frequencies. However, they increase genetic variation by increasing the number of different genotypes.

The number of different phenotypes for a given trait depends on how many genes control the trait. A single-gene trait is controlled by one gene. If there are two alleles for the gene, two or three different genotypes are possible. An example in humans is the presence or absence of widow's peak. A polygenic trait is controlled by two or more genes, and each gene may have more than one allele. An example of a human polygenic trait is height.

Polygenic traits such as height produce many different phenotypes. Variation in a polygenic trait in a population often produces a bell-shaped curve, with most people falling near the middle of the curve.

16–2 Evolution as Genetic Change

Natural selection acts on individuals. Evolution acts on populations. Natural selection acting on individuals leads to the evolution of populations.

Natural selection on a trait controlled by a single gene with two alleles can cause one allele to increase and the other allele to decrease. Natural selection on polygenic traits is more complicated. Natural selection on polygenic traits can occur as directional selection, stabilizing selection, or disruptive selection. Directional selection takes place when individuals at one end of the bell-shaped curve have higher fitness than individuals near the middle or at the other end of the curve. The result of directional selection is a shift in the curve toward the higher fitness end. Stabilizing selection takes place when individuals near the middle of the curve have higher fitness than individuals at either end. The result of stabilizing selection is a narrowing of the curve around the middle. Disruptive selection takes place when individuals at the upper and lower ends of the curve have higher fitness than individuals near the middle. As a result of disruptive selection, the curve develops a peak at each end and a low point in the middle.

Natural selection is not the only source of evolutionary change. In small populations, alleles can become more or less common simply by chance. This kind of change in allele frequency is called genetic drift. It occurs when individuals with a particular allele leave more descendants than other individuals, just by chance. Over time, this can cause an allele to become more or less common in a population.

Genetic drift also may occur when a small group of individuals colonizes a new habitat. By chance, the small group may have different relative allele frequencies than the original population. When this happens, it is called the founder effect.

To understand how evolution occurs, scientists first had to answer the question: Under what conditions does evolution not occur? The answer to this question is called the Hardy-Weinberg principle. The principle states that allele frequencies in a population will remain constant unless one or more factors cause those frequencies to change. The situation in which allele frequencies remain constant is called genetic equilibrium. For a population to be in genetic equilibrium, five conditions are required: random mating, very large population size, no migrations, no mutations, and no natural selection. Random mating assures that each individual has an equal chance of reproducing. Very large population size prevents genetic drift from occurring. If all five conditions are met, relative allele frequencies will not change and evolution will not occur.

16–3 The Process of Speciation

Speciation means the formation of new species. For one species to evolve into two new species, the gene pools of two populations must become separated, or reproductively isolated. Reproductive isolation has occurred when the members of two populations cannot interbreed and produce fertile offspring. Reproductive isolation can involve behavioral, geographic, or temporal isolation.

Behavioral isolation occurs when populations have different courtship rituals or other behaviors involved in reproduction. Geographic isolation occurs when populations are separated by geographic barriers, such as mountains or rivers. Temporal isolation occurs when populations reproduce at different times.

Recently, Peter and Rosemary Grant proved that natural selection is still causing evolution of finches on the Galápagos Islands. The Grants showed that there was enough heritable variation in finch beaks to provide raw material for natural selection. They also showed that differences in beaks produced differences in fitness. These differences in fitness caused directional selection to occur.

Darwin thought that different finch species evolved on the Galápagos Islands from a single species of founding birds. We now know how this could have happened. A few finches may have traveled from mainland South America to one of the islands to found a new population. There, they survived and reproduced. Some birds crossed to a second island, and the two populations became geographically isolated. They no longer shared a gene pool. Seed sizes on the second island favored birds with larger beaks. The population on the second island evolved into a population with larger beaks. Eventually, the large-beaked birds on the second island became reproductively isolated and evolved into a new species.

Evolution continues today. For example, bacteria are evolving to have resistance to drugs. Evolutionary theory can help us understand these changes.

Chapter 16   Evolution of Populations

Section 16–1 Genes and Variation (pages 393–396)

Key Concepts
- What are the main sources of heritable variation in a population?
- How is evolution defined in genetic terms?
- What determines the numbers of phenotypes for a given trait?

Introduction (page 393)

1. Is the following sentence true or false? Mendel's work on inheritance was published after Darwin's lifetime. _____false_____

2. Which two important factors was Darwin unable to explain without an understanding of heredity? __He was unable to explain the source of variation and how heritable traits were__ passed from one generation to the next.

_____

How Common Is Genetic Variation? (page 393)

3. All organisms have additional _____genetic variation_____ that is "invisible" because it involves small differences in biochemical processes.

Variation and Gene Pools (page 394)

4. A group of individuals of the same species that interbreed is a(an) ____population____.

5. All of the genes in a population are called a(an) ____gene pool____.

6. Is the following sentence true or false? A gene pool typically contains just one allele for each inheritable trait. ____false____

7. The number of times that an allele occurs in a gene pool compared with the number of times other alleles for the same gene occur is called the ____relative frequency____ of the allele.

Sources of Genetic Variation (pages 394–395)

8. What is a mutation? __It is any change in a sequence of DNA.__

_____

9. Why do mutations occur? __They occur because of mistakes in the replication of DNA or as a__ result of radiation or chemicals in the environment.

_____

© Pearson Education, Inc., publishing as Pearson Prentice Hall.

10. Complete the concept map.

11. Circle the letter of each choice that is true about mutations.

    a. They do not always change an amino acid.

    b. They always affect lengthy segments of a chromosome.

    c. They always affect an organism's phenotype.

    d. They always affect an organism's fitness.

12. Is the following sentence true or false? Most heritable differences are due to gene shuffling that occurs during the production of gametes. _____true_____

13. Circle the letter of each choice that is true about sexual reproduction.

    a. It is a major source of variation in many populations.

    b. It can produce many different phenotypes.

    c. It can produce many different genetic combinations.

    d. It can change the relative frequency of alleles in a population.

Single-Gene and Polygenic Traits (pages 395–396)

14. Is the following sentence true or false? The number of phenotypes produced for a given trait depends on how many genes control the trait. _____true_____

15. Is the following sentence true or false? Most traits are controlled by a single gene. _____false_____

16. Label the two graphs to show which one represents a single-gene trait and which one represents a polygenic trait.

<u>Polygenic Trait</u>

<u>Single-Gene Trait</u>

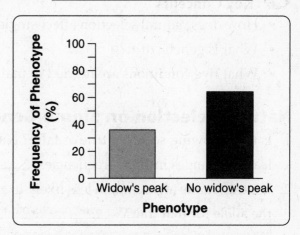

Reading Skill Practice

When you read about related concepts, making a graphic organizer such as a Venn diagram can help you focus on their similarities and differences. Make a Venn diagram comparing and contrasting single-gene and polygenic traits. For more information on Venn diagrams, see Appendix A of your textbook. Do your work on a separate sheet of paper.

Students should show that single-gene and polygenic traits are both controlled by genes but differ in the number of genes that control them and the number of genotypes and phenotypes they produce.

Section 16–2 Evolution as Genetic Change
(pages 397–402)

⬭ **Key Concepts**
- How does natural selection affect single-gene and polygenic traits?
- What is genetic drift?
- What five conditions are needed to maintain genetic equilibrium?

Natural Selection on Single-Gene Traits (pages 397–398)

1. Is the following sentence true or false? Natural selection on single-gene traits cannot lead to changes in allele frequencies. _____false_____

2. If a trait made an organism less likely to survive and reproduce, what would happen to the allele for that trait? __Fewer copies of the allele would pass to future generations, and the__ allele could even disappear from the gene pool completely.

3. If a trait had no effect on an organism's fitness, what would happen to the allele for that trait? __The allele would not be under pressure from natural selection, and its frequency might__ increase, decrease, or remain the same.

Natural Selection on Polygenic Traits (pages 398–399)

4. List the three ways that natural selection can affect the distributions of phenotypes.
   a. Directional selection
   b. Stabilizing selection
   c. Disruptive selection

Match the type of selection with the situation in which it occurs.

	Type of Selection	Situation
b	5. Directional	a. Individuals at the upper and lower ends of the curve have higher fitness than individuals near the middle.
c	6. Stabilizing	b. Individuals at one end of the curve have higher fitness than individuals in the middle or at the other end.
a	7. Disruptive	c. Individuals near the center of the curve have higher fitness than individuals at either end.

8. An increase in the average size of beaks in Galápagos finches is an example of _____directional_____ selection.

9. Is the following sentence true or false? The weight of human infants at birth is under the influence of disruptive selection. _____false_____

10. Draw the missing graph to show how disruptive selection affects beak size.

Disruptive Selection

Largest and smallest seeds become more common.

Population splits into two subgroups specializing in different seeds.

Genetic Drift (page 400)

11. Is the following sentence true or false? Natural selection is the only source of evolutionary change. _____false_____

12. Random change in allele frequencies in small populations is called _____genetic drift_____.

13. A situation in which allele frequencies change as a result of the migration of a small subgroup of a population is known as the _____founder effect_____.

14. What is an example of the founder effect? ___Accept all logical examples. One example is the___ evolution of fruit flies on different Hawaiian Islands.

Evolution Versus Genetic Equilibrium (pages 401–402)

15. What does the Hardy-Weinberg principle state? ___Allele frequencies in a population will___ remain constant unless one or more factors cause them to change.

16. The situation in which allele frequencies remain constant is called _____genetic equilibrium_____.

17. List the five conditions required to maintain genetic equilibrium.

  a. Random mating   **d.** No mutations

  b. Very large population   **e.** No natural selection

  c. No movement into or out of the population

18. Why is large population size important in maintaining genetic equilibrium? Genetic drift has less effect on large populations.

Section 16–3 The Process of Speciation
(pages 404–410)

👄 Key Concepts
- What factors are involved in the formation of new species?
- Describe the process of speciation in the Galápagos finches.

Introduction (page 404)

1. What is speciation? It is the formation of new species.

Isolating Mechanisms (pages 404–405)

2. Is the following sentence true or false? Individuals in different species can have the same gene pool. _____false_____

3. What does it mean for two species to be reproductively isolated from each other? Members of the two species cannot interbreed and produce fertile offspring.

4. What must happen in order for new species to evolve? Populations must be reproductively isolated from one another.

5. List three ways that reproductive isolation occurs.
   a. Behavioral isolation   c. Temporal isolation
   b. Geographic isolation

6. When does behavioral isolation occur? It occurs when populations are capable of interbreeding but have differences in courtship rituals or other types of behavior.

7. Is the following sentence true or false? Eastern and Western meadowlarks are an example of behavioral isolation. _____true_____

8. When does geographic isolation occur? It occurs when populations are separated by geographic barriers such as rivers, mountains, or bodies of water.

9. Abert and Kaibab squirrels in the Southwest are an example of _____geographic_____ isolation.

10. Is the following sentence true or false? Geographic barriers guarantee the formation of new species. _____false_____

11. What is an example of temporal isolation? Each of three similar species of orchid in the same rain forest releases pollen on different days.

Testing Natural Selection in Nature (pages 406–407)

12. Is the following sentence true or false? The basic mechanisms of evolutionary change cannot be observed in nature. _____false_____

13. Circle the letter of each hypothesis about the evolution of Galápagos finches that was tested by the Grants.

   a. The finches' beak size and shape has enough inheritable variation to provide raw material for natural selection.

   b. The different finch species are the descendants of a common mainland ancestor.

   c. Differences in the finches' beak size and shape produce differences in fitness that cause natural selection to occur.

   d. The evolution of the finches is proceeding slowly and gradually.

Speciation in Darwin's Finches (pages 408–409)

14. Complete the flowchart to show how speciation probably occurred in the Galápagos finches.

Founders arrive

↓

Separation of populations

↓

Changes in the gene pool

↓

Reproductive isolation

↓

Ecological competition

↓

Continued evolution

15. How could differences in beak size lead to reproductive isolation? <u>Birds with the same</u> <u>beak size prefer to mate with each other. As a result, big-beaked and smaller-beaked birds would</u> <u>not choose to mate with each other, and their gene pools would remain isolated.</u>

Studying Evolution Since Darwin (page 410)

16. Why is the study of evolution important? <u>By understanding evolutionary theory, we can</u> <u>respond to changes in the living world in ways that improve human life.</u>

Chapter 16 Evolution of Populations

Vocabulary Review

Interpreting Diagrams   *The diagrams show the distribution curves for time of mating in a population of insects. The diagram on the left represents the starting population. The diagram on the right represents the population several generations later. Study the diagrams and answer the questions below.*

1. What type of natural selection has occurred? ___Disruptive selection has occurred.___

_____

2. Which phenotypes are selected against? __Phenotypes near the middle of the distribution__ __are selected against.__

3. Which phenotypes have higher fitness? ___Phenotypes at both ends of the distribution have__ __higher fitness than phenotypes near the middle.__

4. If natural selection continues in this way, what may eventually happen to the population? __The population may eventually evolve into two different species, reproductively isolated by__ __temporal isolation.__

Completion   *Fill in the blanks with terms from Chapter 16.*

5. Any change in the relative frequency of alleles in a population is called ___evolution___.

6. A gene pool consists of all the genes in a(an) ___population___.

7. The two main sources of genetic variation are gene shuffling and ___mutations___.

8. A random change in allele frequency is called ___genetic drift___.

9. When birds cannot interbreed because they have different mating songs, they are characterized by ___behavioral___ isolation.

10. A situation in which allele frequencies change as a result of the migration of a small subgroup of a population is known as the ___founder effect___.

11. Research on Galápagos finches by Peter and Rosemary Grant showed that a type of natural selection called ___directional___ selection was occurring.

12. Two related species that live in the same area but mate during different seasons are separated by ___temporal___ isolation.

Summary

17–1 The Fossil Record

Fossils are preserved traces and remains of ancient life. Scientists who study fossils are called paleontologists. They use fossils to infer what past life forms were like. All the information about past life provided by fossils is called the fossil record. The fossil record shows how life has changed over time. It shows that more than 99 percent of all species that ever lived on Earth have become extinct, or died out.

Few organisms are actually preserved as fossils. Most fossils that do form are found in sedimentary rock. As sediments build up in layers over time, they sometimes bury the remains of dead organisms. These dead organisms eventually turn into fossils.

Relative dating and radioactive dating are used to determine the age of fossils. Relative dating determines whether a fossil is older or younger than other fossils. It is based on where fossils are found in rock layers. Fossils from deeper rock layers are assumed to be older than fossils from rock layers closer to the surface. Index fossils represent species that lived for a short period of time but over a wide geographic range. Index fossils can help determine the relative age of fossils from different places. Radioactive dating determines a fossil's age in years. Radioactive elements in fossils decay, or break down, at a steady rate, called a half-life. A half-life is the length of time needed for half of the radioactive atoms in a sample to decay. A fossil's age is calculated from the half-life and the amount of remaining radioactive atoms the fossil contains.

The geologic time scale is used for evolutionary time. The scale begins with Precambrian Time. Following Precambrian Time, the scale is divided into three eras: the Paleozoic, Mesozoic, and Cenozoic eras. Each era is further divided into smaller lengths of time, called periods.

17–2 Earth's Early History

Earth is about 4.6 billion years old. At first, Earth was very hot and the atmosphere contained toxic gases. The atmosphere also contained water vapor but no oxygen. About 3.8 billion years ago, Earth's surface cooled and water vapor condensed. Thunderstorms soaked the surface, and oceans formed.

In the 1950s, Stanley Miller and Harold Urey simulated conditions on early Earth. They filled a container with water and gases found in Earth's early atmosphere. They passed electric sparks through the mixture to simulate lightning. Soon, organic compounds formed. The experiment showed that molecules needed for life could have evolved under conditions on early Earth. Sometimes large organic molecules form tiny bubbles called proteinoid microspheres. Structures similar to proteinoid microspheres might have become the first living cells. RNA and DNA also could have evolved from simple organic molecules.

The first known life forms evolved about 3.5 billion years ago. They were single celled and looked like modern bacteria. Some were preserved as microscopic fossils, or microfossils. Eventually, photosynthetic bacteria became common. During photosynthesis, the bacteria produced oxygen. The oxygen accumulated in the atmosphere. The rise of oxygen drove some life forms to extinction. At the same time, other life forms evolved that depended on oxygen.

The first eukaryotes, or organisms with nuclei, evolved about 2 billion years ago. One explanation for how eukaryotes evolved is the endosymbiotic theory. This theory proposes that smaller prokaryotes began living inside larger cells and evolved a symbiotic relationship with the larger cells.

Later, sexual reproduction evolved. Sexual reproduction increased genetic variation, so evolution could occur more quickly.

17–3 Evolution of Multicellular Life

During Precambrian Time, life arose and evolved into multicellular forms. However, life still existed only in the oceans. Few fossils exist from the Precambrian, because the animals did not yet have any hard parts.

There is much more fossil evidence from the Paleozoic Era. Animals with hard parts, such as trilobites, evolved then. Other important evolutionary events of the Paleozoic include the evolution of land plants, insects, amphibians, and reptiles. At the end of the Paleozoic, there was a mass extinction, in which many types of organisms became extinct at once.

Important evolutionary events in the Mesozoic Era include the appearance of flowering plants and the dominance of dinosaurs. Reptiles, in general, were so successful during the era that the Mesozoic is called the Age of Reptiles. At the close of the Mesozoic, another mass extinction occurred.

The Cenozoic Era is called the Age of Mammals. During the Cenozoic, mammals evolved adaptations that allowed them to live on land, in water, and in air. The first human fossils may have appeared about 200,000 years ago in Africa.

17–4 Patterns of Evolution

Macroevolution means large-scale evolution, or evolution above the level of the species. Six patterns of macroevolution are extinction, adaptive radiation, convergent evolution, coevolution, punctuated equilibrium, and changes in developmental genes.

Most of the time, extinctions have occurred because species could not compete for resources or adapt to gradually changing environments. Several times, however, mass extinctions have occurred. During these mass extinctions, huge numbers of species became extinct at once. This may have occurred because of a combination of events, such as volcanoes erupting and asteroids striking Earth.

Adaptive radiation is the process in which a single species evolves into diverse species that live in different ways. Convergent evolution is the process in which unrelated species come to look alike because they have evolved similar adaptations to similar environments. Coevolution is the process by which two species evolve in response to changes in each other over time. For example, plants evolved poisons that protected them from insects. In response, insects evolved ways of protecting themselves from the poisons.

Darwin thought evolution occurred slowly and gradually. The fossil record sometimes shows a different pattern of evolution, called punctuated equilibrium. In this pattern, long periods of little or no change are interrupted by short periods of rapid change.

Some genes, called hox genes, control the actions of many other genes. Small changes in hox genes can produce major differences in adult organisms. Some scientists think that changes in hox genes may contribute to major evolutionary changes.

Name_____ Class_____ Date _____

Section 17–1 The Fossil Record (pages 417–422)

🔑 Key Concepts
- What is the fossil record?
- What information do relative dating and radioactive dating provide about fossils?
- What are the main divisions of the geologic time scale?

Fossils and Ancient Life (page 417)

1. Scientists who study fossils are called ___paleontologists___.

2. What is the fossil record? It is information about past life that is based on fossils.

3. What evidence does the fossil record provide? It provides evidence about the history of life on Earth and how different groups of organisms, including species, have changed over time.

4. Species that died out are said to be ___extinct___.

5. Is the following sentence true or false? About half of all species that have ever lived on Earth have become extinct. ___false___

How Fossils Form (page 418)

6. Circle the letter of each sentence that is true about fossils.
   a. Most organisms that die are preserved as fossils.
   b.) Fossils can include footprints, eggs, or other traces of organisms.
   c. Most fossils form in metamorphic rock.
   d.) The quality of fossil preservation varies.

7. How do fossils form in sedimentary rock? Sediments settle to the bottom of lakes and seas and bury dead organisms. The weight of upper layers of sediment compresses lower layers into rock and turns the dead organisms into fossils.

Interpreting Fossil Evidence (pages 418–420)

8. List the two techniques paleontologists use to determine the age of fossils.
   a. Relative dating
   b. Radioactive dating

9. Circle the letter of each sentence that is true about relative dating.

(a.) It determines the age of a fossil by comparing its placement with that of fossils in other layers of rock.

(b.) It uses index fossils.

c. It allows paleontologists to estimate a fossil's age in years.

(d.) It provides no information about absolute age.

10. Is the following sentence true or false? Older rock layers are usually closer to Earth's surface than more recent rock layers. _____false_____

11. Is the following sentence true or false? Scientists use radioactive decay to assign absolute ages to rocks. _____true_____

12. The length of time required for half of the radioactive atoms in a sample to decay is called a(an) _____half-life_____.

13. The use of half-lives to determine the age of a sample is called _____radioactive dating_____.

14. How do scientists calculate the age of a sample using radioactive dating?
They measure the amount of remaining radioactive isotopes it contains. The smaller the
amount, the older the sample.

15. Is the following sentence true or false? All radioactive elements have the same half-life.
_____false_____

Geologic Time Scale (pages 421–422)

16. Fill in the missing eras and periods in the geologic time scale below.

GEOLOGIC TIME SCALE

Era	Cenozoic		Mesozoic			Paleozoic						Precambrian Time
Period	Quaternary	Tertiary	Cretaceous	Jurassic	Triassic	Permian	Carboniferous	Devonian	Silurian	Ordovician	Cambrian	Vendian
Time (millions of years ago)	1.8 – present	65 – 1.8	145 – 65	208 – 145	245 – 208	290 – 245	360 – 290	410 – 360	440 – 410	505 – 440	544 – 505	650 – 544

17. Circle the letter of the choice that lists the eras of the geologic time scale in order from the most recent to the oldest.

a. Mesozioc, Paleozoic, Cenozoic

b. Cenozoic, Paleozoic, Mesozoic

c. Cenozoic, Mesozoic, Paleozoic

d. Paleozoic, Mesozoic, Cenozoic

18. Circle the letter of each sentence that is true about the geologic time scale.

a. The scale is used to represent evolutionary time.

b. Major changes in fossil organisms separate segments of geologic time.

c. Divisions of the scale cover standard lengths of 100 million years.

d. Geologic time begins with the Cambrian Period.

19. After Precambrian time, what are the two basic divisions of the geologic time scale?
Eras and periods

20. During which era did dinosaurs roam the Earth? _____ Mesozoic Era

21. During which era did mammals become common? _____ Cenozoic Era

---

Reading Skill Practice

Writing a summary can help you remember the information you have read. When you write a summary, write only the important points. Write a summary of the information in Section 17–1. Your summary should be shorter than the text on which it is based.

Students' summaries will vary, though all should include descriptions of fossil formation, relative and radioactive dating, and the geological time scale.

Section 17–2 Earth's Early History (pages 423–428)

⬤➤ **Key Concepts**
- What substances made up Earth's early atmosphere?
- What did Miller and Urey's experiments show?
- What occurred when oxygen was added to Earth's atmosphere?
- What hypothesis explains the origin of eukaryotic cells?

Formation of Earth (pages 423–424)

1. List six components of Earth's early atmosphere.

   a. _Hydrogen cyanide_   c. _Carbon monoxide_   e. _Hydrogen sulfide_

   b. _Carbon dioxide_   d. _Nitrogen_   f. _Water_

2. Is the following sentence true or false? Liquid water first occurred on Earth more than 4 billion years ago. _____false_____

The First Organic Molecules (page 424)

3. Label the diagram to show which part of Miller and Urey's apparatus simulated lightning storms on early Earth.

Mixture of gases simulating atmosphere of early Earth

Spark simulating lightning storms

Condensation chamber

Water vapor

Cold water cools chamber, causing droplets to form

Liquid containing amino acids and other organic compounds

4. Circle the letter of each sentence that is true about Miller and Urey's experiments.

 (a.) Their purpose was to determine how the first organic molecules evolved.

 (b.) They led to the formation of several amino acids.

 c. They accurately simulated conditions in Earth's early atmosphere.

 d. The results were never duplicated in experiments by other scientists.

The Puzzle of Life's Origins (page 425)

5. What are proteinoid microspheres? They are tiny bubbles, formed of large organic molecules, that have some characteristics of living cells.

6. Is the following sentence true or false? Scientists know how DNA and RNA evolved. false

7. Why do scientists think that RNA may have evolved before DNA? Experiments show that small sequences of RNA could have formed and replicated on their own in the conditions present on early Earth.

8. Once DNA evolved, why would it have become the primary means of transmitting genetic information? DNA is a more stable information-storing molecule than RNA.

Free Oxygen (page 426)

9. Microscopic fossils are called _____ microfossils _____.

10. Circle the letter of each sentence that is true about the earliest life forms on Earth.

 (a.) They resembled modern bacteria.

 b. They were eukaryotes.

 c. They relied on oxygen.

 d. They were not preserved as fossils.

11. How did early photosynthetic bacteria change Earth? They produced oxygen, which first removed iron from the oceans and then accumulated in the atmosphere.

12. Is the following sentence true or false? The rise of oxygen in the atmosphere drove some life forms to extinction. true

Origin of Eukaryotic Cells (pages 427–428)

13. Is the following sentence true or false? The ancestor of all eukaryotic cells evolved about 2 billion years ago. true

14. What was the first step in the evolution of eukaryotic cells? _The first step was the_
evolution of internal cell membranes.
_____

15. What does the endosymbiotic theory propose? _It proposes that eukaryotic cells arose from_
living communities formed by several organisms.
_____

16. Circle the letter of each choice that provides support for the endosymbiotic theory.

    (a.) The membranes of mitochondria and chloroplasts resemble the plasma membranes of free-living prokaryotes.

    b. Mitochondria and chloroplasts do not have DNA.

    (c.) Mitochondria and chloroplasts have ribosomes that are similar in size and structure to those of bacteria.

    (d.) Mitochondria and chloroplasts reproduce by binary fission, as bacteria do.

Sexual Reproduction and Multicellularity (page 428)

17. How did sexual reproduction speed up the evolutionary process? _Sexual reproduction_
shuffles and reshuffles genes in each generation. This increase in genetic variation greatly
increases the chances of evolutionary change due to natural selection.
_____

18. Is the following sentence true or false? Sexual reproduction evolved after the first multicellular organisms appeared. _____ _false_ _____

Reading Skill Practice

When you read a section that contains new or difficult material, identifying the sentence that best expresses the main topic under each heading can help you focus on the most important points. For each heading in Section 17–2, identify and copy the sentence that best expresses the main topic under that heading. Do your work on a separate sheet of paper.

Topic sentences should express the main point under each heading. Good choices include the
boldface sentences, when they appear.

© Pearson Education, Inc., publishing as Pearson Prentice Hall.

Section 17–3 Evolution of Multicellular Life
(pages 429–434)

👓 **Key Concept**
  • What were the characteristic forms of life in the Paleozoic, Mesozoic, and Cenozoic eras?

Precambrian Time (page 429)

1. Is the following sentence true or false? Almost 90 percent of Earth's history occurred during the Precambrian. _____true_____

2. Circle the letter of each sentence that is true about life in the Precambrian.
   (a.) Anaerobic and photosynthetic forms of life appeared.
   (b.) Aerobic forms of life evolved, and eukaryotes appeared.
   (c.) Multicellular life forms evolved.
   d. Life existed on the land and in the sea.

3. Why do few fossils exist from the Precambrian? _The animals were all soft-bodied._
   _____

Paleozoic Era (pages 429–431)

4. The first part of the Paleozoic Era is the _____Cambrian_____ Period.

5. Is the following sentence true or false? Life was not very diverse during the Cambrian Period. _____false_____

6. Circle the letter of each sentence that is true about the Cambrian Period.
   (a.) Organisms with hard parts first appeared.
   (b.) Most animal phyla first evolved.
   c. Many animals lived on the land.
   (d.) Brachiopods and trilobites were common.

Match the periods of the Paleozoic Era with the evolutionary events that occurred during them.

	Periods	Events
__b__	**7.** Ordovician and Silurian	**a.** Reptiles evolved from amphibians, and winged insects evolved into many forms.
__c__	**8.** Devonian	**b.** The first vertebrates evolved, and insects first appeared.
__a__	**9.** Carboniferous and Permian	**c.** Many groups of fishes were present in the oceans, and the first amphibians evolved.

10. Animals first begin to invade the land during the ____Devonian____ Period.

11. Where does the Carboniferous Period get its name? Vast swampy forests of giant ferns and other plants that grew during that time formed thick deposits of sediment that changed into coal over millions of years.

_____

12. When many types of living things become extinct at the same time, it is called a(an) _____mass extinction_____ .

13. Is the following sentence true or false? The mass extinction at the end of the Paleozoic affected only land animals. _____false_____

Mesozoic Era (pages 431–432)

14. Complete the following table.

PERIODS OF THE MESOZOIC ERA

Period	Evolutionary Event
Triassic	First mammals
Jurassic	First birds
Cretaceous	First flowering plants

15. The Mesozoic Era is called the Age of _____Reptiles_____ .

16. The first dinosaurs appeared in the _____Triassic_____ Period.

17. Is the following sentence true or false? The mammals of the Triassic Period were very small. _____true_____

18. Is the following sentence true or false? Many paleontologists think that birds are close relatives of dinosaurs. _____true_____

19. The dominant vertebrates throughout the Cretaceous Period were _____reptiles_____ .

20. What advantage do flowering plants have over conifers? Their seeds are enclosed in a fruit, which protects the seed and aids in dispersing it to new locations.

_____

21. Describe the mass extinction that occurred at the end of the Cretaceous Period.
More than half of all plant and animals groups were wiped out, including all of the dinosaurs.

_____

_____

Name_____ Class_____ Date_____

Cenozoic Era (pages 433–434)

22. Is the following sentence true or false? During the Cenozoic Era, mammals evolved adaptations that allowed them to live on land, in water, and in the air.

_____true_____

23. The Cenozoic Era is called the Age of _____Mammals_____.

24. What were Earth's climates like during the Tertiary Period? _____They were generally warm and mild._____

25. How did Earth's climate change during the Quaternary Period? _____First it cooled, causing a series of ice ages. Then, it began to warm again._____

26. Is the following sentence true or false? The very earliest ancestors of our species appeared about 100,000 years ago. _____false_____

Reading Skill Practice

When you read a section with many details, writing an outline may help you organize and remember the material. Outline Section 17–3 by first writing the section headings as major topics in the order in which they appear in the book. Then, beneath each major topic, list important details about it.

In their outlines, students should use the blue heads as their major topics. Under each topic, they should list enough details to make the topic clear and informative.

© Pearson Education, Inc., publishing as Pearson Prentice Hall.

Section 17–4 Patterns of Evolution (pages 435–440)

🔑 **Key Concept**
* What are six important patterns of macroevolution?

Introduction (page 435)

1. The large-scale evolutionary changes that take place over long periods of time are referred to as _____macroevolution_____.

2. What are six patterns of macroevolution?

   a. extinction

   b. adaptive radiation

   c. convergent evolution

   d. coevolution

   e. punctuated equilibrium

   f. changes in developmental genes

Extinction (page 435)

3. What are possible causes of mass extinctions? Possible causes include a huge asteroid striking Earth, many large volcanoes erupting, continents changing position, and sea levels changing.

4. What effects have mass extinctions had on the history of life? The disappearance of so many species left habitats open. Often, the result was a burst of evolution that produced many new species.

Adaptive Radiation (page 436)

5. The process of a single species or a small group of species evolving into diverse forms that live in different ways is called _____adaptive radiation_____.

6. What led to the adaptive radiation of mammals? The disappearance of the dinosaurs led to the adaptive radiation of mammals.

Convergent Evolution (pages 436–437)

7. The process by which unrelated organisms come to resemble one another is called _____convergent evolution_____.

8. Circle the letter of each choice that is an example of convergent evolution.

   a. Bird's wing and fish's fin

   (b.) Shark's fin and dolphin's limb

   c. Human's arm and bird's wing

   d. Human's leg and dolphin's limb

Coevolution (pages 437–438)

9. The process by which two species evolve in response to changes in each other over time is called _____coevolution_____.

10. How have plants and plant-eating insects coevolved? __Plants have evolved poisons to__ prevent insects from feeding on them. Insects, in turn, have evolved ways of inactivating or eliminating the poisons.

_____

Punctuated Equilibrium (page 439)

11. The idea that evolution occurs at a slow, steady rate is called _____gradualism_____.

12. What are some reasons rapid evolution may occur after long periods of equilibrium? It may occur when a small population becomes isolated or a small group migrates to a new environment. It may also occur following a mass extinction.

_____

13. The pattern of long, stable periods interrupted by brief periods of more rapid change is called _____punctuated equilibrium_____.

14. Is the following sentence true or false? Evolution has often proceeded at different rates for different organisms. _____true_____

Developmental Genes and Body Plans (page 440)

15. How can hox genes help reveal how evolution occurred? __Homologous hox genes__ establish body plans in animals that have not shared a common ancestor in hundreds of millions of years. In addition, major evolutionary changes may be based on hox genes.

_____

16. Is the following sentence true or false? Changes in the timing of genetic control during embryonic development can contribute to the variation involved in natural selection. _____true_____

Vocabulary Review

Multiple Choice   *In the space provided, write the letter of the answer that best completes each sentence.*

_c_ **1.** Index fossils are used in the type of dating called
    a. radioactive dating.   **c.** relative dating.
    b. periodic dating.   **d.** absolute dating.

_d_ **2.** Oxygen was added to Earth's atmosphere by the process of
    a. macroevolution.   **c.** coevolution.
    b. endosymbiosis.   **d.** photosynthesis.

_a_ **3.** Sexual reproduction evolved before the evolution of
    a. multicellular organisms.   **c.** eukaryotes.
    b. photosynthetic bacteria.   **d.** the earliest life forms.

_c_ **4.** The Age of Mammals occurred during the
    a. Mesozoic Era.   **c.** Cenozoic Era.
    b. Paleozoic Era.   **d.** Precambrian.

_b_ **5.** Dinosaurs were dominant during the
    a. Precambrian.   **c.** Paleozoic Era.
    b. Mesozoic Era.   **d.** Cenozoic Era.

Writing Descriptions   *Describe each pattern of macroevolution.*

6. coevolution   In coevolution, two species evolve in response to changes in each other over time.

7. convergent evolution   Convergent evolution refers to the process by which unrelated organisms come to resemble one another as they evolve similar adaptations to similar environments.

8. mass extinction   Mass extinction is the occurrence of many extinctions around the same time.

9. punctuated equilibrium   Punctuated equilibrium is a pattern of macroevolution in which long, stable periods are interrupted by brief periods of rapid change.

10. adaptive radiation   In adaptive radiation, a single species, or a small group of species, evolves into diverse forms that live in different ways.

Summary

18–1 Finding Order in Diversity

There are millions of different species on Earth. To study this great diversity of organisms, biologists must give each organism a name. Biologists also must organize living things into groups in a logical way. Therefore, biologists need a classification system. Taxonomy is the discipline of naming and classifying organisms. To be useful, the names that are assigned should be universally accepted. A good classification system should also group together organisms that are more similar to each other than they are to organisms in other groups.

Common names for organisms vary by language and region. This creates confusion. By the 1700s, scientists had tried to solve this problem by agreeing to use a single name for each species. At first, the names they used were very long. Then, Carolus Linnaeus developed a two-word naming system, called binomial nomenclature. This system is still used today. In binomial nomenclature, each species is assigned a two-part scientific name. The first part of the name refers to the genus (plural: genera). A genus is a group of closely related species. For example, the genus *Ursus* contains six bear species. The second part of the name, along with the genus name, refers to a single species (plural: species). Recall that species consist of individuals who can interbreed. The name *Ursus maritimus*, for example, refers to the species polar bear.

Linnaeus's system of classification has seven different levels. From smallest to largest, the levels are species, genus, family, order, class, phylum, and kingdom. Each of the levels is called a taxon (plural: taxa). Just as a genus is a group of similar species, a family is a group of similar genera, an order a group of similar families, a class a group of similar orders, a phylum (plural: phyla) a group of similar classes, and a kingdom a group of similar phyla. Linnaeus named two kingdoms of living things, the Animalia (animal) and Plantae (plant) kingdoms.

18–2 Modern Evolutionary Classification

Linnaeus and other taxonomists have always tried to group organisms according to biologically important characteristics. However, they have not always agreed upon which characteristics are most important.

Early classifications were based on visible similarities. Biologists now group organisms according to evolutionary relationships. The study of evolutionary relationships among organisms is called phylogeny. Classification based on evolutionary relationships is called evolutionary classification. Species within one genus are more closely related to each other than to species in another genus. This is because all members of a genus share a recent common ancestor. All genera in a family also share a common ancestor. However, this common ancestor is farther in the past than the common ancestor of species within a genus. The higher the level of the taxon, the farther back in time is the common ancestor of all the organisms in that taxon.

Many biologists now use a method called cladistic analysis to determine evolutionary relationships. Cladistic analysis is based on derived characters. Derived characters are new traits that arise as a group evolves over time. Derived traits are therefore found in closely related organisms but not in their distant ancestors. Derived characters can be used to construct a cladogram. A cladogram is a diagram that shows the evolutionary relationships among a group of organisms. A cladogram is basically an evolutionary tree, much like a family tree.

All organisms have DNA and RNA. Because DNA and RNA are so similar across all forms of life, these molecules can be compared in different species. The more similar the molecules are in different species, the more recently the species shared a common ancestor. Therefore, the more closely related they are.

Comparisons of DNA can also be used to estimate the length of time that two species have been evolving independently. A model called a molecular clock can be used for this purpose. The model assumes that neutral mutations, which do not affect phenotype, accumulate in gene pools. Two species evolving independently from each other will accumulate different neutral mutations through time. The more there are of these different neutral mutations, the longer the two species have been evolving independently.

18–3 Kingdoms and Domains

As biologists learned more about the natural world, they realized that Linnaeus's two kingdoms, Animalia and Plantae, did not represent all life forms. First, microorganisms, such as bacteria, were discovered. Microorganisms did not seem to fit into either kingdom, so they were placed in their own kingdom, called Protista. Then, mushrooms, yeast, and molds were separated from plants and placed in their own kingdom, called Fungi. Later, bacteria were separated from other Protista and placed in another new kingdom, called Monera. Finally, the Monera were divided into two kingdoms: Eubacteria and Archaebacteria. By the 1990s, a six-kingdom system of classification was proposed. It includes the kingdoms Eubacteria, Archaebacteria, Protista, Fungi, Plantae, and Animalia.

A new taxon, called the domain, is now used by many biologists. The domain is one level higher than the kingdom. Three domains are recognized: Bacteria, Archaea, and Eukarya.

The domain Bacteria includes unicellular organisms without a nucleus. They have cell walls containing a substance called peptidoglycan. The domain Bacteria corresponds to the kingdom Eubacteria.

The domain Archaea also includes unicellular organisms without a nucleus. These organisms have cell walls that do not contain peptidoglycan. The domain Archaea corresponds to the kingdom Archaebacteria.

The domain Eukarya includes the four remaining kingdoms: Protista, Fungi, Plantae, and Animalia. All members of the domain Eukarya have cells with a nucleus. Most members of the kingdom Protista are unicellular organisms. Some Protista are autotrophs; others, heterotrophs. Most members of the kingdom Fungi are multicellular, and all are heterotrophs. All members of the kingdom Plantae are multicellular autotrophs. Most plants cannot move about, and their cells have cell walls. All members of the kingdom Animalia are multicellular heterotrophs. Most animals can move about, and their cells lack cell walls.

Section 18–1 Finding Order in Diversity
(pages 447–450)

🔑 Key Concepts
- How are living things organized for study?
- What is binomial nomenclature?
- What is Linnaeus's system of classification?

Why Classify? (page 447)

1. Why do biologists use a classification system to study the diversity of life?
   They use it to name organisms and group them in a logical manner.

2. The science of classifying organisms and assigning them universally accepted names is known as ___taxonomy___.

3. Is the following sentence true or false? In a good system of classification, organisms placed into a particular group are less similar to each other than they are to organisms in other groups. ___false___

Assigning Scientific Names (page 448)

4. Why is it confusing to refer to organisms by common names? Common names vary among languages and even among regions within a single country. Furthermore, different species can share a single common name.

5. Circle the letter of each sentence that is true about early efforts at naming organisms.
   a. Names were usually in English.
   b. Names often described detailed physical characteristics of a species.
   c. Names could be very long.
   d. It was difficult to standardize the names.

6. The two-word naming system developed by Linnaeus is called ___binomial nomenclature___.

7. Circle the letter of each sentence that is true about binomial nomenclature.
   a. The system is no longer in use today.
   b. Each species is assigned a two-part scientific name.
   c. The scientific name is always written in italics.
   d. The second part of the scientific name is capitalized.

8. What is the genus of the grizzly bear, *Ursus arctos*? The genus is *Ursus*.

Linnaeus's System of Classification (pages 449–450)

9. A group or level of organization in taxonomy is called a taxonomic category, or
_____taxon_____.

10. The largest taxonomic category in Linnaeus's system of classification is the
_____kingdom_____, and the smallest is the _____species_____.

11. What two kingdoms did Linnaeus name? He named the Animalia and Plantae kingdoms.
_____

12. Fill in the name of each missing taxonomic category in the chart below.

Grizzly bear Black bear Giant panda Red fox Abert squirrel Coral snake Sea star

KINGDOM
Animalia

PHYLUM
Chordata

CLASS
Mammalia

ORDER
Carnivora

FAMILY
Ursidae

GENUS
Ursus

SPECIES
Ursus arctos

Reading Skill Practice

Taking notes can help you identify and remember the most important information
when you read. Take notes on Section 18–1 by writing the main headings and under
each heading listing the most important points. Include in your notes the boldface
terms and sentences. Do your work on a separate sheet of paper.

Students should list all the headings in the section and under each heading write enough additional
information, including the boldface terms and sentences, to make the topic clear and informative.

Section 18–2 Modern Evolutionary Classification (pages 451–455)

Key Concepts
- How are evolutionary relationships important in classification?
- How can DNA and RNA help scientists determine evolutionary relationships?

Introduction (page 451)

1. What traits did Linnaeus consider when classifying organisms? <u>He tried to group</u>
<u>organisms according to biologically important characteristics.</u>
_____
_____

Which Similarities Are Most Important? (page 451)

2. What problems are faced by taxonomists who rely on body-structure comparisons?
<u>It is difficult to decide which similarities and differences are most important.</u>
_____
_____
_____

Evolutionary Classification (page 452)

3. Is the following sentence true or false? Darwin's theory of evolution changed the way biologists thought about classification. _____<u>true</u>_____

4. How do biologists now group organisms into categories? <u>They group them into categories</u>
<u>that represent lines of evolutionary descent, not just physical similarities.</u>
_____
_____

5. Is the following sentence true or false? Genera placed within a family should be less closely related to one another than to members of any other family. _____<u>false</u>_____

6. The strategy of grouping organisms together based on their evolutionary history is called _____<u>evolutionary classification</u>_____.

Classification Using Cladograms (page 453)

7. Circle the letter of each sentence that is true about cladistic analysis.
   (a.) It considers only traits that are evolutionary innovations.
   b. It considers all traits that can be measured.
   c. It considers only similarities in body structure.
   (d.) It is a method of evolutionary classification.

8. Characteristics that appear in recent parts of a lineage, but not in its older members, are called _____<u>derived characters</u>_____.

Name_____ Class_____ Date_____

9. A diagram that shows the evolutionary relationships among a group of organisms is called a(an) _____cladogram_____.

10. Is the following sentence true or false? Derived characters are used to construct a cladogram. _____true_____

Similarities in DNA and RNA (page 454)

11. Is the following sentence true or false? Some organisms do not have DNA or RNA. _____false_____

12. How do similarities in genes show that humans and yeasts share a common ancestry?
Both humans and yeasts have a gene that codes for a myosin protein. This similarity at the
molecular level indicates a shared common ancestry.
_____
_____

Molecular Clocks (page 455)

13. A model that uses DNA comparisons to estimate the length of time that two species have been evolving independently is known as a(an) _____molecular clock_____.

14. A molecular clock relies on the repeating process of _____mutations_____.

15. Why are only neutral mutations useful for molecular clocks? _____Neutral mutations_____
accumulate in the DNA of different species at about the same rate because they are unaffected by
natural selection.
_____
_____

16. Is the following sentence true or false? The degree of dissimilarity in DNA sequences is an indication of how long ago two species shared a common ancestor. _____true_____

17. Why are there many molecular clocks in a genome instead of just one?
Some genes accumulate mutations faster than others.
_____
_____

Section 18–3 Kingdoms and Domains (pages 457–461)

Key Concepts
- What are the six kingdoms of life as they are now identified?
- What is the three-domain system of classification?

The Tree of Life Evolves (pages 457–458)

1. Is the following sentence true or false? The scientific view of life was more complex in Linnaeus's time. _____false_____

2. What fundamental traits did Linnaeus use to separate plants from animals?
   Animals were mobile organisms that used food for energy. Plants were green, photosynthetic
   organisms that used energy from the sun.
   _____

3. What type of organisms were later placed in the kingdom Protista?
   Microorganisms were later placed in this kingdom.
   _____

4. Mushrooms, yeast, and molds have been placed in their own kingdom, which is
   called_____Fungi_____.

5. Why did scientists place bacteria in their own kingdom, the Monera? Bacteria lack the
   nuclei, mitochondria, and chloroplasts found in other forms of life.
   _____

6. List the two groups into which the Monera have been separated.
   a. Eubacteria _____
   b. Archaebacteria _____

7. Complete the concept map.

© Pearson Education, Inc., publishing as Pearson Prentice Hall.

The Three-Domain System (page 458)

8. A more inclusive category than any other, including the kingdom, is the _____domain_____.

9. What type of analyses have scientists used to group modern organisms into domains? They have used molecular analyses.

10. List the three domains.

    a. Bacteria_____

    b. Archaea_____

    c. Eukarya_____

11. Complete the chart below.

CLASSIFICATION OF LIVING THINGS

Domain	Kingdom	Examples
Bacteria	Eubacteria	*Streptococcus, Escherichia coli*
Archaea	Archaebacteria	Methanogens, halophiles
Eukarya	Protist	Amoeba, paramecium, slime molds, giant kelp
	Fungi	Mushrooms, yeasts
	Plantae	Mosses, ferns, flowering plants
	Animalia	Sponges, worms, insects, fishes, mammals

Domain Bacteria (page 459)

12. Circle the letter of each sentence that is true about members of the domain Bacteria.

    a. They are multicellular.

    (b.) They are prokaryotes.

    (c.) They have rigid cell walls.

    (d.) The cell walls contain peptidoglycans.

13. Is the following sentence true or false? All members of the domain Bacteria are parasites. _____false_____

Name_____ Class_____ Date _____

Domain Archaea (page 459)

14. Circle the letter of each sentence that is true about members of the domain Archaea.

(a.) They are unicellular.

b. They are eukaryotes.

c. They lack cell walls.

d. They lack cell membranes.

15. Is the following sentence true or false? Many members of the domain Archaea can survive only in the absence of oxygen. _____true_____

Domain Eukarya (pages 460–461)

16. Circle the letter of each sentence that is true about all the members of the domain Eukarya.

(a.) They have a nucleus.

b. They are multicellular.

c. They are heterotrophs.

d. They have cell walls and chloroplasts.

Match each kingdom with the description that applies to members of that kingdom.

	Kingdom	Description
c	**17.** Protista	**a.** They have cell walls of chitin.
a	**18.** Fungi	**b.** They have no cell walls or chloroplasts.
d	**19.** Plantae	**c.** They include slime molds and giant kelp.
b	**20.** Animalia	**d.** They include mosses and ferns.

Chapter 18   Classification

Vocabulary Review

Crossword Puzzle   *Complete the puzzle by entering the term that matches each numbered description.*

Across
7. type of classification that is based on evolutionary history
8. discipline of classifying and naming organisms
10. taxon composed of similar orders
11. taxon composed of similar classes
12. type of clock that estimates how long species have been evolving independently

Down
1. kingdom in the Eukarya domain that includes single-celled autotrophs
2. study of evolutionary relationships among organisms
3. new taxon that is higher than the kingdom
4. taxon composed of similar genera
5. taxon composed of closely related species
6. diagram based on derived characters
8. general term for any level, or category, in a taxonomic system
9. taxon composed of similar families

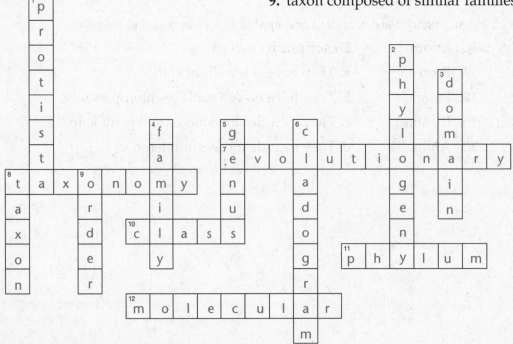

Answering Questions   *Write one or more sentences to answer each question.*

13. In what ways are members of the domain Bacteria and the domain Archaea similar?

    Possible answer: Members of both domains are unicellular, are prokaryotes, have cell walls, and can be autotrophic or heterotrophic.

14. Which domain includes only organisms with a nucleus in their cells?   All members of the domain Eukarya have a nucleus in their cells.

15. What are two ways that most members of the kingdom Plantae and the kingdom Animalia differ?   Possible answer: Most Plantae cannot move about, and their cells have cell walls; most Animalia can move about, and their cells do not have cell walls.

Summary

19–1 Bacteria

The smallest and most common microorganisms are prokaryotes, which are unicellular organisms that lack a nucleus. Prokaryotes are divided into two kingdoms: Eubacteria and Archaebacteria. Eubacteria live almost everywhere. Eubacteria are usually surrounded by a cell wall, which contains a carbohydrate called peptidoglycan. Inside the cell wall is a cell membrane that surrounds the cytoplasm. Archaebacteria look very similar to eubacteria. Archaebacteria lack the peptidoglycan of eubacteria and have different membrane lipids. Also, the DNA sequences of key archaebacterial genes are more like those of eukaryotes than those of eubacteria. Archaebacteria may be the ancestors of eukaryotes.

Prokaryotes are identified by characteristics such as shape, the chemical nature of their cell walls, the way they move, and the way they obtain energy. Three differently shaped prokaryotes are bacilli, cocci, and spirilla. Bacilli (singular: bacillus) are rod-shaped; cocci (singular: coccus) are sphere-shaped; and spirilla (singular: spirillum) are spiral or corkscrew-shaped. Two different types of cell walls are found in prokaryotes. A method called Gram staining is used to tell them apart. Gram-positive bacteria appear violet when stained, while Gram-negative bacteria appear pink. Prokaryotes move in a variety of ways.

Most prokaryotes are heterotrophs—organisms that obtain energy by consuming other organisms. Other prokaryotes are autotrophs, organisms that can make their own food. Heterotrophic prokaryotes include chemoheterotrophs and photoheterotrophs. Autotrophic prokaryotes include photoautotrophs and chemoautotrophs.

Prokaryotes release energy by both cellular respiration and fermentation. Organisms that require a constant supply of oxygen to live are called obligate aerobes. Organisms that do not require oxygen are called obligate anaerobes. Organisms that can survive with or without oxygen are called facultative anaerobes.

When a bacterium has grown so that it has nearly doubled, it replicates its DNA and divides in half, producing two identical "daughter" cells. This asexual reproduction is called binary fission. Bacteria are also able to exchange genetic information by a process called conjugation. Many bacteria can form an endospore when conditions are bad.

Bacteria are vital to maintaining the living world. Some are producers that carry out photosynthesis. Others are decomposers that break down dead matter. Some soil bacteria convert natural nitrogen gas into a form plants can use through a process called nitrogen fixation. Humans use bacteria in industry, food production, and other ways.

19–2 Viruses

Viruses are particles of nucleic acid, protein, and, in some cases, lipids. All viruses have one thing in common: They enter living cells and, once inside, use the machinery of the infected cell to produce more viruses. A typical virus is composed of a core of DNA or RNA surrounded by a protein coat. A virus's protein coat is called its capsid. Viruses that infect bacteria are called bacteriophages.

Once the virus is inside a host cell, two different processes may occur. In a lytic infection, a virus enters a cell, makes copies of itself, and causes the cell to burst, releasing new virus particles that can attack other cells. The virus uses the materials of the host cell to make copies of its own DNA molecule. In a lysogenic infection, a virus integrates its DNA into the DNA of the host cell, and the viral genetic information replicates along with the host cell's DNA. The viral DNA that is embedded in the host's DNA is called a prophage. The prophage may remain part of the DNA of the host cell for many generations. Eventually, the prophage will remove itself from the host cell DNA and make new virus particles.

Some viruses, called retroviruses, contain RNA as their genetic information. In a retrovirus, the genetic information is copied backward—from RNA to DNA instead of from DNA to RNA. The virus that causes the disease AIDS is a retrovirus.

Viruses must infect a living cell in order to reproduce. Viruses are parasites. Because viruses are not made up of cells and cannot live independently, viruses are not considered to be living things.

19–3 Diseases Caused by Bacteria and Viruses

Disease-causing agents are known as pathogens. Bacteria and viruses can cause disease. Not all bacteria are pathogens. Some live in and on the human body and help the body perform essential functions. Other bacteria can produce human diseases such as tuberculosis, strep throat, and tooth decay.

Bacteria produce disease in one of two general ways. Some bacteria damage the cells and tissues of the infected organism directly by breaking down the cells for food. Other bacteria release toxins (poisons) that travel throughout the body interfering with the normal activity of the host.

Many bacterial diseases can be prevented by using a vaccine. A vaccine is a preparation of weakened or killed pathogens. A vaccine can prompt the body to produce immunity to the disease. Immunity is the body's natural way of killing pathogens. When a bacterial infection does occur, antibiotics can be used to fight the disease. Antibiotics are compounds that block the growth and reproduction of bacteria. Animals also suffer from bacterial diseases.

There are various methods to control bacterial growth, including sterilization, disinfectants, and food storage and food processing. Disinfectants include soaps and cleaning solutions. Food storage includes using a refrigerator.

Viruses produce disease by disrupting the body's normal equilibrium. In many viral infections, viruses attack and destroy certain body cells, causing the symptoms of the disease. Viral diseases in humans include the common cold, influenza, AIDS, chickenpox, and measles. Viruses produce other serious diseases in both animals and plants.

Two other viruslike particles can cause disease. Viroids are single-stranded RNA molecules that have no surrounding capsids. Viroids cause disease in plants. Prions are particles that contain only protein—there is no DNA or RNA. Prions cause disease in animals, including humans.

Chapter 19   Bacteria and Viruses

Section 19–1 Bacteria (pages 471–477)

🔑 **Key Concepts**
- How do the two groups of prokaryotes differ?
- What factors are used to identify prokaryotes?
- What is the importance of bacteria?

Introduction (page 471)

1. What are prokaryotes? _They are unicellular organisms that lack a nucleus._

_____

2. Is the following sentence true or false? Prokaryotes are much smaller than most eukaryotic cells. _____ _true_

Classifying Prokaryotes (pages 471–472)

3. What are the two different groups of prokaryotes?

   a. _Eubacteria_   b. _Archaebacteria_

4. Which is the larger of the two kingdoms of prokaryotes? _Eubacteria_

5. Where do eubacteria live? _They live almost everywhere—including in water, on land, and on_ _and within the human body._

6. What protects a prokaryotic cell from injury? _The cell wall protects it._

_____

7. Circle the letter of what is within the cell wall of a prokaryote.

   a. another cell wall   c. archaebacteria

   (b.) cell membrane   d. pili

8. What is peptidoglycan? _It is a carbohydrate in the cell walls of eubacteria._

_____

9. Some eubacteria have a second _____ _membrane_ outside the cell membrane.

10. Circle the letter of each sentence that is true about archaebacteria.

    (a.) Their membrane lipids are different from those of eubacteria.

    b. They lack a cell wall.

    (c.) They lack peptidoglycan.

    (d.) They look very similar to eubacteria.

11. What is significant about the DNA sequences of key archaebacterial genes?
    They are more like those of eukaryotes than those of eubacteria.

_____

12. How are archaebacteria related to eukaryotes? _Scientists reason that archaebacteria may_ _be the ancestors of eukaryotes._

Name_____ Class_____ Date _____

13. What are methanogens, and where do they live? They are prokaryotes that produce
methane gas. They live in oxygen-free environments, such as thick mud and the digestive tracts of
animals.

Identifying Prokaryotes (page 473)

14. Complete the illustration of a typical prokaryote by labeling the parts.

15. What are four characteristics used to identify prokaryotes?

a. Their shape

b. The chemical nature of their cell walls

c. The way they move

d. The way they obtain energy

16. What are each of the differently shaped prokaryotes called?

a. The rod-shaped are called _____ bacilli _____.

b. The spherical-shaped are called _____ cocci _____.

c. The corkscrew-shaped are called _____ spirilla _____.

17. A method of telling two different types of eubacteria apart by using dyes is called
_____ Gram staining _____.

18. What colors are Gram-positive and Gram-negative bacteria under the microscope
when treated with Gram stain? Gram-positive bacteria appear violet, and Gram-negative
bacteria appear red.

19. What are flagella? They are whiplike structures used for movement.

20. Is the following sentence true or false? Some prokaryotes do not move at all.
_____ true _____

© Pearson Education, Inc., publishing as Pearson Prentice Hall.

Metabolic Diversity (pages 473–474)

21. Complete the table about prokaryotes classified by the way they obtain energy.

GROUPS OF PROKARYOTES

Group	Description
Photoautotroph	Organism that carries out photosynthesis in a manner similar to that of plants
Chemoautotroph	Organism that obtains energy directly from chemical reactions involving inorganic molecules
Heterotroph	Organism that takes in organic molecules and then breaks them down
Photoheterotroph	Organism that captures sunlight for energy and also needs organic molecules as a carbon source

22. Members of which group of photoautotrophs contain a bluish pigment and chlorophyll *a*? _____ Cyanobacteria _____

23. How do the chemoautotrophs that live near hydrothermal vents on the ocean floor obtain energy? They obtain energy from hydrogen sulfide gas that flows from the vents.
_____

24. Complete the table about prokaryotes classified by the way they release energy.

GROUPS OF PROKARYOTES

Group	Description
Obligate aerobes	Organisms that require a constant supply of oxygen
Obligate anaerobes	Organisms that must live in the absence of oxygen
Facultative anaerobes	Organisms that can survive with or without oxygen

25. Facultative anaerobes can switch between cellular respiration and _____ fermentation _____.

Growth and Reproduction (page 475)

26. What occurs in the process of binary fission? It is a type of asexual reproduction in which a prokaryote grows to nearly double its size, replicates its DNA, and divides in half, producing two identical "daughter" cells.

27. What occurs during conjugation? A hollow bridge forms between two cells, and genes move from one cell to the other.

28. Is the following sentence true or false? Most prokaryotes reproduce by conjugation.
_____ false _____

Name_____ Class_____ Date _____

29. What is an endospore? It is a type of spore that is formed when a bacterium produces a thick internal wall that encloses its DNA and a portion of its cytoplasm.

Importance of Bacteria (pages 476–477)

30. How do decomposers help the ecosystem recycle nutrients when a tree dies? Armies of bacteria attack and digest the dead tissue. The bacteria break down dead matter into simpler materials, which are released into the soil.

31. What would happen to plants and animals if decomposers did not recycle nutrients? Plants would drain the soil of minerals and die, and animals that depend on plants for food would starve.

32. Why do plants and animals need nitrogen? They need nitrogen to make amino acids, which are the building blocks of proteins.

33. How does nitrogen fixation help plants? Plants use the nitrogen to build amino acids.

34. What kind of relationship do many plants have with nitrogen-fixing bacteria? They have symbiotic relationships.

35. How can bacteria be used to clean up an oil spill? One type of bacterium can digest petroleum.

36. What have biotechnology companies begun to realize about bacteria adapted to extreme environments? Those bacteria may be a rich source of heat-stable enzymes, which can be used in medicine, food production, and industrial chemistry.

Reading Skill Practice

Writing a summary can help you remember the information you have read. When you write a summary, write only the most important points. Write a summary of the information under the green heading Decomposers. Your summary should be shorter than the text on which it is based. Do your work on a separate sheet of paper.

Students' summaries should include the main points about how some bacteria are critical in recycling nutrients in the environment.

© Pearson Education, Inc., publishing as Pearson Prentice Hall.

216 Chapter 19

Name_____ Class_____ Date_____

Section 19–2 Viruses (pages 478–483)

🔑 **Key Concepts**
- What is the structure of a virus?
- How do viruses cause infection?

What Is a Virus? (pages 478–479)

1. What are viruses? _They are particles of nucleic acid, protein, and in some cases lipids that can_ _reproduce only by infecting living cells._

2. What do all viruses have in common? _They enter living cells and, once inside, use the_ _machinery of the infected cell to produce more viruses._

3. Is the following sentence true or false? Most viruses are so small that they can be seen only with the aid of a powerful electron microscope. _____true_____

4. What is the structure of a typical virus? _A typical virus is composed of a core of either DNA_ _or RNA surrounded by a protein coat._

5. Complete the illustration of a T4 bacteriophage by labeling the parts.

Head

DNA

Tail sheath

Tail Fiber

6. A virus's protein coat is called a(an) _____capsid_____.

7. How does a typical virus get inside a cell? _The capsid proteins bind to receptors on the_ _surface of a cell and "trick" the cell into allowing it inside._

Reading and Study Workbook **217**

8. What occurs when viruses get inside cells? Once inside, the viral genes are expressed. The cell transcribes and translates the viral genetic information into viral capsid proteins. Sometimes the program may cause the cell to make copies of the virus, and in the process the host cell is destroyed.

9. Why are most viruses highly specific to the cells they infect? Viruses must bind precisely to proteins on the cell surface and then use a host's genetic system.

10. What are bacteriophages? They are viruses that infect bacteria.

Viral Infection (pages 480–481)

11. Why is a lytic infection given that name? The host cell is lysed and destroyed.

12. Circle the letter of each sentence that is true about a lysogenic infection.
    a. The virus lyses the host cell immediately.
    (b.) The virus embeds its DNA into the host's DNA.
    (c.) The virus's DNA is replicated along with the host cell's DNA.
    (d.) A host cell makes copies of the virus indefinitely.

13. Complete the flowchart about a lytic infection.

> The bacteriophage attaches to the bacterium's _____cell wall_____.

⬇

> The bacteriophage injects its _____DNA_____ into the cell.

⬇

> The cell makes mRNA from the bacteriophage's _____genes_____.

⬇

> The virus wrecks the cell, causing it to _____burst_____.

⬇

> The bursting of the cell releases new bacteriophage _____particles_____.

14. What is a prophage? It is the viral DNA that is embedded in the host's DNA.

Retroviruses (page 482)

15. What are retroviruses? They are viruses that contain RNA as their genetic information.
_____

16. What happens when retroviruses infect a cell? They produce a DNA copy of their RNA.
This DNA is inserted into the DNA of the host cell.
_____

Viruses and Living Cells (pages 482–483)

17. Circle the letter of each reason why some biologists do not consider viruses to be alive.

 a. They can't infect living cells.

 b. They can't evolve.

 c. They can't regulate gene expression.

 (**d.**) They can't reproduce independently.

18. Complete the table comparing viruses and cells.

Virus and Cells

Characteristic	Virus	Cell
Structure	DNA or RNA core, capsid	Cell membrane, cytoplasm; eukaryotes also contain nucleus and organelles
Reproduction	Only within a host cell	Independent cell division either asexually or sexually
Genetic Code	DNA or RNA	DNA
Growth and Development	No	Yes
Obtain and Use Energy	No	Yes
Response to the Environment	No	Yes
Change Over Time	Yes	Yes

Name_____ Class_____ Date _____

Section 19–3 Diseases Caused by Bacteria and Viruses (pages 485–490)

Key Concepts
- How do bacteria cause disease?
- How can bacterial growth be controlled?
- How do viruses cause disease?

Bacterial Disease in Humans (pages 485–486)

1. What are pathogens? They are disease-causing agents.

2. What are the two general ways that bacteria cause disease?

   a. Some damage the tissues of the infected organism directly by breaking them down for food.

   b. Others release toxins that harm the body.

3. What kind of tissue do the bacteria that cause tuberculosis break down?
   They break down lung tissue.

4. What are antibiotics? They are compounds that block the growth and reproduction of bacteria.

5. What do you think is one of the major reasons for the dramatic increase in life expectancy during the past two centuries? There is an increased understanding of how to prevent and cure bacterial infections.

Bacterial Disease in Animals (page 486)

6. What is one example of a bacterial disease in animals? Example given in the textbook is anthrax; however, accept all correct answers.

Controlling Bacteria (pages 487–488)

7. What is sterilization? It is a way of destroying all bacteria by subjecting them to great heat.

8. A chemical solution that kills pathogenic bacteria is called a(an) _____disinfectant_____.

9. Why will food stored at low temperatures keep longer? The bacteria in the food will take much longer to multiply.

Viral Disease in Humans (page 488)

10. What are some human diseases that viruses cause? Viruses cause polio, measles, AIDS, mumps, influenza, yellow fever, smallpox, the common cold, and many other diseases.

220 Chapter 19

Viral Disease in Animals (page 489)

11. What is one example of a viral disease in animals? <u>Example given in text is foot-and-mouth</u> <u>disease; however, accept all correct answers.</u>

12. Cancer-causing viruses are known as <u>oncogenic viruses</u> .

Viral Disease in Plants (page 489)

13. Why do plant viruses have a difficult time entering the cells they infect? <u>Because plant</u> <u>cells are surrounded by a cell wall, viruses can't break through. Instead, viruses enter a plant cell</u> <u>through tears in leaves, stems, or roots.</u>

14. How are most plant viruses spread? <u>They are spread by insects.</u>

Viroids and Prions (page 490)

15. What are viroids? <u>Viroids are single-stranded RNA molecules that have no surrounding capsids.</u>

16. A disease-causing particle that contains only protein and not DNA or RNA is called a(an) <u>prion</u> .

Vocabulary Review

Matching   *In the space provided, write the letter of the definition that best matches each term.*

___f___ **1.** lysogenic infection

___t___ **2.** eubacteria

___l___ **3.** chemoautotroph

___p___ **4.** toxin

___b___ **5.** prion

___n___ **6.** bacteriophage

___h___ **7.** coccus

___d___ **8.** chemoheterotroph

___r___ **9.** antibiotic

___e___ **10.** virus

___j___ **11.** prokaryote

___a___ **12.** spirillum

___o___ **13.** prophage

___g___ **14.** pathogen

___i___ **15.** lytic infection

___m___ **16.** endospore

___c___ **17.** bacillus

___k___ **18.** binary fission

___s___ **19.** obligate anaerobe

___q___ **20.** vaccine

a. spiral-shaped bacterium

b. pathogen that causes disease in animals by forming a protein clump

c. rod-shaped bacterium

d. organism that must take in organic molecules for both energy and a supply of carbon

e. a particle of nucleic acid, protein, and in some cases, lipids

f. process in which viral DNA becomes part of a host cell's DNA

g. disease-causing agent

h. spherical bacterium

i. process in which a host cell bursts after being invaded by a virus

j. organism consisting of one cell that lacks a nucleus

k. process in which a bacterium replicates its DNA and divides in half

l. organism that obtains energy from inorganic molecules

m. spore formed by bacteria when growth conditions become unfavorable

n. virus that infects bacteria

o. viral DNA that is embedded in the host's DNA

p. substance produced by some bacteria that poisons host cells

q. preparation of weakened or killed pathogens

r. compound that can destroy bacteria

s. organism that can live only in an oxygen-free environment

t. the larger of the two kingdoms of prokaryotes

Summary

20–1 The Kingdom Protista

The kingdom Protista is a diverse group. Protists are eukaryotes that are not members of the kingdoms Plantae, Animalia, or Fungi. Most protists are unicellular. The first eukaryotic organisms on Earth were protists.

Protists, which first appeared about 1.5 billion years ago, were the first group of eukaryotes to evolve. One explanation for the way the first eukaryotes developed from prokaryotes has been credited to Lynn Margulis. Margulis's hypothesis states that the first eukaryote—and the first protist—was formed by a symbiosis among several prokaryotes. Evidence to support this hypothesis includes structural similarities between certain eukaryotic organelles and bacteria.

Because protists are such a diverse group, scientists don't always agree on how to classify them. One way to classify protists is according to the way they obtain nutrition. There are animallike protists, plantlike protists, and funguslike protists.

20–2 Animallike Protists: Protozoans

Animallike protists—also called protozoans—are heterotrophs. The four phyla of animallike protists are classified according to they way they move.

Animallike protists that swim using flagella are classified in the phylum Zoomastigina. They are called zooflagellates. Members of the phylum Sarcodina move by means of temporary projections of cytoplasm known as pseudopods. Sarcodines use pseudopods for feeding and movement. Sarcodines called amoebas have thick pseudopods. The phylum Ciliophora is named for cilia, which are short hairlike projections similar to flagella. Ciliates use cilia for feeding and movement. Some of the best-known ciliates belong to the genus *Paramecium*. Members of the phylum Sporozoa are parasites and do not move on their own. Sporozoans reproduce by means of sporozoites.

Some animallike protists cause serious diseases. The sporozoan *Plasmodium* causes malaria. The zooflagellate *Trypanosoma* causes African sleeping sickness. Some animallike protists are beneficial to organisms. *Trichonympha* lives within the digestive system of termites and helps termites digest wood.

20–3 Plantlike Protists: Unicellular Algae

Plantlike protists are commonly called algae. Plantlike protists include four phyla that contain unicellular organisms. One of the key traits used to classify algae is the photosynthetic pigments they contain. Chlorophyll includes three forms. Each form absorbs a different wavelength of light. Many algae also have compounds called accessory pigments that absorb light at different wavelengths than chlorophyll.

Euglenophytes—members of the phylum Euglenophyta—are plantlike protists that have two flagella but no cell wall. Euglenophytes have chloroplasts, but in most other ways they are like the protozoans called zooflagellates.

Chrysophytes—members of the phylum Chrysophyta—are a diverse group of plantlike protists that have gold-colored chloroplasts. Diatoms—members of the phylum Bacillariophyta—produce thin, delicate cell walls rich in silicon. Silicon (Si) is the main component of glass. These walls are shaped like the two sides of a petri dish or a flat pillbox.

Dinoflagellates—members of the phylum Pyrrophyta—generally have two flagella. About half of the dinoflagellates are photosynthetic. The other half live as heterotrophs.

Plantlike protists play a major ecological role on Earth by being a considerable part of the phytoplankton. Phytoplankton are made up of the population of small photosynthetic organisms found near the surface of the ocean. Many protists grow rapidly in regions where sewage is dumped into water. When the amount of waste is excessive, algae grow into enormous masses called algal blooms.

20–4 Plantlike Protists: Red, Brown, and Green Algae

Three phyla of plantlike protists contain mostly multicellular organisms. The most important differences among these phyla are their photosynthetic pigments. Red algae—members of phylum Rhodophyta—are able to live at great depths due to their efficiency in harvesting light energy. Red algae contain chlorophyll *a* and reddish accessory pigments called phycobilins.

Brown algae—members of the phylum Phaeophyta—contain chlorophyll *a* and *c* as well as a brown accessory pigment called fucoxanthin. The largest alga is giant kelp, a brown alga that grows to be more than 60 meters in length.

Green algae—members of the phylum Chlorophyta—share many characteristics with plants. They share the same photosynthetic pigments, chlorophyll *a* and *b*. Both plants and green algae have cellulose in their cell walls. Also, green algae are like plants in that they store food in the form of starch. These shared characteristics lead scientists to hypothesize that the ancestors of modern land plants looked like green algae. Green algae include the unicellular *Chlamydomonas*. Several species of green algae live in multicellular colonies. *Ulva*, called "sea lettuce," is a true multicellular green alga.

The life cycles of many algae include both a diploid and a haploid generation. The process of switching back and forth between haploid stages and diploid stages in a life cycle is called alternation of generations.

Algae produce much of Earth's oxygen through photosynthesis. Algae are a major food source in the oceans. People also use algae for food. Industry uses algae in making plastics and other products.

20–5 Funguslike Protists

Funguslike protists are like fungi in that they are heterotrophs that absorb food from dead or decaying organic matter. Unlike most true fungi, though, funguslike protists have centrioles. They also lack the chitin cell walls of true fungi.

Slime molds are funguslike protists that play key roles in recycling organic material. At one stage of their life cycle, slime molds look just like amoebas. At other stages, they form moldlike clumps that produce spores, almost like fungi. In cellular slime molds, individual cells remain distinct during every phase of the life cycle. They spend most of their lives as free-living cells. In acellular slime molds, cells fuse to form large cells with many nuclei. These structures are known as plasmodia. Fruiting bodies, or sporangia, spring up from a plasmodium.

Water molds, or oomycetes, are members of the phylum Oomycota. Oomycetes thrive on dead or decaying organic matter in water. Some oomycetes are plant parasites on land.

Slime molds and water molds are important recyclers of organic material. Some funguslike protists can cause diseases in plants. An oomycete caused a disease in the Irish potato crop in 1845 and 1846, leading to mass starvation.

Section 20–1 The Kingdom Protista (pages 497–498)

Key Concept
- What are protists?

What Is a Protist? (page 497)

1. What is a protist? It is any organism that is not a plant, an animal, a fungus, or a prokaryote.

2. Circle the letter of each sentence that is true about protists.

   a. All are unicellular.

   (b.) All cells have a nucleus.

   (c.) All cells have membrane-bound organelles.

   d. All are multicellular.

3. Why are some organisms that consist of thousands of cells considered to be protists? They are considered protists because they are so similar to others that are truly unicellular.

Evolution of Protists (page 498)

4. The first eukaryotic organisms on Earth were _____protists_____.

5. What is biologist Lynn Margulis's hypothesis about where the first protists came from? The first eukaryotic cells may have evolved from a symbiosis of several cells. Mitochondria and chloroplasts found in eukaryotic cells may be descended from aerobic and photosynthetic prokaryotes that began to live inside larger cells.

Classification of Protists (page 498)

6. Complete the table about protist classification.

GROUPS OF PROTISTS

Group	Method of Obtaining Food
Animallike protists	Consume other organisms
Plantlike protists	Produce their own food by photosynthesis
Funguslike protists	Obtain food by external digestion, as either decomposers or parasites

7. What don't categories of protists based on the way they obtain food reflect about these organisms? _They don't reflect their evolutionary history._
_____

Reading Skill Practice

By looking at illustrations in textbooks, you can help yourself remember better what you have read. Look carefully at Figure 20–1 on page 497. What important idea do these photographs communicate? Do your work on a separate sheet of paper.

Students should infer that the main idea these photographs communicate is that the kingdom Protista consists of an extremely diverse group of organisms and that protists are defined less by what they are than by what they are not.

Section 20–2 Animallike Protists: Protozoans
(pages 499–505)

🗝 Key Concepts
- What are the distinguishing features of the major phyla of animallike protists?
- How do animallike protists harm other living things?

Introduction (page 499)

1. At one time, what were all animallike protists called? _____Protozoa_____

2. How are the four phyla of animallike protists distinguished from one another?
   They are distinguished by their means of movement.
   _____
   _____

Zooflagellates (page 499)

3. What kind of protists are classified in the phylum Zoomastigina? They are animallike
   protists that swim using flagella.

4. How many flagella does a zooflagellate have? Most have either one or two flagella, though
   a few species have many flagella.

5. Zooflagellates reproduce asexually by means of _____mitosis and cytokinesis_____.

6. Is the following sentence true or false? Some zooflagellates have a sexual life cycle.
   _____true_____

Sarcodines (page 500)

7. Sarcodines are members of the phylum _____Sarcodina_____.

8. What are pseudopods? They are temporary projections of cytoplasm.
   _____

9. What do sarcodines use pseudopods for? They use pseudopods for feeding and movement.
   _____

10. The best known sarcodines are the _____amoebas_____.

11. What is amoeboid movement? It is a type of locomotion that occurs when the cytoplasm of
    the cell streams into a pseudopod, and the rest of the cell follows.

12. What is a food vacuole? It is a small cavity in the cytoplasm that temporarily stores food.
    _____

13. How do amoebas capture and digest food? They surround a food particle or cell and take it
    inside themselves to form a food vacuole. Once inside the cell, the material is digested rapidly.
    _____

14. Amoebas reproduce by means of _____binary fission_____.

15. Circle the letter of each example of a sarcodine.
    a. foraminiferan   **b.** paramecium   **c.** amoeba   **d.** heliozoan

Ciliates (pages 501–502)

16. Ciliates are members of the phylum _____Ciliophora_____.

17. What are cilia? They are short hairlike projections similar to flagella.

18. What do ciliates use cilia for? They use them for feeding and movement.

Match the ciliate structure with its description.

Structure	Description
c **19.** Trichocysts	**a.** Indentation on one side of a ciliate into which food is swept
e **20.** Macronucleus	
b **21.** Micronucleus	**b.** Smaller nucleus containing a "reserve copy" of the cell's genes
a **22.** Gullet	
d **23.** Anal pore	**c.** Small, bottle-shaped structures used for defense
f **24.** Contractile vacuole	**d.** Region of cell membrane where waste-containing food vacuoles fuse
	e. Larger nucleus containing multiple copies of most of the cell's genes
	f. Cavity in cytoplasm specialized to collect and pump out water

25. Label the illustration of a paramecium.

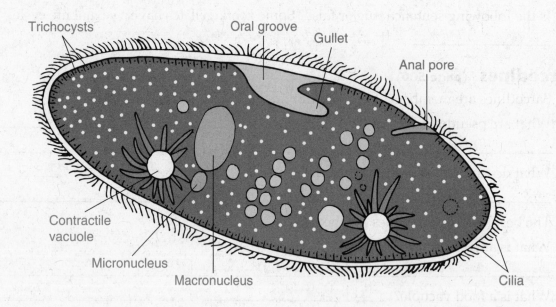

26. What is conjugation? It is a process that allows ciliates to exchange genetic information with other individuals.

27. Within a large population, how does conjugation benefit ciliates? The process helps to create and maintain genetic diversity.

Sporozoans (page 502)

28. Sporozoans are members of the phylum _____Sporozoa_____.

29. Circle the letter of each sentence that is true about sporozoans.

   (a.) They are parasitic.   c. All have only one host.

   (b.) They do not move on their own.   (d.) They reproduce by means of sporozoites.

Animallike Protists and Disease (pages 503–504)

30. What causes malaria? It is caused by the sporozoan *Plasmodium*.

_____

31. Complete the flowchart about the cycle of malarial infection.

An infected *Anopheles* mosquito bites a human and deposits *Plasmodium* spores into the _____bloodstream_____.

↓

The spores travel to the _____liver_____.

↓

Infected liver cells burst, releasing parasites that infect _____red blood_____ cells.

↓

The human experiences the symptoms of _____malaria_____.

↓

A mosquito bites the infected human and picks up the _____*Plasmodium*_____ cells.

Ecology of Animallike Protists (page 505)

32. Is the following sentence true or false? Some animallike protists recycle nutrients by breaking down dead organic matter. _____true_____

33. How does the zooflagellate *Trichonympha* make it possible for termites to eat wood?

Termites do not have enzymes to break down the cellulose in wood. The zooflagellate in a termite's gut manufactures the enzyme cellulase, which breaks the chemical bonds in cellulose. With the help of their protist partners, then, the termites can eat wood.

_____

_____

Section 20–3 Plantlike Protists: Unicellular Algae (pages 506–509)

👄 **Key Concepts**
- What is the function of chlorophyll and accessory pigments in algae?
- What are the distinguishing features of the major phyla of unicellular algae?

Introduction (page 506)

1. Plantlike protists are commonly called _____algae_____.

2. Is the following sentence true or false? Algae include only multicellular organisms. _____false_____

Chlorophyll and Accessory Pigments (page 506)

3. In the process of photosynthesis, what substances trap the energy of sunlight? Chlorophyll and the accessory pigments trap the energy of sunlight.

4. How does water affect the sunlight that passes through it? Water absorbs much of the light's energy.

5. Why does the dim blue light that penetrates deep into the sea contain little energy that chlorophyll *a* can use? Chlorophyll *a* is most efficient at capturing red and violet light.

6. How have various groups of algae adapted to conditions of limited light? They have evolved different forms of chlorophyll.

7. What are accessory pigments? They are compounds that absorb light at different wavelengths than chlorophyll.

8. Why are algae such a wide range of colors? The accessory pigments in algae reflect different wavelengths of light than chlorophyll.

Euglenophytes (page 507)

9. Euglenophytes are members of the phylum _____Euglenophyta_____.

10. Circle the letter of each sentence that is true about euglenophytes.

   (a.) They are remarkably similar to zooflagellates.
   (b.) They possess chloroplasts.
   c. They have a cell wall.
   (d.) They have two flagella.

11. What is an eyespot, and what is its function? It is a cluster of reddish pigment near one

end of a euglena that helps the organism find sunlight to power photosynthesis.

_____

12. Euglenas have a tough, intricate membrane called a(an) _____pellicle_____.

13. How do euglenas reproduce? They reproduce asexually by means of binary fission.

14. Label the illustration of a euglena.

Chloroplast

Flagella

Eyespot   Nucleus   Contractile
vacuole

Chrysophytes (page 507)

15. The yellow-green algae and the golden-brown algae are members of the phylum

_____Chrysophyta_____.

16. What color are the chloroplasts of chrysophytes? _____Gold_____

17. Circle the letter of each sentence that is true about chrysophytes.

(**a.**) The cell walls of some contain the carbohydrate pectin.

b. They reproduce sexually but not asexually.

(**c.**) They generally store food in the form of oil.

(**d.**) Some form threadlike colonies.

Diatoms (page 507)

18. Diatoms are members of the phylum _____Bacillariophyta_____.

19. Circle the letter of each sentence that is true about diatoms.

a. They are very rare in almost all environments.

(**b.**) Their cell walls are rich in silicon.

(**c.**) They are shaped like a petri dish or flat pillbox.

(**d.**) They are among the most abundant organisms on Earth.

Dinoflagellates (page 508)

20. Dinoflagellates are members of the phylum _____Pyrrophyta_____.

21. How do dinoflagellates obtain nutrition? About half of dinoflagellates are photosynthetic; the other half live as heterotrophs.

22. Circle the letter of each sentence that is true about dinoflagellates.

   a. They generally have one flagellum.

   (b.) Many species are luminescent.

   (c.) Most reproduce by binary fission.

Ecology of Unicellular Algae (pages 508–509)

23. How do plantlike protists make much of the diversity of aquatic life possible? They are at the base of the food chain.

24. What are phytoplankton? Phytoplankton constitute the population of small, photosynthetic organisms found near the surface of the ocean.

25. What are algal blooms? They are enormous masses of algae.

26. How can an algal bloom be harmful? A bloom can quickly deplete the water of nutrients, and cells begin to die in great numbers. The decomposition of the dead algae can rob the water of its oxygen, choking its resident fish and invertebrate life.

Section 20–4 Plantlike Protists: Red, Brown, and Green Algae (pages 510–515)

Key Concepts
- What are the distinguishing features of the major phyla of multicellular algae?
- How do multicellular algae reproduce?

Introduction (page 510)

1. What are seaweeds? They are multicellular algae._____

2. What are the most important differences among the three phyla of multicellular algae?
   The most important involve their photosynthetic pigments._____
   _____

Red Algae (page 510)

3. Red algae are members of the phylum _____Rhodophyta_____.

4. Why are red algae able to live at great depths? They are efficient in harvesting light energy.
   _____

5. What pigments do red algae contain? They contain chlorophyll *a* and the reddish accessory
   pigments called phycobilins._____

6. Which color of light are phycobilins especially good at absorbing?
   a. red   **b.** green   **c.** yellow   **(d.)** blue

7. Circle the letter of each sentence that is true about red algae.
   (a.) They can grow in the ocean at depths up to 260 meters.
   b. Most are unicellular.
   c. All are red or reddish-brown.
   (d.) Coralline algae play an important role in coral reef formation.

Brown Algae (page 511)

8. Brown algae are members of the phylum _____Phaeophyta_____.

9. What pigments do brown algae contain? They contain chlorophyll *a* and *c*, as well as a
   brown accessory pigment, fucoxanthin._____

Match each structure with its description.

	Structure	Description
c	10. Holdfast	**a.** Flattened stemlike structure
a	11. Stipe	**b.** Gas-filled swelling
d	12. Blade	**c.** Structure that attaches alga to the bottom
b	13. Bladder	**d.** Leaflike structure

14. Where are brown algae commonly found growing? They are found in cool, shallow
coastal waters of temperate or arctic areas.

15. What is the largest known alga? Giant kelp

Green Algae (pages 511–512)

16. Green algae are members of the phylum Chlorophyta.

17. What characteristics do green algae share with plants? They have cellulose in their cell
walls, contain chlorophyll a and b, and store food in the form of starch.

18. What do scientists think is the connection between mosses and green algae?
They think mosses and green algae share an algaelike ancestor from millions of years ago.

19. The freshwater alga *Spirogyra* forms long threadlike colonies called
filaments.

20. How can the cells in a *Volvox* colony coordinate movement? They are connected to one
another by strands of cytoplasm.

21. "Sea lettuce" is the multicellular alga Ulva.

Reproduction in Green Algae (pages 512–514)

22. What occurs in the process known as alternation of generations? The process involves
switching back and forth between haploid and diploid stages during an organism's life cycle.

23. The single-celled *Chlamydomonas* reproduces asexually by producing
zoospores.

24. Circle the letter of each sentence that is true about sexual reproduction in
Chlamydomonas.

   a. If conditions become unfavorable, cells release gametes.

   b. Paired gametes form a diploid zygote.

   c. A zygote quickly grows into an adult organism.

   d. The gametes are called male and female.

25. Complete the table about the generations in an organism's life cycle.

GENERATIONS IN A LIFE CYCLE

Generation	Definition	Diploid or Haploid?
Gametophyte	Gamete-producing phase	Haploid
Sporophyte	Spore-producing phase	Diploid

© Pearson Education, Inc., publishing as Pearson Prentice Hall.

26. Complete the life cycle of *Ulva* by labeling the sporophyte, the male gametophyte, and the female gametophyte. Also, label the places where the processes of fertilization, mitosis, and meiosis occur.

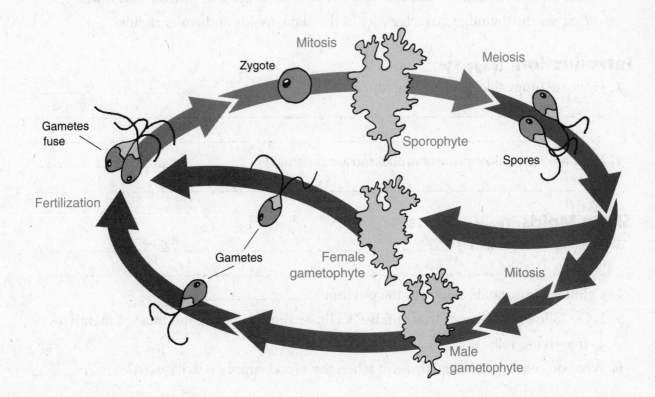

Human Uses of Algae (page 515)

27. Why have algae been called the "grasses" of the sea? <u>They make up much of the base of</u> <u>the food chain upon which animals "graze."</u>

28. Through photosynthesis, algae produce much of Earth's _____oxygen_____.

29. What is the compound agar derived from, and how is it used? <u>Agar is derived from</u> <u>seaweed, and it is used to thicken nutrient mixtures scientists use to grow bacteria and other</u> <u>microorganisms.</u>

© Pearson Education, Inc., publishing as Pearson Prentice Hall.

Name_____ Class_____ Date _____

Section 20–5 Funguslike Protists (pages 516–520)

⊙ Key Concepts
- What are the similarities and differences between funguslike protists and fungi?
- What are the defining characteristics of the slime molds and water molds?

Introduction (page 516)

1. How are funguslike protists like fungi? Both are heterotrophs that absorb nutrients from dead or decaying organic matter.

2. How are funguslike protists unlike most true fungi? Funguslike protists have centrioles, and they also lack chitin cell walls.

Slime Molds (pages 516–518)

3. What are slime molds? They are funguslike protists that play key roles in recycling organic material.

4. Cellular slime molds belong to the phylum ___Acrasiomycota___.

5. Is the following sentence true or false? Cellular slime molds spend most of their lives as free-living cells. ___true___

6. What do cellular slime molds form when their food supply is exhausted? They form a sluglike colony of thousands of cells.

7. What structure does a cellular slime mold colony produce, and what is that structure's function? It produces a fruiting body, which produces and sends out spores. Each spore gives rise to a single amoeba-like cell.

8. Acellular slime molds belong to the phylum ___Myxomycota___.

9. What is a plasmodium? It is an aggregation of acellular slime molds that is a single structure with many nuclei.

10. The plasmodium eventually produces sporangia, which in turn produce haploid ___spores___.

Water Molds (pages 518–519)

11. Water molds, or oomycetes, are members of the phylum ___Oomycota___.

12. Water molds produce thin filaments known as ___hyphae___.

236 Chapter 20

© Pearson Education, Inc., publishing as Pearson Prentice Hall.

13. What are zoosporangia? They are the spore cases that portions of water mold hyphae
produce in asexual reproduction.

14. Where are male and female nuclei produced in water mold sexual reproduction?
Male nuclei are produced by a structure formed by hyphae called the antheridium. Female nuclei
are produced by a structure called the oogonium.

15. Fertilization in water molds occurs in the _____oogonium_____.

Ecology of Funguslike Protists (page 519)

16. Why aren't there bodies of dead animals and plants littering the woods and fields you
walk through? After these organisms die, their tissues are quickly broken down by slime molds,
water molds, mushrooms, and other decomposers.

17. What are examples of plant diseases that water molds cause? They include mildews and
blights of grapes and tomatoes.

Water Molds and the Potato Famine (page 520)

18. What produced the Great Potato Famine of 1846? It was produced by a potato blight,
which was caused by a water mold, *Phytophthora infestans*, that destroys all parts of potato
plants.

19. What did the Great Potato Famine lead to? It led to the immediate migration of more
than 1 million Irish people to the United States.

Vocabulary Review

Matching   *In the space provided, write the letter of the description that best matches each organism.*

___d___ **1.** sarcodines

___g___ **2.** ciliates

___f___ **3.** euglenophytes

___a___ **4.** diatoms

___h___ **5.** brown algae

___c___ **6.** green algae

___b___ **7.** slime molds

___e___ **8.** water molds

a. unicellular algae that produce thin, delicate cell walls rich in silicon

b. funguslike protists that look just like amoebas at one stage of their life cycles

c. plantlike protists that share many characteristics with plants

d. protozoans that use pseudopods for feeding and movement

e. funguslike protists that thrive on dead or decaying organic matter in water

f. unicellular algae that have two flagella but no cell wall

g. protozoans that include those belonging to the genus *Paramecium*

h. multicellular algae that contain fucoxanthin

Completion   *Fill in the blanks with terms from Chapter 20.*

9. Any organism that is not a plant, an animal, a fungus, or a prokaryote is a(an) _____protist_____.

10. A temporary cytoplasmic projection used in feeding and movement is called a(an) _____pseudopod_____.

11. The disease _____malaria_____ is caused by the sporozoan *Plasmodium*.

12. Many algae have compounds called _____accessory_____ pigments that absorb light at different wavelengths than chlorophyll.

13. _____Phytoplankton_____ are the population of small, photosynthetic organisms found near the surface of the ocean.

14. The process of switching back and forth between haploid and diploid stages in a life cycle is known as _____alternation_____ of generations.

15. The single structure with many nuclei produced by an acellular slime mold is called a(an) _____plasmodium_____.

Chapter 21   Fungi

Summary

21–1 The Kingdom Fungi

Fungi are eukaryotic heterotrophs that have cell walls. The cell walls of fungi are made up of chitin, a complex carbohydrate. Fungi do not ingest their food, as animals do. Instead, fungi digest food outside their bodies and then absorb it. Many fungi feed by absorbing nutrients from decaying matter. Some fungi are parasites.

All fungi except for yeasts are multicellular. Multicellular fungi are composed of thin filaments called hyphae. Each hypha is only one cell thick. The bodies of multicellular fungi are composed of many hyphae tangled together into a thick mass called a mycelium. The fruiting body of a fungus—such as the above-ground part of a mushroom—is a reproductive structure growing from the mycelium in the soil beneath it.

Most fungi reproduce both asexually and sexually. Asexual reproduction can occur when cells or hyphae break off and begin to grow on their own. Some fungi also produce spores. In some fungi, spores are produced in structures called sporangia. Sporangia are found at the tips of hyphae called sporangiophores. Sexual reproduction in fungi usually involves two different mating types.

Spores of fungi are found in almost every environment. Many fungi produce dry, almost weightless spores that are easily scattered in the wind.

21–2 Classification of Fungi

Fungi are classified according to their structure and method of reproduction. The four main groups of fungi are the common molds (phylum Zygomycota), the sac fungi (phylum Ascomycota), the club fungi (phylum Basidiomycota), and the imperfect fungi (Deuteromycota).

The common molds—zygomycetes—grow on meat, cheese, and bread. Zygomycetes have a life cycle that includes a zygospore. A zygospore is a resting spore that contains zygotes formed during the sexual phase of the mold's life cycle. The zygomycetes include the black bread mold, *Rhizopus stolonifer*. Black bread mold has two different kinds of hyphae. The rootlike hyphae that penetrate the bread's surface are rhizoids. The stemlike hyphae that run along the surface of bread are stolons. During the sexual phase in the bread mold, hyphae from different mating types fuse to produce gamete-forming structures called gametangia.

Sac fungi—ascomycetes—have a reproductive structure called an ascus, which contains spores. Sac fungi include the large cup fungi as well as the unicellular yeasts. The life cycle of an ascomycete includes both asexual and sexual reproduction. In asexual reproduction, tiny spores called conidia form at the tips of specialized hyphae called conidiophores. In sexual reproduction, haploid hyphae from two different mating types (+ and −) grow close together and produce a fruiting body. An ascus forms within the fruiting body. Two nuclei of different mating types fuse within the ascus to form a diploid zygote. Yeasts are unicellular ascomycetes. The process of asexual reproduction in yeasts is called budding.

The club fungi—basidiomycetes—have a specialized reproductive structure that resembles a club. The cap of the fruiting body of a basidiomycete—such as the familiar mushroom—is composed of tightly packed hyphae. The lower side of the cap is composed of gills, which are thin blades of tissue lined with basidia. A basidium is a spore-bearing structure. Two nuclei in each basidium fuse to form a diploid zygote cell. The zygote cell undergoes meiosis, forming clusters of spores called basidiospores. A single mushroom can produce billions of basidiospores. Club fungi include mushrooms, shelf fungi, and puffballs.

The imperfect fungi—deuteromycetes—include those fungi that are not placed in other phyla because researchers have never been able to observe a sexual phase in their life cycles. Most imperfect fungi look like ascomycetes, though others are similar to basidiomycetes or zygomycetes. An example of an imperfect fungus is *Penicillium notatum*, a mold that grows on fruit. It is the source of the antibiotic penicillin.

21–3 Ecology of Fungi

All fungi are heterotrophs. Many fungi are saprobes, which are organisms that obtain food from decaying organic matter. Others are parasites, and still others live in symbiosis with other species.

Fungi play an essential role in maintaining equilibrium in nearly every ecosystem. Fungi do this by recycling nutrients as they break down the bodies and wastes of other organisms. Many fungi feed by releasing digestive enzymes that break down organic material into simple molecules. Fungi food includes wastes and dead organisms. In breaking down this material, fungi promote the recycling of nutrients and essential chemicals. Without such decomposers, the energy-rich compounds that organisms accumulate would be lost forever.

Parasitic fungi cause serious plant and animal diseases. A few cause diseases in humans. Fungal diseases in plants include corn smut and wheat rust. Fungal diseases in humans include athlete's foot and ringworm, thrush, and yeast infections of the female reproductive tract.

Some fungi form symbiotic relationships in which both partners benefit, such as lichens and mycorrhizae. Lichens are not single organisms. Rather, lichens are symbiotic associations between a fungus and a photosynthetic organism. The photosynthetic organism in a lichen is either a green alga or a cyanobacterium, or both. The alga or cyanobacterium provides the fungus with a source of energy by carrying out photosynthesis. The fungus, in turn, provides the photosynthetic organism with water and minerals. The fungus also shades the alga or cyanobacterium from intense sunlight.

Mutualistic associations of plant roots and fungi are called mycorrhizae. The plant's roots are woven into a partnership with the web of fungal hyphae. The hyphae of fungi aid plants in absorbing water and minerals. In addition, the fungi release enzymes that free nutrients from the soil. The plants, in turn, provide the fungi with the products of photosynthesis. The presence of mycorrhizae is essential for the growth of many plants. Mycorrhizal associations were an adaptation that was critical in the evolution of plants.

Chapter 21   Fungi

Section 21–1 The Kingdom Fungi (pages 527–529)

🔑 Key Concepts
- What are the defining characteristics of fungi?
- What is the internal structure of a fungus?
- How do fungi reproduce?

What Are Fungi? (page 527)

1. Circle the letter of each sentence that is true about fungi.
   - **(a.)** They are heterotrophs.
   - **(b.)** They have cell walls.
   - c. They are photosynthetic.
   - **(d.)** They are eukaryotic.

2. The cell walls of fungi are made of a complex carbohydrate called _____chitin_____.

3. How do fungi digest their food? _They digest food outside their bodies and then absorb it._
   _____

4. Is the following sentence true or false? Some fungi are parasites. _____true_____

Structure and Function of Fungi (pages 527–528)

5. Which group of fungi are not multicellular? _____Yeasts_____

6. What are hyphae? _They are the tiny filaments that compose multicellular fungi._
   _____

7. How thick is each hypha? _Each hypha is one cell thick._

8. In some fungi, what divides the hyphae into cells containing one or two nuclei?
   _____Cross walls_____

9. What is a mycelium? _A mycelium is a thick mass of many hyphae tangled together. It_
   composes the body of a multicellular fungus.
   _____

10. Why is a mycelium well suited to absorb food? _It permits a large surface area to come in_
    contact with the food source through which it grows.
    _____

11. What is a fruiting body of a fungus? _It is a reproductive structure growing from_
    the mycelium in the soil beneath it.
    _____
    _____

12. What is a fairy ring, and why does it form? <u>A fairy ring is composed of the fruiting bodies</u>
<u>of mushrooms that developed at the outer edges of a single mycelium. It forms because as time</u>
<u>goes by soil nutrients near the center of the mycelium become depleted and mushrooms sprout</u>
<u>only at the edges.</u>

13. Label the parts of the fungus.

Fruiting body

Hyphae

Mycelium

Reproduction in Fungi (pages 528–529)

14. Is the following sentence true or false? Most fungi can reproduce only asexually.
_____false_____

15. How does asexual reproduction occur in fungi? <u>It takes place when cells or hyphae break</u>
<u>off from a fungus and begin to grow on their own. Some fungi also produce spores, which can</u>
<u>scatter and grow into new organisms.</u>
_____

16. In some fungi, spores are produced in structures called _____sporangia_____.

17. Where are sporangia found in a fungus? <u>They are found at the tips of specialized hyphae</u>
<u>called sporangiophores.</u>
_____

18. Sexual reproduction in fungi usually involves two different _____mating types_____.

19. What is a gametangium? <u>It is a structure in a fungus that forms gametes.</u>
_____
_____

20. How does a zygote form in fungal sexual reproduction? When the hyphae of opposite mating types meet, their two gametangia join, and the haploid nuclei contained in them fuse to form a diploid nucleus, or zygote.

21. Circle the letter of each sentence that is true about sexual reproduction in fungi.

(**a.**) The zygote is often the only diploid cell in the fungus's entire life cycle.

b. Mating types are called male and female.

(**c.**) Gametes of both mating types are about the same size.

(**d.**) One mating type is a "+" (plus) and the other is a "–" (minus).

How Fungi Spread (page 529)

22. Is the following sentence true or false? The spores of many fungi scatter easily in the wind. _____ true _____

23. For a fungal spore to grow, where must it land? It must land in a favorable environment where there is a proper combination of temperature, moisture, and food.

Section 21–2 Classification of Fungi (pages 530–536)

🔁 Key Concept
- What are the characteristics of the four main phyla of fungi?

Introduction (page 530)

1. Complete the concept map about the four main groups of fungi.

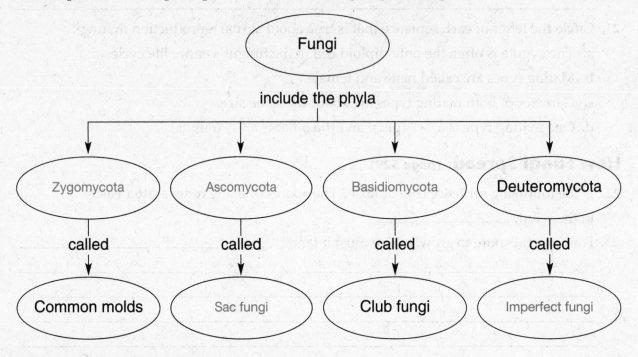

The Common Molds (pages 530–531)

2. What are zygomycetes? <u>They are the familiar molds that grow on meat, cheese, and bread;</u>
<u>and they are members of the phylum Zygomycota.</u>

_____

3. The resting spore formed during the sexual phase of the mold's life cycle is called a(an)
_____<u>zygospore</u>_____.

4. Is the following sentence true or false? The hyphae of zygomycetes are generally
divided by cross walls. _____<u>false</u>_____

5. What is the common name for *Rhizopus stolonifer*? <u>Black bread mold</u>

6. Complete the table about the kinds of hyphae of black bread mold.

KINDS OF HYPHAE

Kind	Description
Rhizoids	Rootlike hyphae that penetrate the surface of a slice of bread
Stolons	Stemlike hyphae that run along the surface of bread
Sporangiophores	Hyphae that push up into the air and form sporangia at their tips

© Pearson Education, Inc., publishing as Pearson Prentice Hall.

7. Complete the flowchart about sexual reproduction in zygomycetes.

> Two hyphae from different mating types come together, forming _____gametangia_____.

> Haploid gametes from the mating types fuse to form diploid zygotes, which make up a single
>
> _____zygospore_____.

> The zygospore eventually germinates, and a(an) _____sporangium_____ emerges.

> The sporangium reproduces asexually by releasing _____spores_____.

The Sac Fungi (pages 532–533)

8. What is an ascus? __It is a tough sac in ascomycetes that contains spores.__

_____

9. Is the following sentence true or false? Ascomycetes make up the largest phylum in the
kingdom Fungi. _____true_____

10. What occurs among sac fungi during asexual reproduction? __Tiny spores called conidia__
__are formed at the tips of specialized hyphae, called conidiophores. If conidia land in a suitable__
__environment, they grow into haploid mycelium.__

11. Complete the flowchart about sexual reproduction in ascomycetes.

> Gametangia from two different mating types _____fuse_____ together.

> That fusion produces hyphae that contain haploid _____nuclei_____.

> The N + N hyphae produce a fruiting body, inside of which the _____ascus_____ forms.

> Within the ascus, meiosis and mitosis occur to produce cells known as _____ascospores_____.

> In a favorable environment, an ascospore germinates and grows into a haploid _____mycelium_____.

12. Is the following sentence true or false? Yeasts are multicellular ascomycetes.
_____false_____

13. Why are yeasts classified as ascomycetes? They form asci with ascospores during the
sexual phase of their life cycle.

14. What process do yeasts carry out to obtain energy when they are in a nutrient
mixture such as bread dough? Alcoholic fermentation

The Club Fungi (pages 534–536)

15. From what does the phylum Basidiomycota get its name? It gets its name from a
specialized reproductive structure, the basidium, that resembles a club.

16. Label the parts of a mushroom.

Cap

Gills

Stalk

Base

17. Where are basidia found on a basidiomycete? They are found on the gills that grow on the
underside of mushroom caps.

_____

18. The cap of a basidiomycete is composed of tightly packed _____hyphae_____.

19. Is the following sentence true or false? The remarkable growth of mushrooms
overnight is caused by cell enlargement. _____true_____

20. Circle the letter of each example of basidiomycetes.
(a.) puffballs   (b.) shelf fungi   (c.) rusts   d. yeasts

21. Why should you never pick or eat any mushrooms found in the wild?
Many are poisonous, and many poisonous mushrooms look almost identical to edible mushrooms.

_____

22. Complete the flowchart about reproduction in basidiomycetes.

> A basidiospore germinates to produce a haploid primary ___mycelium___.

> The mycelia of different mating types fuse to produce a(an) ___secondary mycelium___.

> A fruiting body pushes above ground, forming a(an) ___button___ at the soil's surface.

> Two nuclei in each basidium fuse to form a diploid ___zygote cell___.

> Each zygote undergoes meiosis, forming clusters of diploid ___basidiospores___.

The Imperfect Fungi (page 536)

23. The phylum Deuteromycota is composed of what fungi? It is composed of those fungi that are not placed in other phyla because researchers have never been able to observe a sexual phase in their life cycles.

24. What is *Penicillium notatum*, and where does it grow naturally? It is a deuteromycete mold that frequently grows on fruit.

25. What is produced from *Penicillium notatum*? The antibiotic penicillin is produced from it.

Reading Skill Practice

You can often increase your understanding of what you've read by making comparisons. A compare-and-contrast table helps you to do this. On a separate sheet of paper, make a table to compare the four main groups of fungi you read about in Section 21–2. For more information about compare-and-contrast tables, see Organizing Information in Appendix A of your textbook.

Students' tables should include the basic information about the common molds, the sac fungi, the club fungi, and the imperfect fungi.

Name_____ Class_____ Date_____

Section 21–3 Ecology of Fungi (pages 537–542)

⊂ Key Concepts
- What is the main role of fungi in natural ecosystems?
- What problems do parasitic fungi cause?
- What kinds of symbiotic relationships do fungi form with other organisms?

All Fungi Are Heterotrophs (page 537)

1. Fungi cannot manufacture their own food because they are ___heterotrophs___.
2. What are saprobes? They are organisms that obtain food from decaying organic matter.
_____
_____

Fungi as Decomposers (page 538)

3. Fungi recycle nutrients breaking down the bodies and wastes of other ___organisms___.
4. How do fungi break down leaves, fruit, and other organic material into simple molecules? They feed by releasing digestive enzymes that speed the breakdown of these materials.
_____

Fungi as Parasites (pages 538–539)

5. Parasitic fungi cause serious plant and animal ___diseases___.
6. Circle the letter of each example of a fungal plant disease.
   (a.) wheat rust   (b.) corn smut   c. thrush   (d.) mildews
7. Rusts are members of the phylum ___Basidiomycota___.
8. What two kinds of plants do wheat rusts need to complete their life cycle?
They need barberry plants and wheat plants.
_____
_____

9. One deuteromycete can infect the areas between the human toes, causing an infection known as ___athlete's foot___.
10. What happens when the fungus that causes athlete's foot infects other areas of the body? It produces a red scaling sore known as ringworm.
_____

© Pearson Education, Inc., publishing as Pearson Prentice Hall.

Symbiotic Relationships (pages 540–542)

11. Lichens and mycorrhizae are both examples of what kind of symbiotic relationship?
Mutualistic associations

12. What are lichens? They are symbiotic associations between a fungus and a photosynthetic organism.

13. What is the photosynthetic organism in a lichen? It is either a green alga or a cyanobacterium.

14. Where do lichens grow? They often grow on rocks and in other environments where few organisms can survive.

15. What benefits do the fungus and the photosynthetic organism derive from the association in a lichen? The alga or cyanobacterium provides the fungus with a source of energy. The fungus provides the photosynthetic organism with water, minerals, and protection.

16. What are mycorrhizae? They are associations of plant roots and fungi.

17. Why is the presence of mycorrhizae essential for the growth of many plants?
The seeds of some plants cannot germinate in the absence of mycorrhizal fungi.

Chapter 21   Fungi

Vocabulary Review

Labeling Diagrams   *Use terms from Chapter 21 to label the diagram.*

2. _____ sporangium
3. _____ sporangiophore
4. _____ zygospore
1. _____ spores
5. _____ gametangia
6. _____ stolons
7. _____ rhizoids

Completion   *Fill in the blanks with terms from Chapter 21.*

8. Multicellular fungi are composed of thin filaments called _____hyphae_____.

9. The bodies of multicellular fungi are composed of many hyphae tangled together into a thick mass called a(an) _____mycelium_____.

10. A(An) _____fruiting_____ body is a fungal reproductive structure growing from the mycelium.

11. The process of asexual reproduction in yeasts is called _____budding_____.

12. The spore-bearing structure of a club fungus is called the _____basidium_____.

13. The phylum composed of fungi that have never been observed to have a sexual phase in their life cycles is the _____imperfect_____ fungi.

14. Organisms that obtain food from decaying organic matter are called _____saprobes_____.

15. A(An) _____lichen_____ is a symbiotic association between a fungus and a photosynthetic organism.

Summary

22–1 Introduction to Plants

Plants provide the base for food chains on land. They also provide shade, shelter, and oxygen for animals. Plants are multicellular organisms with cells walls made of cellulose. They make their own food in the process of photosynthesis using green pigments called chlorophyll *a* and *b*.

Plant life cycles have two phases that alternate. This is known as alternation of generations. A diploid (2N) phase, called the sporophyte, alternates with a haploid (N) phase, called the gametophyte. The sporophyte produces haploid spores. The spores grow into haploid gametophytes. The gametophyte produces male and female reproductive cells, called gametes. Male and female gametes fuse during fertilization to produce a new sporophyte.

In order to survive, all plants need sunlight, water, minerals, oxygen, carbon dioxide, and a way to move water and nutrients to their cells. Plants have many adaptations to get these things.

Early land plants evolved from an organism that was like the multicellular green algae living today. As early land plants adapted to a dry habitat, several major groups of plants evolved. Botanists divide modern plants into four groups based on water-conducting tissues, seeds, and flowers. These four plant groups are mosses and their relatives, ferns and their relatives, cone-bearing plants, and flowering plants.

22–2 Bryophytes

Mosses, liverworts, and hornworts belong to the group called bryophytes. Bryophytes do not have tubes to move water and nutrients through the plant. Water simply moves from cell to cell. It moves from areas where there is plenty of water to areas where water is needed. Examples of bryophytes include mosses, liverworts, and hornworts.

Bryophytes do not have true leaves, stems, and roots. Instead of roots, they have structures called rhizoids. Rhizoids anchor the plant to the ground.

Bryophytes reproduce sexually and asexually. They have several structures that produce reproductive cells. Structures called antheridia make sperm. Structures called archegonia produce egg cells.

Sperm cells must swim through water to fertilize eggs. This is why bryophytes must live in moist habitats. After fertilization, the diploid zygote grows to become a sporophyte. The sporophyte is made up of a capsule and a long stalk that remains attached to the gametophyte. It relies on the gametophyte for food and water. Spores are made inside the capsule. When the capsule ripens, it opens and the spores are carried off by wind and water. When a spore lands in a moist place, it grows into the plant we think of as moss. This green plant is the haploid gametophyte.

22–3 Seedless Vascular Plants

Ferns and their relatives were the first plants to have special tissues that carry water and food throughout a plant. These tissues are called vascular tissues. There are two types of vascular tissue. Xylem moves water from the roots to all parts of the plant. Special cells called tracheids make up xylem. They have thick, strong cell walls. The other type of vascular tissue is phloem. Phloem carries nutrients and food from place to place within the plant. Both xylem and phloem can move fluids through the plant body against the force of gravity. Many plants contain lignin, a substance that makes cell walls rigid.

Seedless vascular plants include club mosses, horsetails, and ferns. These plants have true roots, leaves, and stems. Roots absorb water and minerals. Leaves make food by photosynthesis. Stems support the plant and connect leaves and roots.

In the life cycle of ferns, the diploid sporophyte is the dominant stage. Fern sporophytes produce spores on the underside of the fronds in structures called sporangia. These spores are haploid. When spores are ripe, they burst from sporangia and are carried by wind and water. In the right conditions, they will grow to form haploid gametophytes.

The haploid gametophyte is a thin, heart-shaped structure. The antheridia and archegonia are found on the underside of the gametophyte. When mature, sperm from the antheridia swim to the archegonia to fertilize the eggs.

22–4 Seed Plants

Seed plants are divided into two groups: gymnosperms and angiosperms. Gymnosperms, or cone-bearing plants, produce seeds directly on the surface of cones. Angiosperms, which are flowering plants, produce seeds inside a tissue that protects them. Seed plants can live just about anywhere, because they do not need water for reproduction.

Like other plants, seed plants have alternation of generations. All of the seed plants that we see are sporophytes. The gametophytes of seed plants are made up of only a few cells. They grow and mature within flowers and cones. The entire male gametophyte fits in a tiny structure called a pollen grain. Pollen is carried to the female gametophyte by wind, birds, mammals, or insects. This process is called pollination.

Seeds protect the zygote of seed plants. After fertilization, the zygote grows into a tiny plant. This plant is called an embryo. When conditions are right, the embryo grows. It uses a supply of stored food inside the seed when it starts growing. A seed coat surrounds the embryo, protecting it from drying out.

Gymnosperms are the oldest surviving seed plants. Gymnosperms include gnetophytes, cycads, ginkgoes, and conifers. These plants produce seeds that are protected by a seed coat. However, the cone does not cover the seeds. This is why they are called naked seed plants.

22–5 Angiosperms—Flowering Plants

Angiosperms have reproductive organs called flowers. Flowers attract animals, which carry pollen from flower to flower. This is a more efficient way of pollination than the wind pollination of most gymnosperms. Unlike gymnosperms, the seeds of angiosperms are protected. The structure that protects the seeds develops into a fruit.

There are two groups of angiosperms: monocots and dicots. Monocot embryos have one seed leaf, or cotyledon. Dicot embryos have two cotyledons. Other differences between monocots and dicots include the arrangement of veins in leaves, the number of flower petals, the structure of roots, and the arrangement of vascular tissue in the stem.

Flowering plants can also be subdivided according to the characteristics of their stems. Woody plants—such as trees, shrubs, and vines—have cells with thick cell walls that support the plant body. Plant stems that are smooth and nonwoody are characteristic of herbaceous plants. Herbaceous plants include zinnias, petunias, and sunflowers.

Flowering plants have three different life spans. Annuals complete their life cycle within one growing season. Biennials complete their life cycle in two years. They produce seeds and die in the second growing season. Perennials live through many years. Some die each winter and regrow in spring.

Chapter 22   Plant Diversity

Section 22–1 Introduction to Plants (pages 551–555)

🔑 **Key Concepts**
- What is a plant?
- What do plants need to survive?
- How did the first plants evolve?

What Is a Plant? (page 551)

1. Circle the letter of each sentence that is true about plants.

    a. Plants are multicellular prokaryotes.

    (b.) Plants carry out photosynthesis.

    (c.) Plants have cell walls made of cellulose.

    (d.) Plants develop from multicellular embryos.

2. What pigments do plants use to carry out photosynthesis? <u>They use the green pigments</u>
<u>chlorophyll *a* and *b*.</u>

3. Is the following sentence true or false? All plants are autotrophs. _____<u>false</u>_____

The Plant Life Cycle (page 552)

4. All plants have a life cycle that is characterized by _____<u>alternation of generations</u>_____
_____.

5. Complete the diagram of the plant life cycle by writing the name of the plant generation in the correct place. For each generation, indicate whether it is haploid or diploid by writing either *N* or *2N*.

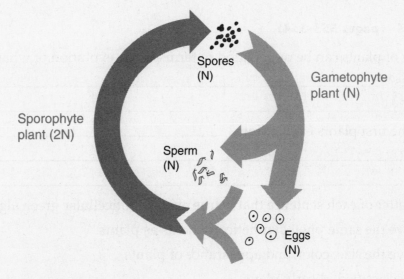

Spores (N)

Gametophyte plant (N)

Sporophyte plant (2N)

Sperm (N)

Eggs (N)

© Pearson Education, Inc., publishing as Pearson Prentice Hall.

6. Complete the table about plant generations.

PLANT GENERATIONS

Generation	Description	Haploid or Diploid?
Gametophyte	Gamete-producing plant	Haploid
Sporophyte	Spore-producing plant	Diploid

7. Seed plants have evolved reproductive cycles that can be carried out without _____water_____.

What Plants Need to Survive (page 552)

8. What are the four basic needs of plants?

a. Sunlight

b. Water and minerals

c. Gas exchange

d. Transport of water and nutrients throughout plant body

9. Why are plant leaves typically broad and flat? Their shape maximizes light absorption.

10. Circle the letter of each sentence that is true about the basic needs of plants.

(a.) Plants require oxygen to support cellular respiration.

b. Plants must get rid of water as quickly as possible.

(c.) Water is one of the raw materials of photosynthesis.

(d.) Plants have specialized tissues to carry nutrients upward.

Early Plants (pages 553–554)

11. The history of plants can be understood in terms of the evolution of what kind of structures? It can be understood in terms of the evolution of structures that acquire, transport, and conserve water.

12. What did the first plants evolve from? The first plants evolved from an organism much like the multicellular green algae living today.

13. Circle the letter of each sentence that is true about multicellular green algae.

(a.) They have the same photosynthetic pigments as plants.

(b.) They have the size, color, and appearance of plants.

c. They are classified as early plants.

(d.) They have reproductive cycles that are similar to those of early plants.

14. How were early plants similar to today's mosses? They were simple in structure and grew close to the damp ground.

15. From the first plants, at least two major groups of plants evolved. What did those groups develop into? One group developed into mosses and their relatives. The other group developed into all other plants, including ferns, cone-bearing plants, and flowering plants.

Overview of the Plant Kingdom (page 555)

16. Circle the letter of each of the important features that botanists use to divide the plant kingdom into four groups.

(a.) seeds

(b.) water-conducting tissue

c. stems

(d.) flowers

17. What are the four main groups of living plants?

a. Mosses and their relatives

b. Ferns and their relatives

c. Cone-bearing plants

d. Flowering plants

18. The great majority of plants alive today are flowering plants.

Reading Skill Practice

Finding the main ideas of a section can help you organize the important points you need to remember. Skim Section 22–1 to find the main ideas. Write them on the left-hand side of a separate sheet of paper. Then, make a list of supporting details for each main idea on the right-hand side of the sheet.

Students should note a main idea for each of the section's subsections. These should include the section's boldface key concepts. For each main idea, students should list supporting details.

Section 22–2 Bryophytes (pages 556–559)

Key Concepts
- What adaptations of bryophytes enable them to live on land?
- What are the three groups of bryophytes?
- How do bryophytes reproduce?

Introduction (page 556)

1. Mosses and their relatives are generally called _____bryophytes_____.
2. Bryophyte life cycles are highly dependent on _____water_____.
3. How does the lack of vascular tissue keep bryophytes small? Lacking vascular tissue, they can draw up water by osmosis only a few centimeters above the ground.

4. Why must bryophytes live in places where there is standing water for at least part of the year? During at least one stage of their life cycle, they produce gametes that must swim through water to reach other individuals.

Groups of Bryophytes (pages 556–557)

5. What are the three groups of plants that bryophytes include?
   a. Mosses
   b. Liverworts
   c. Hornworts

6. Where would you expect to find mosses growing? In areas with water, such as in swamps and bogs, near streams, and in rain forests

7. Why are mosses the most abundant plants in polar regions? They can tolerate low temperatures.

8. Why is the thin, upright shoot of a moss plant not considered to be a true stem?
   It has no vascular tissue.

9. Complete the illustration by identifying which part of a typical moss plant is the gametophyte and which part is the sporophyte.

Sporophyte

Gametophyte

10. What do the mature gametophytes of liverworts look like? When they mature, they produce structures that look like tiny green umbrellas.

11. What are gemmae? They are small multicellular reproductive structures of liverworts.

12. How do liverworts reproduce asexually? When haploid cells are washed out of a gemma cup, the gemmae can divide by mitosis and produce a new individual.

13. What does the hornwort sporophyte look like? It looks like a tiny green horn.

14. In what sort of soil would liverworts and hornworts be expected to be found?
They are generally found only in soil that is damp nearly year-round.

Life Cycle of Bryophytes (pages 558–559)

15. In bryophytes, which stage of the life cycle is dominant and carries out most of the plant's photosynthesis? _____Gametophyte_____

16. What fact of reproduction limits the distribution of bryophytes to habitats near water?

Fertilization can occur only when the gametophytes are soaked with rainwater or dew, so that

sperm cells can swim to egg cells.

_____

17. When a moss spore germinates, what does it grow into? It grows into a mass of tangled

green filaments called a protonema.

_____

18. Complete the table about bryophyte reproductive structures.

BRYOPHYTE REPRODUCTIVE STRUCTURES

Structure	Description	Structure Produces
Antheridia	Male reproductive structure	Sperm
Archegonia	Female reproductive structure	Egg cells

19. What does the zygote depend on for water and nutrients? It depends on the body of the

gametophyte.

_____

Human Use of Mosses (page 559)

20. In certain environments, the dead remains of sphagnum accumulate to form thick

deposits of _____peat_____.

21. Why do gardeners add peat moss to soil? It improves the soil's ability to retain water.

_____

_____

Name_____ Class_____ Date _____

Section 22–3 Seedless Vascular Plants
(pages 560–563)

Key Concepts
- How is vascular tissue important to ferns and their relatives?
- What are the characteristics of the three phyla of seedless vascular plants?
- What are the stages in the life cycles of ferns?

Evolution of Vascular Tissue: A Transport System (page 560)

1. What is vascular tissue? It is a type of tissue that is specialized to conduct water and nutrients.

2. What kind of cells did the first vascular plants have that were specialized to conduct water? Tracheids

3. Circle the letter of each sentence that is true about tracheids.
   (a.) They are hollow cells.
   (b.) They are connected end to end.
   (c.) Their thick cell walls resist pressure.
   d. They are the key cells of phloem.

4. What is the function of xylem? Carries water upward from the roots to every part of a plant

5. What is the function of phloem? Transports nutrients and carbohydrates produced by photosynthesis

6. Is the following sentence true or false? Phloem and xylem cannot move water and nutrients against the force of gravity. false

7. What is lignin? It is a substance that makes cell walls rigid.

Ferns and Their Relatives (pages 561–562)

8. Complete the table about plant structures.

PLANT STRUCTURES

Structure	Description
Roots	Underground organs that exchange water and minerals with the environment
Leaves	Photosynthetic organs that contain one or more bundles of vascular tissue
Stems	Supporting structures that connect roots and leaves, carrying water and nutrients between them

© Pearson Education, Inc., publishing as Pearson Prentice Hall.

9. Spore-bearing vascular plants include what three types of plants?

   a. Club mosses _____

   b. Horsetails _____

   c. Ferns _____

10. Is the following sentence true or false? Vascular plants have true roots and stems. _____ true

11. The fossilized remains of ancient forests of club mosses exist today as huge beds of _____ coal _____.

12. Circle the letter of each structure a horsetail has.

    (a.) stems   b. cones   (c.) leaves   (d.) roots

13. Ferns are members of phylum _____ Pterophyta _____.

14. What are rhizomes? They are the creeping, underground stems of ferns. _____

15. The large leaves of ferns are called _____ fronds _____.

16. Fronds grow from what fern structures? They grow from rhizomes. _____

17. In what kind of habitats are ferns most abundant? They are found in wet, or at least _____ seasonally wet, habitats around the world. _____

Life Cycle of Ferns (pages 562–563)

18. What is the dominant stage in the life cycle of ferns and other spore-bearing vascular plants? The diploid sporophyte is the dominant stage. _____

19. Fern sporophytes produce haploid spores on the underside of their fronds in tiny containers called _____ sporangia _____.

20. What are sori? Sori are clusters of sporangia. _____

21. Are the spores of ferns haploid or diploid? _____ Haploid _____

22. Label each drawing of a fern as either the sporophyte or the gametophyte.

Gametophyte _____

Sporophyte _____

23. Where are the antheridia and archegonia found in ferns? They are found on the
underside of the gametophyte.

24. Why does fertilization in ferns require at least a thin film of water? The water allows the
sperm to swim to the eggs.

25. Circle the letter of each sentence that is true about the life cycle of ferns.

    a. The zygote grows into a new gametophyte.

    b. The sporophyte is a heart-shaped, green structure.

    c. Fern sporophytes often live several years.

    d. When spores germinate, they grow into haploid gametophytes.

Section 22–4 Seed Plants (pages 564–568)

👄 Key Concepts
- What adaptations allow seed plants to reproduce without standing water?
- What are the four groups of gymnosperms?

Introduction (page 564)

1. Complete the table about the two groups of seed plants.

SEED PLANTS

Group	Description	Examples
Gymnosperms	Seed plants that bear seeds directly on the surfaces of cones	Conifers, cycads
Angiosperms	Seed plants that bear their seeds within a layer of protective tissue	Grasses, flowering trees and shrubs, wildflowers, cultivated flowers

Reproduction Free From Water (pages 564–565)

2. What are three features that allow seed plants to reproduce without water?

   a. Reproduction in flowers or cones

   b. The movement of gametes by pollination

   c. The protection of embryos in a seed

3. What are cones and flowers? Cones are the seed-bearing structures of gymnosperms, and flowers are the seed-bearing structures of angiosperms.

4. Why don't the gametophytes or the gametes of seed plants need standing water to function? They don't need water because the gametophyte generation develops within the sporophyte plant.

5. What is pollination? It is the transfer of pollen from the male reproductive structure to the female reproductive structure.

Match the structure with its description.

	Structure	Description
d	6. pollen grain	a. An embryo encased in a protective covering
a	7. seed	b. Structure that surrounds and protects the plant embryo
e	8. endosperm	c. Early developmental stage of an organism
c	9. embryo	d. Male gametophyte of seed plants
b	10. seed coat	e. Seed's food supply

11. What tissues or structures do seeds have that aid in their dispersal to other habitats? The seed coat can be textured so that it sticks to the fur or feathers of animals, or the entire seed can be contained in fleshy tissues that are then eaten and dispersed by animals.

12. What is the strategy that allows seeds to survive long periods of bitter cold, extreme heat, or drought? The embryo stops growing when it is still small and contained within the seed. It begins to grow only when conditions are right.

Evolution of Seed Plants (page 566)

13. How did conditions on Earth change during the Carboniferous and Devonian periods, and how did those changes affect plants? Land environments were much wetter than they are today, and tree ferns and other spore bearers flourished and developed into lush forests that covered much of Earth.

14. What link do seed ferns represent in the fossil record? They represent a link between ferns that do not form seeds and seed plants.

15. What adaptations did seed plants have that allowed them to replace spore-bearing plants as continents became drier? Seed plants had adaptations that equipped them to deal with drier conditions.

Name_____ Class_____ Date _____

Gymnosperms—Cone Bearers (pages 566–568)

16. Complete the concept map about gymnosperms.

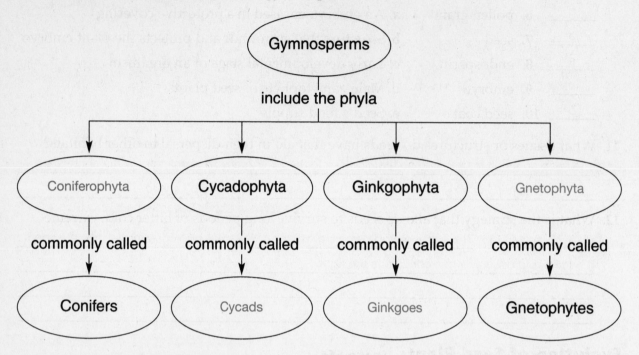

17. Where are the reproductive scales of gnetophytes found? <u>They are clustered into cones.</u>

_____

18. What do cycads look like? <u>They are palmlike plants that reproduce with large cones.</u>

_____

19. In what kinds of habitats can cycads be found growing naturally today?

<u>They can be found in tropical and subtropical places.</u>

_____

20. Why is the ginkgo tree sometimes called a living fossil? <u>It looks similar to its fossil</u>

<u>ancestors.</u>

_____

21. What kinds of plants do conifers include? <u>They include pines, spruces, firs, cedars,</u>

<u>sequoias, redwoods, junipers, and yews.</u>

_____

22. Why are the leaves of most conifers long and thin, such as pine needles?

<u>That shape reduces the surface area from which water can be lost by evaporation.</u>

_____

© Pearson Education, Inc., publishing as Pearson Prentice Hall.

23. In addition to the shape of the leaves, what are two other adaptations that help conifers conserve water?

a. Conifer leaves have a thick, waxy covering.

b. The openings of leaves that allow for gas exchange are below the surface of the leaves.

_____

24. Circle the letter of the reason conifers never become bare.

a. They never lose their needles.

b. The gametophyte supplies needles to the sporophyte.

c. Older needles are gradually replaced by newer needles.

d. The needles conserve water throughout the year.

25. How are larches and baldcypresses different from most other conifers?

They lose their needles every fall.

_____

Section 22–5 Angiosperms—Flowering Plants
(pages 569–572)

⊂▢ **Key Concepts**
- What are the characteristics of angiosperms?
- What are monocots and dicots?
- What are the three categories of plant life spans?

Flowers and Fruits (page 569)

1. Angiosperms are members of the phylum ____Anthophyta____.
2. Angiosperms have unique reproductive organs known as ____flowers____.
3. During which geologic period did flowering plants first appear? _They first appeared_ during the Cretaceous Period. _____

_____

4. In flowering plants, the seed is encased in a(an) ____ovary____.
5. What is a fruit? _It is a wall of tissue surrounding the seed._
6. Why is using fruit to attract animals one of the reasons for the success of flowering plants? _An animal eats the fruit, and by the time the seeds leave its digestive system the animal_ _may have traveled many miles. By using fruit to attract animals, flowering plants increase the ranges_ _they inhabit._

_____

Diversity of Angiosperms (pages 570–572)

7. The seed leaves of plant embryos are called ____cotyledons____.
8. Complete the table about classes of angiosperms.

CLASSES OF ANGIOSPERMS

Class	Common Name	Number of Seed Leaves	Examples
Monocotyledonae	Monocots	One	Corn, wheat, lilies, orchids, palms
Dicotyledonae	Dicots	Two	Roses, clover, tomatoes, oaks, daisies

9. Circle the letter of each plant feature that is characteristic of dicots.
   a. Parallel leaf veins
   b. Floral parts in multiples of 4 or 5
   c. Roots include a taproot
   d. Vascular bundles scattered throughout stem

10. Classify each of the following plants as either woody or herbaceous by writing the correct term on the line.

a. Rose shrubs _____Woody_____

b. Oaks _____Woody_____

c. Tomato plants _____Herbaceous_____

d. Sunflowers _____Herbaceous_____

e. Grape vines _____Woody_____

f. Dandelions _____Herbaceous_____

11. Woody plants are made primarily of what kind of cells? They are made primarily of cells with thick cell walls that support the plant body.

_____

12. What characteristics do the stems of herbaceous plants have? Their plant stems are smooth and nonwoody.

_____

13. Complete the table about plant life spans.

PLANT LIFE SPANS

Category	Definition	Examples
Annuals	Angiosperms that complete a life cycle within one growing season	Marigolds, petunias, pansies, wheat, corn, cucumbers
Biennials	Angiosperms that complete a life cycle in two years	Parsley, celery, foxgloves
Perennials	Angiosperms that live more than two years	Peonies, asparagus, grasses, palm trees, sagebrush, oak trees, honeysuckle

Vocabulary Review

Labeling Diagrams   *Use the following words to label the diagrams of the stages in a fern's life cycle:* antheridia, archegonia, frond, rhizoid, rhizome, root, sori.

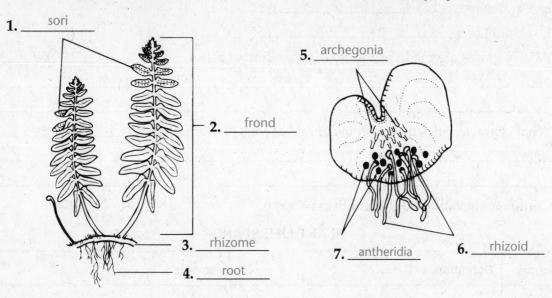

Sporophyte

1. _____ sori

2. _____ frond

3. _____ rhizome

4. _____ root

Gametophyte

5. _____ archegonia

7. _____ antheridia

6. _____ rhizoid

Completion   *Fill in the blanks with terms from Chapter 22.*

8. A(An) _____ sporophyte _____ is the diploid phase of the plant life cycle.

9. A(An) _____ gymnosperm _____ produces seeds directly on the surface of cones.

10. The seed-bearing structures of angiosperms are _____ flowers _____ .

11. The transfer of pollen from the male to the female reproductive structures is called _____ pollination _____ .

12. A(An) _____ seed _____ is a plant embryo with its food supply that is protected by a seed coat.

13. The _____ fruit _____ is a wall of tissue surrounding the seed.

14. An angiosperm that has one cotyledon, or seed leaf, is called a(an) _____ monocot _____ .

15. Flowering plants that complete an entire life cycle within one growing season are called _____ annuals _____ .

Summary

23–1 Specialized Tissues in Plants

The cells of seed plants are organized into different tissues and organs. The three main plant organs are roots, stems, and leaves. These organs are made up of three main kinds of tissues: dermal tissue, vascular tissue, and ground tissue.

Dermal tissue is like the "skin" of a plant. It protects the plant and prevents water loss. Dermal tissue is made up of epidermal cells that have different shapes and functions.

Vascular tissue moves water and nutrients throughout the plant. It consists of xylem tissue and phloem tissue. Xylem tissue moves water. It is made up of two kinds of specialized cells called tracheids and vessel elements. Phloem tissue moves sugars. It consists of sieve tube elements and companion cells.

Ground tissue is made up of all the cells that lie between dermal and vascular tissues. Ground tissue is made up mostly of parenchyma cells. Parenchyma cells have thin cell walls and function in photosynthesis and storage. Collenchyma and sclerenchyma cells are also part of ground tissue. These cells have thick cell walls that help support the plant.

A fourth kind of tissue is responsible for plant growth. Meristematic tissue produces new cells by mitosis. These new cells have not yet become specialized for specific functions. As the new cells mature, they develop specialized structures and functions, a process called differentiation. Meristematic tissue is found at the tips of stems and roots.

23–2 Roots

As soon as a seedling begins to grow, it sends out a primary root. Other roots branch out from the primary root. They are called secondary roots.

In some plants, the primary root grows long and thick. The secondary roots stay small. This kind of primary root is called a taproot. In other plants, secondary roots grow and branch. The roots of these plants are called fibrous roots.

Roots are made up of cells from the four tissue systems—dermal, vascular, ground, and meristematic. A mature root has an outside layer of dermal tissue called the epidermis. It also has a central cylinder of vascular tissue called the vascular cylinder. Between these two tissues lies ground tissue, which is called the cortex. A thin layer of cells called the endodermis completely surrounds the vascular cylinder, separating it from the cortex. An apical meristem in the root causes it to grow in length.

Roots have two functions. One function is to anchor a plant in the ground. The other function is to absorb water and dissolved nutrients from the soil.

Once absorbed by the root hairs, water and nutrients move inward through the cortex. After passing through the endodermis into the vascular cylinder, the water cannot leave. This causes pressure to build up. This pressure is called root pressure. Root pressure forces water upward through the xylem toward the stem.

23–3 Stems

Stems have three important jobs. They produce leaves, branches, and flowers. They hold leaves up to the sunlight. They also carry water and nutrients between roots and leaves.

Like the rest of the plant, the stem is composed of dermal, vascular, and ground tissue. Stems are surrounded by a layer of epidermal cells that have thick cell walls and a waxy protective coating.

In most plants, stems contain nodes (where leaves are attached) and internodes (regions between the nodes). Small buds are found where leaves attach to the nodes. Buds contain tissue that can produce new stems and leaves.

The arrangement of tissues in a stem differs among seed plants. In monocots, vascular bundles are scattered throughout the stem. In dicots and most gymnosperms, vascular bundles are arranged in a ring. These vascular bundles contain xylem and phloem tissue.

Plant stems can grow in two different ways. They have primary growth and secondary growth. In primary growth, stems grow longer as meristematic tissue at the ends of the stems produces new cells. In secondary growth, a stem grows wider as meristematic tissue on its sides produces new cells. This growth produces wood and bark. Only plants with woody stems have secondary growth.

23–4 Leaves

The leaves of a plant are its main organs of photosynthesis. In photosynthesis, plants make food. Sugars, starches, and oils made by plants provide food for all land animals.

Leaves have a structure that enables them to absorb light and make food. Most leaves have thin, flattened sections called blades to collect sunlight. The blade is attached to the stem at the petiole. Most leaves are also made up of a specialized ground tissue called mesophyll. Mesophyll cells have many chloroplasts. It is in these cells that photosynthesis occurs.

Xylem and phloem tissues in leaves are gathered in bundles called veins. These veins are connected to the xylem and phloem in the stem.

Plants must exchange gases with the air around them. They can lose a lot of water during this process. Leaves have an adaptation to prevent water loss. They allow air in and out of their waterproof covering only through small openings called stomata. Guard cells on the undersides of the leaves control the stomata and thus regulate the movement of gases into and out of leaf tissues. In general, the stomata are open during the day, when photosynthesis is active, and closed at night.

23–5 Transport in Plants

Xylem tissue forms tubes that stretch from roots through stems and out into leaves. Root pressure forces water and nutrients into the xylem. Other forces pull water and nutrients through the plant.

Water can be pulled up through xylem because its molecules are pulled together by a force called cohesion. Water molecules are also attracted to other molecules. This force is called adhesion. Together, cohesion and adhesion cause water to move upward. This movement is called capillary action.

Capillary action is too weak to pull water up the xylem tubes in a large plant. Another force pulls water up to the leaves. It is called transpiration pull. Transpiration pull happens because water moves from areas where there is plenty of water to areas where there is little water. When water evaporates from leaves, water is drawn upward from the roots to replace it.

Phloem transports the sugars made in photosynthesis. It carries sugars from the leaves into the stems and roots. The food is then either used or stored.

Scientists have only formed hypotheses to explain how phloem transport happens. One hypothesis is called the pressure-flow hypothesis. This hypothesis explains that sugars move from areas of high concentration to areas of low concentration. When sugars are pumped into or removed from phloem, the change in concentration causes a movement of sugars in that same direction.

Chapter 23   Roots, Stems, and Leaves

Section 23–1 Specialized Tissues in Plants
(pages 579–583)

Key Concepts
- What are the three principal organs and tissues of seed plants?
- What are the three main tissue systems of plants?
- What specialized cells make up vascular tissue?
- How does meristematic tissue differ from other plant tissue?

Seed Plant Structure (page 579)

1. What are the three principal organs of seed plants?

   a. Roots   b. Stems   c. Leaves

2. Circle the letter of each sentence that is true about a function that roots perform.

   (a.) They anchor plants in the ground.

   b. They compete with other plants for sunlight.

   (c.) They absorb water and nutrients from soil.

   (d.) They hold plants upright.

3. What does the transport system of stems do? It lifts water from the roots up to the leaves and sends the products of photosynthesis from the leaves down to the roots.

4. The principal organs in which plants carry out photosynthesis are the ___leaves___.

5. What do the adjustable pores of leaves help conserve, and what do they allow to enter and leave a plant? The pores conserve water while allowing oxygen and carbon dioxide to enter and leave a leaf.

Plant Tissue Systems (page 580)

6. What are the three tissue systems of plants?

   a. Dermal tissue   c. Ground tissue

   b. Vascular tissue

Dermal Tissue (page 580)

7. Dermal tissue typically consists of a single layer of ___epidermal cells___.

8. What is the cuticle, and what is its function? The cuticle is a thick, waxy layer that often covers the exposed outer surfaces of epidermal cells. It protects against water loss and injury.

9. What is the function of the tiny projections known as trichomes? They help protect the leaf.

10. What does dermal tissue consist of in roots, and what is its function? Dermal tissue in roots consists of root hair cells that have a large amount of surface area and aid in water absorption.

Vascular Tissue (pages 580–581)

11. Complete the table about the types of vascular tissue.

TYPES OF VASCULAR TISSUE

Type	Function	Cell Types Within Tissue
Xylem	Transports water	Tracheids, vessel elements
Phloem	Transports food	Sieve tube elements, companion cells

Match the vascular-tissue cells with their descriptions.

Vascular-Tissue Cells

___b___ **12.** Tracheids

___d___ **13.** Vessel elements

___a___ **14.** Sieve tube elements

___c___ **15.** Companion cells

Description

a. The main phloem cells

b. Long, narrow xylem cells with walls that are impermeable to water

c. Phloem cells that surround sieve tube elements

d. Xylem cells arranged end to end on top of one another

16. How can water move from one tracheid into a neighboring cell? The cell walls of
tracheids are pierced by openings that connect neighboring cells to one another.

17. How can materials move from one sieve tube element into the next? The end walls of
sieve tube elements have many small holes in them. Material can move through these holes from
one cell to another adjacent cell.

18. What cells support the phloem cells? Companion cells

Ground Tissue (page 582)

19. The cells that lie between dermal and vascular tissue make up what kind of tissue?
Ground tissue

20. Complete the table about ground-tissue cells.

GROUND-TISSUE CELLS

Type of Cell	Structure	Function
Parenchyma	Cells with thin cell walls and large central vacuoles	The site of most of a plant's photosynthesis
Collenchyma	Cells with strong, flexible cell walls	Help support larger plants
Sclerenchyma	Cells with extremely thick, rigid cell walls	Make ground tissue tough and strong

Plant Growth and Meristematic Tissue (pages 582–583)

21. What does indeterminate growth mean in a plant? Indeterminate growth means that new cells are produced at the tips of roots and stems for as long as the plant lives.

_____

_____

22. Where are these cells produced? In the meristems

_____

23. The only plant tissue that produces new cells by mitosis is called meristematic tissue .

24. What occurs as meristematic cells mature? They differentiate into one of the three main tissues of a plant.

_____

25. What is an apical meristem? An apical meristem is a group of undifferentiated cells that divide to produce increased length of stems and roots.

_____

26. Where else on many plants is there meristematic tissue other than at apical meristems? Many plants grow in width as a result of meristematic tissue that lines the stems and roots of a plant.

_____

Name_____ Class_____ Date_____

Section 23–2 Roots (pages 584–588)

Key Concepts
- What are the two main types of roots?
- What are the main tissues in a mature root?
- What are the different functions of roots?

Types of Roots (page 584)

1. How are primary roots and secondary roots different in some plants? <u>The primary root</u>
   <u>grows long and thick, whereas the secondary roots remain small.</u>

2. Complete the table about types of roots.

TYPES OF ROOTS

Type of Root	Description	Mainly in Dicots or Monocots?	Examples
Taproots	Long and thick primary roots that grow deep into the soil	Dicots	Oak and hickory trees, carrots, dandelions, beets, radishes
Fibrous roots	Roots that are usually shallow and consist of many thin roots	Monocots	Grasses

Root Structure and Growth (page 585)

3. Label the parts of a root on the illustration.

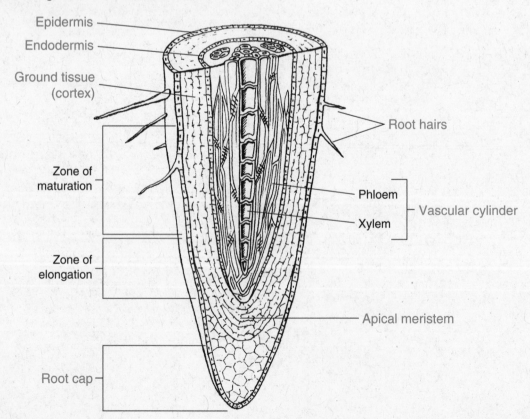

Epidermis

Endodermis

Ground tissue (cortex)

Root hairs

Zone of maturation

Phloem

Xylem

Vascular cylinder

Zone of elongation

Apical meristem

Root cap

© Pearson Education, Inc., publishing as Pearson Prentice Hall.

4. What is the structure of a mature root? A mature root has an outside layer, the epidermis, and a central cylinder of vascular tissue. Between these two tissues lies a large area of ground tissue.

5. Water enters the plant through the large surface area provided by the _____ root hairs _____.

6. What does the cortex of a root consist of? It consists of a spongy layer of ground tissue.

7. The vascular tissue in the central region of a root is called the _____ vascular cylinder _____.

8. What protects the apical meristem of a root? The root cap protects it.

9. Where does most of the increase in root length occur? It occurs immediately behind the meristem, where cells are growing longer.

Root Functions (pages 586–588)

10. What are two functions of a plant's roots?
    a. Roots anchor a plant in the ground.
    b. Roots absorb water and dissolved nutrients from the soil.

11. Is the following sentence true or false? The ingredients of a soil can determine what kinds of plants grow in it. _____ true _____

12. Circle the letter of each sentence that is true about active transport of minerals in roots.
    a. Water molecules move into the plant by active transport.
    b. ATP is the source of energy used to pump mineral ions from the soil into the plant.
    c. The cell membranes of root hairs contain active transport proteins.
    d. Using active transport, a root actually pumps water into the plant.

13. What happens to the water and dissolved minerals after they move into the cortex? They pass the inner boundary of the cortex and enter the endodermis.

14. Each of the cells of a root's endodermis is surrounded on four sides by a waterproof strip called a(an) _____ Casparian strip _____.

15. Why is there a one-way passage of materials into the vascular cylinder in plant roots? Because water and minerals cannot pass through the waxy Casparian strip, once they pass through the endodermis, they are trapped in the vascular cylinder.

16. What is root pressure? Root pressure is caused by the trapped water and minerals in the vascular cylinder. The pressure forces water upward through the xylem toward the stem.

Section 23–3 Stems (pages 589–594)

Key Concepts

- What are the three main functions of stems?
- How do monocot and dicot systems differ?
- How do primary growth and secondary growth occur in stems?

Stem Structure and Function (page 589)

1. What are the two important functions of stems?

   a. They hold leaves up to the sunlight.

   b. They transport substances between roots and leaves.

2. What three tissue systems compose a stem? Dermal, vascular, and ground tissue

Match the stem structure with its description.

	Structure	Description
c	**3.** Node	**a.** A region between nodes
a	**4.** Internode	**b.** Contains undeveloped tissue that can produce new stems and leaves
b	**5.** Bud	**c.** Where leaves are attached

Monocot and Dicot Stems (page 590)

6. How does the arrangement of tissues in a stem differ among seed plants?

   In monocots, vascular bundles are scattered throughout the stem. In dicots and most

   gymnosperms, vascular bundles are arranged in a cylinder.

7. In a monocot stem, what does each vascular bundle contain? Each contains xylem and phloem tissue.

8. The parenchyma cells inside the ring of vascular tissue in a dicot stem are known

   as _____pith_____.

9. What do the parenchyma cells outside the ring of vascular tissue form in a dicot stem?

   They form the cortex of the stem.

Primary Growth of Stems (page 590)

10. What is primary growth in a plant? Primary growth is the increase in plant length caused by

    the production of new cells at the tips of roots and shoots.

© Pearson Education, Inc., publishing as Pearson Prentice Hall.

11. Primary growth of stems is produced by cell division in the ____apical meristem____.

12. Is the following sentence true or false? Only dicot plants undergo primary growth. _____false_____

Secondary Growth of Stems (pages 591–594)

13. The pattern of growth in which stems increase in width is called ____secondary growth____.

14. In conifers and dicots, where does secondary growth take place? __It takes place in lateral__ __meristematic tissues called the vascular cambium and cork cambium.__

15. What type of lateral meristematic tissue produces vascular tissues and increases the thickness of stems over time? __Vascular cambium__

16. What does cork cambium produce? __It produces the outer covering of stems.__

17. Circle the letter of each sentence that is true about the formation of vascular cambium.

    (a.) Vascular cambium forms between the xylem and phloem of individual vascular bundles.

    (b.) Divisions of vascular cambium give rise to new layers of xylem and phloem.

    (c.) Once secondary growth begins, vascular cambium appears as a thin layer.

    d. The production of new layers of xylem and phloem causes the stem to shrink when secondary growth begins.

18. Is the following sentence true or false? Most of what we call "wood" is actually layers of phloem. _____false_____

19. What is heartwood? __It is the darker wood near the center of the stem that no longer conducts__ __water.__

20. The wood that is active in fluid transport and therefore lighter in color is called ____sapwood____.

21. The alternation of dark and light wood produces what we commonly call ____tree rings____.

22. How can you estimate the age of a tree? __You can estimate a tree's age by counting the rings__ __in a cross section of the tree.__

23. On most trees, what does bark include? __Bark includes all tissues outside the vascular__ __cambium, including phloem, the cork cambium, and cork.__

24. Circle the letter of each sentence that is true about cork.

   (**a.**) Cork cells usually contain fats, oils, or waxes.

   b. Cork cells cause the loss of water from a stem.

   (**c.**) The outermost cork cells are usually dead.

   (**d.**) Cork cambium produces a thick, protective layer of cork.

25. Label the parts of the illustration of the cross section of a tree. Use the following terms : wood, bark, heartwood, cork, sapwood, cork cambium, vascular cambium, phloem.

26. What are four kinds of modified stems that store food?

   a. Tuber

   b. Bulb

   c. Rhizome

   d. Corm

© Pearson Education, Inc., publishing as Pearson Prentice Hall.

Section 23–4 Leaves (pages 595–598)

🔑 Key Concepts
- How does the structure of a leaf enable it to carry out photosynthesis?
- How does gas exchange take place in a leaf?

Leaf Structure (page 595)

1. The structure of a leaf is optimized for what purposes? _It is optimized for absorbing light_ _and carrying out photosynthesis._

2. What is a leaf blade? _A blade is the thin, flattened section of a leaf._

3. The blade is attached to the stem by a thin stalk called a(an) ____petiole____.

4. Circle the letter of the type of tissue that covers a leaf.

   a. vascular   (**b.**) dermal   **c.** ground   **d.** petiole

5. The vascular tissues of leaves are connected directly to the vascular tissues of _____stems_____.

Leaf Functions (pages 596–598)

6. The bulk of most leaves is composed of a specialized ground tissue known as ____mesophyll____.

7. How do the carbohydrates produced in photosynthesis get to the rest of the plant? _They move from mesophyll cells into phloem vessels, which carry them to the_ _rest of the plant._

Match the leaf structure with its description.

	Structure	Description
c	8. Palisade mesophyll	**a.** A bundle of xylem and phloem tissues
e	9. Spongy mesophyll	**b.** Specialized cells that control the opening and closing of stomata
a	10. Vein	**c.** A layer of mesophyll cells that absorb much of the light that enters the leaf
d	11. Stomata	
b	12. Guard cells	**d.** Openings in the underside of the leaf
		e. A loose tissue with many air spaces between its cells

13. How do the air spaces in the spongy mesophyll connect with the exterior of the leaf?
They connect with the exterior through stomata.

14. What is transpiration? _Transpiration is the loss of water from a plant through its leaves._

15. Why must a plant have its stomata open at least part of the time? _The stomata must be_ _open part of the time to allow gas exchange between air spaces in the spongy mesophyll and the_ _exterior._

16. What would probably happen to a plant that kept its stomata open all the time?

The water loss due to transpiration would be so great that the plant would be unable to take in

enough water to survive.

17. What is the balance plants maintain that prevents them from losing too much water?

Plants keep their stomata open just enough to allow photosynthesis to take place but not so much

that they lose an excessive amount of water.

18. Complete the flowchart about guard cells.

Guard cells are forced into a curved shape when water pressure becomes _____high_____.

↓

The guard cells pull away from one another, opening the _____stoma_____.

↓

Guard cells straighten out when water pressure _____decreases_____.

↓

The guard cells pull together, closing the _____stoma_____.

19. Is the following sentence true or false? In general, stomata are closed at night. _____true_____

20. How is the structure of the leaves of a pine tree an adaptation to dry conditions?

The structure reduces water loss from the leaf.

21. What are cactus leaves adapted for? Cactus leaves are actually nonphotosynthetic thorns

that protect against herbivores.

22. Why must carnivorous plants rely on insects for their source of nitrogen?

Carnivorous plants typically live in nutrient-poor soils.

Reading Skill Practice

Writing a summary can help you remember the information that you have read. When you write a summary, write only the most important points. Write a summary of the information under the blue heading Leaf Functions. Your summary should be shorter than the text on which it is based. Do your work on a separate sheet of paper.

Students' summaries should include definitions of the boldface terms, as well as the main points under each of the three subheadings.

Section 23–5 Transport in Plants (pages 599–602)

 Key Concepts
- How is water transported throughout a plant?
- How are the products of photosynthesis transported throughout a plant?

Water Transport (pages 599–601)

1. What combination of factors provides enough force to move water through the xylem tissue of even the tallest plant? The combination of root pressure, capillary action, and transpiration moves water through the xylem of plants.

2. Complete the table about attraction between molecules.

ATTRACTION BETWEEN MOLECULES

Type of Attraction	Definition
Cohesion	Attraction between molecules of the same substance
Adhesion	Attraction between unlike molecules

3. The tendency of water to rise in a thin tube is called _____capillary action_____.

4. How does the thinness of a tube affect how high water will rise because of capillary action? Show your answer by drawing how high water would rise in each of the tubes on the illustration.

5. The tubelike structures of what two kinds of cells use capillary action to raise water above the level of ground?

   a. Tracheids _____ b. Vessel elements _____

6. How do vessel elements form continuous tubes through which water can move freely?
Their cell walls are lost at both ends when the cells die.

7. What causes the process known as transpiration pull? When water is lost through
transpiration, osmotic pressure moves water out of the vascular tissue of the leaf. The movement
of water out of the leaf "pulls" water upward through the vascular system from the roots.

8. What normally keeps a plant's leaves and stems rigid? Osmotic pressure on the plant's
cell walls keeps the leaves and stems rigid.

9. High transpiration rates can lead to water loss that is severe enough to
cause _____wilting_____.

10. How does the loss of osmotic pressure in leaves slow down the rate of transpiration?
The loss of osmotic pressure causes guard cells to close, thereby slowing down the rate of
transpiration.

Nutrient Transport (pages 601–602)

11. How is the water content of a leaf kept constant? When water is abundant, it flows into the
leaf. This raises the water pressure in the guard cells, which then open the stomata. When water is
scarce, the water pressure in the leaf falls, and the guard cells close the stomata.

12. How does wilting help a plant to conserve water? Wilting results from the loss of water—
and therefore pressure in a plant's cells. Without the internal pressure, the plant's cell walls bend
inward, and the leaves and stems wilt. This slows down transpiration.

13. The movement of sugars out of leaves and through stems to fruits takes place in what
kind of vascular tissue? _____Phloem_____

14. Is the following sentence true or false? Many plants pump food down into their roots
for winter storage. _____true_____

15. The hypothesis that considers plants in terms of where they produce and use materials
from photosynthesis is called the _____pressure-flow hypothesis_____.

16. Complete the flowchart about the pressure-flow hypothesis.

Photosynthesis produces a high concentration of sugars in a cell, called the _____source_____ cell.

↓

Sugars move from the cell to phloem, and water also moves into the phloem by the process of _____osmosis_____.

↓

Water moving into the phloem causes an increase in _____pressure_____.

↓

The pressure causes fluid to move through the phloem toward a cell where sugars are lower in concentration, called the _____sink_____ cell.

Reading Skill Practice

When you read a section, taking notes can help you organize and remember the information. As you read or review Section 23–5, take notes by writing each heading and listing the main points under each heading. Do your work on a separate sheet of paper.

Students should make note of the main points on pages 599–602. Their notes should include enough detail to be clear and informative.

Vocabulary Review

Multiple Choice   *In the space provided, write the letter of the answer that best completes each sentence or answers the question.*

___b___ **1.** The main phloem cells are
  a. epidermal cells.
  b. sieve tube elements.
  c. vessel elements.
  d. meristems.

___a___ **2.** Which of the following cells are found in ground tissue and have thin cell walls and large vacuoles?
  a. parenchyma
  b. sclerenchyma
  c. collenchyma
  d. companion cells

___c___ **3.** The spongy layer of ground tissue just inside the epidermis of a root is called the
  a. root cap.
  b. endodermis.
  c. cortex.
  d. vascular cylinder.

___b___ **4.** The meristematic tissue that produces the outer covering of stems is called
  a. pith.
  b. cork cambium.
  c. vascular cambium.
  d. bark.

___c___ **5.** Which of the following is made up of tall, columnar cells that absorb light?
  a. petioles
  b. spongy mesophyll
  c. palisade mesophyll
  d. stomata

Matching   *In the space provided, write the letter that best matches each term.*

___c___ **6.** apical meristem
___h___ **7.** differentiation
___f___ **8.** root hairs
___a___ **9.** Casparian strip
___j___ **10.** bud
___d___ **11.** heartwood
___g___ **12.** mesophyll
___i___ **13.** transpiration
___b___ **14.** adhesion
___e___ **15.** capillary action

a. structure that makes cells of the endodermis waterproof
b. force of attraction between unlike molecules
c. cells that divide to increase root and stem length
d. older xylem that no longer conducts water
e. tendency of water to rise in a thin tube
f. tiny projections on the root epidermis that absorb water
g. specialized ground tissue in leaves where photosynthesis occurs
h. process in which cells develop special structures and functions
i. loss of water through leaves
j. part of a stem that contains undeveloped tissue

Summary

24–1 Reproduction With Cones and Flowers

Seed plants are completely adapted to life on land. Because they do not need water for reproduction, seed plants can reproduce nearly everywhere.

In the seed plant life cycle, the spore-producing generation (sporophyte) alternates with the gamete-producing generation (gametophyte). In seed plants, the familiar form of the plant is the sporophyte. The gametophyte of seed plants is hidden within the cones and flowers. Cones and flowers are two different methods of reproduction.

Pine trees and other gymnosperms use cones for reproduction. Pollen cones produce the male gametophyte, which are called pollen grains. Seed cones produce the female gametophyte in ovules. A few large egg cells form within the ovules. When a pollen grain lands near an ovule, it grows a pollen tube into the ovule. A sperm from the pollen tube fertilizes the egg in the ovule. A zygote forms and grows into an embryo. The embryo becomes enclosed in a seed.

Angiosperms, or flowering plants, reproduce with flowers. Flowers are organs that are made up of four kinds of leaves: sepals, petals, stamens, and carpels. Sepals make up the outermost circle of floral parts and are often green. They protect the flower bud. Colorful petals form the next circle. Petals attract insects and other pollinators to the flower.

The inner circles of a flower are fertile leaves. Stamens form the first inner circle. Each stamen has a long filament that supports an anther. The anther produces male gametophytes. One or more carpels form the innermost circle. Carpels, also called pistils, produce female gametophytes. Each carpel has a broad base called the ovary. The carpel's stalk is called the style. At the top of the style is the stigma. The stigma has a sticky surface where pollen grains land. Angiosperms may have stamens and carpels within the same flower or in separate flowers on the same plant.

Reproduction in flowering plants takes place inside the flower. Inside the anthers, each cell undergoes meiosis to produce four haploid spore cells. Each of these cells becomes a pollen grain. Inside the ovaries are the ovules, where the female gametophyte develops. A single cell goes through meiosis to produce four haploid cells. One of these cells goes through mitosis, producing the embryo sac. This is the female gametophyte. Within the embryo sac is the egg cell.

During pollination, pollen is transferred from the anther to the stigma. Most gymnosperms are wind pollinated. Animals pollinate most angiosperms. Animal-pollinated flowers have many adaptations to attract the animals. Animals have evolved body shapes that let them reach nectar deep within the flowers. Animal pollination is more efficient than wind pollination.

When a pollen grain lands on a stigma, it grows a pollen tube to the ovary. Two sperm nuclei enter the embryo sac. Two distinct fertilizations take place in the embryo sac. First, one sperm nucleus fuses with the egg to form a diploid zygote. The zygote will grow into the plant embryo. Then, the other sperm nucleus fuses with two other nuclei in the embryo sac to form the endosperm. The endosperm provides food for the embryo. This is known as double fertilization.

© Pearson Education, Inc., publishing as Pearson Prentice Hall.

24–2 Seed Development and Germination

Seeds helped to make angiosperms successful on land. Seeds nourish and protect embryos. As angiosperm seeds mature, the ovary walls thicken to form a fruit. The fruit encloses the seed. Some fruits are fleshy like grapes. Others are tough like pea pods.

Fleshy fruits often attract animals. When animals eat the fruit, they also eat the seeds. The animals disperse the seeds in their feces, often in areas far from the parent plant. Seeds that are spread by wind and water are usually lightweight. They easily float in the air or on water.

Many seeds enter a period of dormancy. They are alive but not growing. Dormancy gives time for seeds to spread to new areas or wait for better growing conditions. The right temperature and moisture can cause seeds to germinate, ending dormancy.

Germination is the stage of early growth of the plant embryo. When seeds germinate, they absorb water. This makes a seed swell and crack open. The young root emerges through the crack and begins to grow. In most monocots, a shoot emerges, protected by a sheath. The cotyledon stays underground. In some dicots, the cotyledons emerge above the ground. They protect the stem and the first leaves. In other dicots, the cotyledons stay underground to provide food for the seedling.

24–3 Plant Propagation and Agriculture

The production of seeds and fruits is sexual reproduction. Many plants also reproduce asexually by vegetative reproduction. This enables a single plant to produce many offspring that are genetically identical.

Plants reproduce asexually in many different ways. Some plants send out long, horizontal stems that produce roots or new shoots. Other plants produce tiny plants, called plantlets, on their leaves or stems. These plantlets detach and grow into new plants. Some plants can even produce new plants when a leaf drops to the ground and grows roots.

Plant growers often use vegetative reproduction to make exact copies of a useful or pretty plant. One method is to make a cutting of a stem that has meristematic tissue. The stem is partially buried in soil and treated with a special rooting mixture.

Grafting and budding are other methods used by plant growers. New plants are grown on plants that have a strong root system. A scion is a piece cut from the parent plant. It is attached to the plant with strong roots, called the stock. In grafting, stems are used as scions. In budding, buds are used as scions.

Agriculture, or the cultivation of plants, is the foundation of human society. Farmers in North America produce enough food to feed millions of people around the world. Most people of the world depend on a few crop plants—wheat, rice, and corn. Most food from crop plants is taken from the seeds.

Over time, farmers have increased the amount of crops they can harvest in an acre of land. Selective breeding of crop plants and improved farming techniques have made crop production more efficient.

Section 24–1 Reproduction With Cones and Flowers (pages 609–616)

👉 **Key Concepts**
- What are the reproductive structures of gymnosperms and angiosperms?
- How does pollination differ between angiosperms and gymnosperms?

Alternation of Generations (page 609)

1. Circle the letter of each sentence that is true about alternation of generations in plants.

   (a.) In all plants, the sporophyte generation is diploid.

   (b.) The gametophyte in seed plants is hidden within the sporophyte plant.

   c. The recognizable part of a seed-bearing plant is the gametophyte.

   (d.) In all plants, the gametophyte generation is haploid.

2. An important trend in plant evolution is the reduction in the size of the _____gametophyte_____.

3. Where are the gametophytes found in gymnosperms and angiosperms?
   They are found inside the cones in gymnosperms and inside flowers in angiosperms.
   _____

Life Cycle of Gymnosperms (pages 610–611)

4. Reproduction in gymnosperms takes place in _____cones_____.

5. Circle the letter of what produces cones in gymnosperms.

   (a.) mature sporophyte   c. pine trees

   b. mature gametophyte   d. pollen seeds

6. What kind of cone produces male gametophytes? ___Pollen cones___

7. The male gametophytes of gymnosperms are called ___pollen grains___.

8. Circle the letter of each sentence that is true about seed cones.

   a. They produce pollen grains.

   (b.) They produce female gametophytes.

   (c.) They have two ovules at the base of each scale.

   (d.) They are generally much larger than pollen cones.

9. Is the following sentence true or false? Each mature female gametophyte contains hundreds of egg cells ready for fertilization. ___false___

10. How long does the gymnosperm life cycle typically take to complete?
    It typically takes two years.

11. In the gymnosperm life cycle, how do the pollen grains reach the female cones? The pollen grains are released by the male cones, and some are carried to the female cones by the wind.

12. What ensures that pollen grains stay on the scales of a female cone? A sticky material, called pollination drop, ensures that the pollen grains stay.

13. A structure grown by a pollen grain that contains two sperm nuclei is called a(an) _____pollen tube_____.

14. What happens to the two sperm cells once the pollen tube reaches the female gametophyte? One sperm nucleus disintegrates, and the other fertilizes the egg contained in the female gametophyte.

15. Circle the letter of what a gymnosperm embryo can be called.
    a. mature gametophyte
    b. new sporophyte
    c. mature sporophyte
    d. new gametophyte

16. What are the three generations of the gymnosperm life cycle that are contained in a gymnosperm seed? The outer seed coat is part of the old sporophyte generation, the haploid cells surrounding the embryo are part of the female gametophyte, and the embryo is the new sporophyte plant.

Structure of Flowers (pages 612–613)

17. What are the four kinds of specialized leaves that compose a flower?
    a. Sepals
    b. Petals
    c. Stamens
    d. Carpels

© Pearson Education, Inc., publishing as Pearson Prentice Hall.

Name_____ Class_____ Date _____

Match the floral part with its description.

	Floral Part	**Description**
_d_	**18.** Sepals	**a.** Stalk with the stigma at the top
_i_	**19.** Petals	**b.** Structures where male gametophytes are produced
_h_	**20.** Stamen	**c.** Flower part that contains one or more ovules
_e_	**21.** Filament	**d.** Outermost, green floral parts
_b_	**22.** Anthers	**e.** Long, thin structure that supports an anther
_f_	**23.** Carpels	**f.** Innermost floral parts that produce female gametophytes
_c_	**24.** Ovary	**g.** Sticky, top portion of style
_a_	**25.** Style	**h.** Male structure made up of an anther and a filament
_g_	**26.** Stigma	**i.** Brightly colored parts just inside the sepals

27. Label the parts of the flower on the illustration.

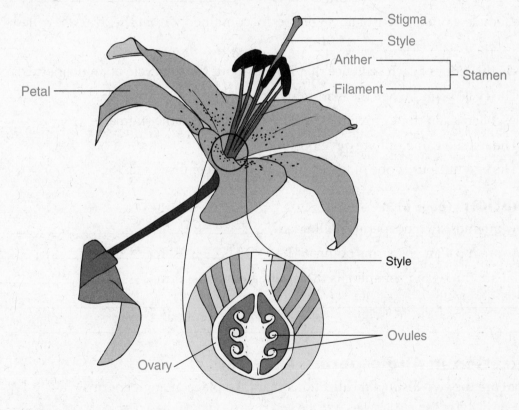

28. What is a pistil? It is a reproductive structure formed from the fusion of several carpels.
_____

29. What are the separate male and female flowers on a corn plant? The tassel is a flower
that produces male gametophytes, and the silk is the style of a flower that contains the female
gametophyte.
_____

Life Cycle of Angiosperms (pages 614–615)

30. Where does reproduction in angiosperms take place? It takes place within the flower.
_____

31. Inside the anthers, each cell undergoes meiosis and produces four haploid cells that each develop into a(an) pollen grain .

32. In angiosperms, the pollen grain is the entire male gametophyte .

33. The female gametophyte of an angiosperm, contained within the ovary, is called the embryo sac .

34. Circle the letter of each sentence that is true about the life cycle of angiosperms.

(**a.**) The cycle begins when the mature sporophyte produces flowers.

b. A pollen grain stops growing when it is released from the stigma.

(**c.**) The female gametophyte develops in the ovule.

(**d.**) The egg nucleus is one of the eight nuclei in the embryo sac.

Pollination (page 615)

35. How are most gymnosperms pollinated? Most are pollinated by the wind.

36. How are most angiosperms pollinated? Most are pollinated by animals.

37. What are three kinds of animals that pollinate angiosperms? Insects, birds, and
mammals pollinate angiosperms.
_____

Fertilization in Angiosperms (page 616)

38. What are the two distinct fertilizations that take place in angiosperms?

a. One of the sperm nuclei fuses with the egg nucleus to produce a diploid zygote cell.
_____

b. The other sperm nucleus fuses with two other nuclei in the embryo sac to form a triploid cell.
_____

Name_____ Class_____ Date _____

39. The food-rich tissue that nourishes a seedling as it grows is known as
_____endosperm_____.

40. Why is fertilization in angiosperms known as double fertilization? __Two distinct__
fertilization events take place between the male and female gametophytes.

_____

41. Complete the flowchart about the life cycle of angiosperms.

Inside the anthers, each cell undergoes _____meiosis_____ to produce megaspores.

Each megaspore becomes a(an) _____pollen grain_____.

The nucleus of each pollen grain produces two haploid _____nuclei_____.

The pollen grain lands on a stigma and begins to grow a(an) _____pollen tube_____
that eventually reaches the ovary and enters the _____ovule_____.

One of the sperm nuclei fuses with the egg nucleus to produce a(an) _____zygote_____, and
the other sperm nucleus fuses with two other nuclei to form a cell that grows into the _____endosperm_____.

Reading Skill Practice

Outlining is a way you can help yourself understand better and remember what you have read. Write an outline for Section 24–1, Reproduction With Cones and Flowers. In your outline, use the blue headings for the first level and the green subheadings for the second level. Then, list the details that support, or back up, the main ideas.

Students should use the section's six blue headings for the first level of their outline and use the green headings where appropriate. Supporting details should include the highlighted, boldface vocabulary terms and the key concepts.

Section 24–2 Seed Development and Germination (pages 618–621)

🗝 **Key Concepts**
- How do fruits form?
- How are seeds dispersed?
- What factors influence the dormancy and germination of seeds?

Seed and Fruit Development (page 618)

1. What is a fruit? It is a ripened ovary that contains angiosperm seeds.

2. What happens as angiosperm seeds mature after fertilization is complete?
   The ovary walls thicken to form a fruit that encloses the developing seeds.

3. The outer layer of the seed that protects the embryo and its food supply is called a(an)
   seed coat .

4. Is the following sentence true or false? Both cucumbers and tomatoes are fruits.
   true

5. Circle the letter of each sentence that is true about fruits.
   (a.) As seeds mature, the ovary walls thicken to form a fruit.
   (b.) Fruits can carry one seed or several seeds.
   (c.) A fruit is a ripened ovary that encloses a seed or seeds.
   d. The inner wall of the ovary never touches the seed.

Seed Dispersal (page 619)

6. Why are seeds that are dispersed by animals typically contained in fleshy, nutritious
   fruits? These fruits provide nutrition for the animal and also help the plant disperse its seeds.

7. Circle the letter of why seeds dispersed by animals are covered with tough coatings.
   a. The seeds need to be able to float on water.
   (b.) The coatings enable the seeds to pass through an animal unharmed.
   c. The seeds need to be digested by the animal that eats them.
   d. The coatings prevent the seeds from being eaten by animals.

8. Why are seeds dispersed by wind or water typically lightweight?
   Being lightweight allows the seeds to be carried in the air or to float on the surface of the water.

9. How are the seeds of ash and maple trees dispersed long distances from the parent
   plants? Their seeds are encased in winglike structures that spin and twirl as they are released,
   helping them glide considerable distances.

10. What adaptation does a coconut seed have that helps its dispersal? <u>The seed contains a</u> <u>liquid endosperm layer that makes a coconut buoyant enough to float in sea water within its</u> <u>protective coating for many weeks.</u>

Seed Dormancy (page 620)

11. What is dormancy? <u>It is a period in which the plant embryo is alive but not growing.</u>

12. What are two environmental factors that can cause a seed to end dormancy and germinate?

a. <u>Temperature</u>   b. <u>Moisture</u>

13. What are two purposes served by seed dormancy?

a. <u>It can allow for long-distance dispersal.</u>

b. <u>It can allow seeds to germinate under ideal growth conditions.</u>

14. Is the following sentence true or false? Some pine tree seeds remain dormant until the high temperatures generated by a forest fire cause cones to open and release the seeds. <u>true</u>

Seed Germination (page 621)

15. What is seed germination? <u>Seed germination is the early growth stage of the plant embryo.</u>

16. Complete the flowchart about seed germination.

> When a seed germinates, it absorbs ____<u>water</u>____.

> ↓

> The water causes the endosperm to swell, which cracks open the ____<u>seed coat</u>____.

> ↓

> Through the cracked seed coat, the young ____<u>root</u>____ begins to grow.

17. Circle the letter of each sentence that is true about seed germination.

(a.) In some dicots, the cotyledons protect the first foliage leaves.

(b.) In most monocots, the cotyledon remains within the seed.

(c.) In some dicots, the cotyledons remain below the soil and provide food for the seedling.

d. In most monocots, the cotyledon emerges above ground to protect the leaves.

Section 24–3 Plant Propagation and Agriculture
(pages 622–626)

👄 **Key Concepts**
- What forms of vegetative reproduction occur in plants?
- What is plant propagation?
- Which crops are the major food supply for humans?

Vegetative Reproduction (page 622)

1. The method of asexual reproduction used by many flowering plants is called _____vegetative reproduction_____.

2. What does vegetative reproduction enable a single plant that is well adapted to the environment to do? _It enables the plant to produce many offspring genetically identical to_ itself.

3. Vegetative reproduction includes the production of new plants from what three kinds of plant structures?

   a. _Horizontal stems_

   b. _Plantlets_

   c. _Underground roots_

4. Why does vegetative reproduction enable plants to reproduce very quickly?
   It does not involve pollination or seed formation.

5. What do spider plants produce that allows them to reproduce vegetatively?
   They produce plantlets.

6. Is the following sentence true or false? New plants can grow from the leaves of a parent plant if the leaves fall to the ground and the conditions are right.
   _____true_____

7. How do strawberry plants reproduce vegetatively? _They send out long trailing stems called_ stolons that produce roots when they touch the ground. Once the roots are well established, each stolon may be broken, forming a new, independent plant.

8. How do bamboo plants reproduce asexually? _They grow long underground stems that can_ send up new shoots in several places.

Plant Propagation (page 623)

9. What do horticulturists use plant propagation for? _They use it to make many identical_ copies of plants or to produce offspring from seedless plants.

© Pearson Education, Inc., publishing as Pearson Prentice Hall.

10. Why might a horticulturist not want a plant to reproduce sexually by seeds?
The growers want to avoid the variation that would result if the plant reproduced sexually.

11. Circle the letter of what a cutting must have to form roots when placed in a rooting mixture.

a. Several stolons   (**c.**) Buds containing meristematic tissue

b. A taproot   **d.** Buds without meristematic tissue

12. When a piece of stem or a lateral bud is cut from a parent plant and attached to another plant, what are the cut piece and the plant to which it is attached called?
The cut piece is called a scion, and the plant to which it is attached is called the stock.

13. When stems are used as scions, the process is called _____ grafting _____ .

14. What is the process called when buds are used as scions? It is called budding.

15. In what kind of cases do growers use grafting and budding? Grafting and budding are
used to reproduce seedless plants and varieties of woody plants that do not produce strong root
systems.

Agriculture (pages 624–626)

16. Circle the letter showing when evidence suggests that agriculture developed in many parts of the world.

a. about 1–2 million years ago   (**c.**) about 10,000–12,000 years ago

b. about 1000–2000 years ago   **d.** about 100,000 years ago

17. What are three crop plants that most people of the world depend on for the bulk of their food supply?

a. Wheat   **b.** Rice   **c.** Corn

18. The food taken from crops such as wheat, rice, and corn is stored in their
_____ seeds _____ .

19. What are the four crops that 80 percent of all U.S. cropland is used to grow?
They include wheat, corn, soybeans, and hay.

20. What important crops were unknown in Europe before they were introduced there from the Americas? Important crops include corn, peanuts, beans, and potatoes.

21. What are two ways in which the efficiency of agriculture has been improved?

a. Selective breeding of crop plants

b. Improvements in farming techniques

22. How has the use of pesticides and fertilizers affected crop yields? Pesticides and
fertilizers have been responsible for dramatic improvements in crop yields.

Chapter 24   Reproduction of Seed Plants

Vocabulary Review

Labeling Diagrams   *Use the following words to label the parts of the flower:* anther, carpel, filament, ovary, ovule, petal, sepal, stamen, stigma, and style.

4. _____ Ovule _____

3. _____ Stigma _____

5. _____ Ovary _____

6. _____ Anther _____

2. _____ Style _____

7. _____ Filament _____

8. _____ Carpel _____

1. _____ Stamen _____

9. _____ Petal _____

10. _____ Sepal _____

Completion   *Fill in the blanks with terms from Chapter 24.*

11. In gymnosperms, pollen grains form in _____ pollen cones _____.

12. The female gametophyte is produced by _____ seed cones _____ in gymnosperms.

13. When a pollen grain lands on a stigma, it begins to grow a(an) _____ pollen tube _____.

14. Brightly colored _____ petals _____ attract pollinators to flowers.

15. In angiosperms, pollen grains are produced within the _____ anther _____.

16. The sticky portion of the carpel where pollen grains often land is called the _____ stigma _____.

17. The female gametophyte of the flowering plant consisting of eight nuclei and the surrounding membrane is called the _____ embryo sac _____.

18. A food-rich tissue that nourishes the seedling as it grows is called the _____ endosperm _____.

19. The process of _____ double fertilization _____ in angiosperms produces a diploid zygote and a triploid endosperm.

20. During _____ dormancy _____, plant embryos are alive but not growing.

21. Seed _____ germination _____ is the early growth stage of the plant embryo.

22. When flowering plants reproduce asexually, it is called _____ vegetative reproduction _____.

23. Strawberry plants send out long trailing stems called _____ stolons _____ that produce roots when they touch the ground.

24. In _____ grafting _____, stems are used as scions.

25. When buds are used as scions, the process is called _____ budding _____.

Summary

25–1 Hormones and Plant Growth

Plant growth is not precisely determined. However, plant growth still follows general growth patterns that differ among species. Plant growth never stops. New cells are always being made in meristems. Meristems are found at the tips of stems and roots. New cells later develop into specialized tissues.

Plants grow in response to environmental factors like light, moisture, gravity, and temperature. Certain plant chemicals also control plant growth. These chemicals are called hormones. A hormone is a substance that is produced in one part of an organism and affects another part of the same organism. The part of the organism affected by a hormone is the target cell or target tissue. Different kinds of target cells can respond to the same hormone. A single hormone may affect two different tissues in different ways.

One important group of plant hormones is auxins. Auxins have different effects on different tissues. Auxins make stems grow toward light and away from the pull of gravity. The tendency of a plant to grow toward light is called phototropism. Gravitropism is the response of a plant to the pull of gravity. Auxins make roots grow away from light and toward the pull of gravity. Auxins also control plant branching by keeping the buds on the sides of the stem from growing.

Growing roots and developing fruits and seeds make hormones called cytokinins. Cytokinins stimulate cell division and make dormant seeds sprout. Their effects are often opposite to the effects of auxins.

In the 1920s, Japanese scientists identified a substance produced by a fungus that stimulated plant growth. They named this substance gibberellin. Later, scientists learned that plants also produce gibberellins. Gibberellins cause dramatic increases in size and rapid growth.

Ethylene is another plant hormone. Plants release ethylene in response to auxins. Ethylene stimulates fruits to ripen.

25–2 Plant Responses

Plants respond to changes in their environment. They respond to gravity, light, and touch. These responses are called tropisms. Gravitropism is the response of a plant to gravity. Phototropism is the response of a plant to light. A plant's response to touch is called thigmotropism.

Some plants have a rapid response to touch that does not involve growth. This kind of response is caused by changes in the osmotic pressure of some cells. These pressure changes cause leaves to fold up or snap shut. This response enables a Venus' flytrap to trap an insect.

Many plants respond to periods of light and darkness. This is called photoperiodism. It is caused by changes in the length of periods of light and darkness. These changes affect plant pigments called phytochromes, causing plants to flower. Some plants, known as short-day plants, flower when days are short. Others, known as long-day plants, flower when the days are long.

Some plants lose their leaves and become dormant during the winter. Auxins and other hormones work together to control this. Changes in the length of light and dark periods cause a change in the chemistry of phytochrome. This change in phytochrome causes auxin production to drop. The production of ethylene increases. The leaves stop making chlorophyll. Other pigments in the leaves become visible as the green coloring disappears. The cells that join a leaf to the stem become weak, and an abscission layer forms. The abscission layer seals the leaf off from the rest of the plant. The leaves fall from the tree. Thick, waxy bud scales form. They cover the buds at the ends of the branches. The bud scales protect the buds from winter cold.

25–3 Plant Adaptations

Flowering plants live in many different environments. Through natural selection, plants have evolved different adaptations to live successfully in each environment.

Aquatic plants often live in mud that does not contain much oxygen. To get enough oxygen, many aquatic plants have air-filled spaces in their tissues. Oxygen diffuses through these spaces from the leaves to the roots.

Some plants can grow in salt water or in very salty air near the ocean. Many salt-tolerant plants have special cells that pump salt out of the plant tissues and onto the leaf surface. There, the rain washes off the salt.

Plants that live in the desert are called xerophytes. These plants must tolerate high daytime heat, sandy soil, strong winds, and little rain. These plants often have extensive roots, reduced leaves, and thick stems that can store water. Seeds of many desert plants can remain dormant for years. These seeds will germinate only when enough moisture guarantees them a chance to survive.

Some plants grow in soil with few nutrients. Carnivorous plants and parasites have adapted to living in environments with poor soil. Carnivorous plants trap and digest insects to get nitrogen. Parasites get water and nutrients directly from a host plant. Like all parasites, these plants harm their host plants.

Epiphytes are plants that are not rooted in soil. They grow directly on the bodies of other plants. Epiphytes are not parasites. They gather their own moisture, generally from rainfall. They also make their own food. Most epiphytes live in rain forests.

Many plants produce chemicals that are poisonous to the animals that eat them. These chemical defenses protect plants from potential predators.

Section 25–1 Hormones and Plant Growth
(pages 633–638)

🔑 Key Concepts
- What are plant hormones?
- How do auxins, cytokinins, gibberellins, and ethylene affect plant growth?

Patterns of Plant Growth (page 633)

1. Is the following sentence true or false? Plant growth follows patterns that are the same for all species. _____false_____

2. Circle the letter of each sentence that is true about plant growth.
   (a.) Chemicals direct, control, and regulate plant growth.
   (b.) Meristems are found at places where plants grow rapidly.
   c. Plants stop growing when they reach maturity.
   (d.) Even very old plants continue to grow.

Plant Hormones (page 634)

3. What is a hormone? A hormone is a substance that is produced in one part of an organism and affects another part of the same individual.

_____

4. What are two ways in which plant hormones control plant growth?
   a. They control a plant's patterns of growth and development.

   _____

   b. They control the plant's responses to environmental conditions.

   _____

5. What is a target cell? It is the portion of an organism affected by a particular hormone.

_____

6. Circle the letter of each sentence that is true about hormones and plant growth.
   (a.) Plant hormones are produced in growing flowers and fruits.
   (b.) A single hormone may affect two different tissues in different ways.
   (c.) Hormones can activate the transcription of certain genes.
   d. All plant cells are affected by all plant hormones.

Auxins (pages 634–636)

7. What is phototropism? It is the tendency of a plant to grow toward a source of light.

_____

8. From their experiment with oak seedlings, what did the Darwins suspect about the seedlings? They suspected that the tip of each seedling produced substances that regulated cell growth.

© Pearson Education, Inc., publishing as Pearson Prentice Hall.

9. How do auxins affect plant cells? They stimulate cell elongation._____

10. Where are auxins produced, and how are they distributed in a plant? Auxins are produced ___ in the apical meristem and diffuse downward into the rest of the plant._____

_____

11. Complete the flowchart about phototropism.

When light hits one side of a stem, a higher concentration of auxins develops on the _____shaded_____ side.

↓

The concentration of auxins stimulates cells on the shaded side to _____elongate_____.

↓

As a result, the stem bends toward the _____light_____.

12. What is gravitropism? It is the response of a plant to the force of gravity._____

_____

13. Circle the letter of each sentence that is true about auxins.

(**a.**) Auxins cause roots to grow downward.

(**b.**) Auxins regulate cell division in meristems.

(**c.**) Snipping off the tip of a plant removes the source of auxins.

d. In roots, auxins stimulate cell elongation.

14. What is a lateral bud? It is a meristematic area on the side of a stem that gives rise to side ___ branches.

15. The closer a bud is to the stem's tip, the more it is inhibited. What is this phenomenon called? It is called apical dominance._____

16. What are herbicides? They are compounds that are toxic to plants._____

_____

Cytokinins (page 636)

17. What are cytokinins? They are plant hormones that are produced in growing roots and in ___ developing roots and seeds.

_____

18. Circle the letter of each sentence that is true about cytokinins.

   (a.) They delay the aging of leaves.

   b. They stop cell division and the growth of lateral buds.

   (c.) They often produce effects opposite to those of auxins.

   (d.) They cause dormant seeds to sprout.

19. What are two examples of how cytokinins produce effects opposite to those of auxins?

   a. Auxins stimulate cell elongation, whereas cytokinins inhibit elongation and cause cells to grow thicker.

   b. Auxins inhibit the growth of lateral buds, whereas cytokinins stimulate lateral bud growth.

Gibberellins (page 637)

20. What are gibberellins? They are growth-producing substances produced by plants.

21. Particularly in stems and fruits, gibberellins produce dramatic increases in _____ size _____.

Ethylene (page 638)

22. What do fruit tissues do in response to auxins? They release small amounts of the hormone ethylene.

23. Ethylene is a plant hormone that causes fruits to _____ ripen _____.

Section 25–2 Plant Responses (pages 639–642)

⬤ Key Concepts
- What are plant tropisms?
- What is photoperiodism?
- How do deciduous plants prepare for winter?

Tropisms (page 639)

1. What are tropisms? They are responses of plants to external stimuli.
   _____

2. What do tropisms demonstrate about plants? Tropisms demonstrate the ability of plants to
   respond effectively to external stimuli such as gravity, light, and touch.
   _____

3. Complete the table about plant tropisms.

PLANT TROPISMS

Tropism	Definition
Gravitropism	The response of a plant to gravity
Phototropism	The response of a plant to light
Thigmotropism	The response of a plant to touch

4. Circle the letter of each sentence that is true about the effects of thigmotropism.
   - (a.) The tendrils of a grapevine wrap tightly around any object they encounter.
   - (b.) A plant that is touched regularly may be stunted in growth.
   - (c.) The stems of climbing plants don't grow straight up.
   - d. When the tip of a vine encounters an object, it breaks off.

Rapid Responses (page 640)

5. The folding together of mimosa leaflets when touched is the result of what
   changes in cells at the base of each leaflet? It is the result of changes in
   osmotic pressure.

6. What does a fly trigger in a Venus' flytrap that causes the leaf to snap shut?
   It triggers sensory cells on the inside of the flytrap's leaf.

Photoperiodism (page 641)

7. Why are plants such as chrysanthemums and poinsettias called short-day plants?
   They flower when days are short.

8. What are long-day plants? They are plants that flower when days are long.

© Pearson Education, Inc., publishing as Pearson Prentice Hall.

9. What is photoperiodism? It is the response of plants to periods of light and darkness.

10. What is photoperiodism in plants responsible for? It is responsible for the timing of seasonal activities such as flowering and growth.

11. What plant pigment is responsible for photoperiodism? Phytochrome

12. How does phytochrome control photoperiodism? It absorbs red light and activates a number of signaling pathways within plant cells. Plants respond to regular changes in these pathways, and these changes determine the patterns of a variety of plant responses.

Winter Dormancy (pages 641–642)

13. What is dormancy? It is the period during which an organism's growth and activity decrease or stop.

14. How do shorter days and lower temperatures affect photosynthesis? They gradually reduce the efficiency of photosynthesis.

15. As cold weather approaches, what happens to deciduous plants? They turn off photosynthetic pathways, transport materials from leaves to roots, and seal leaves off from the rest of the plant.

16. When days shorten at summer's end, what changes start a series of events that gradually shuts down the leaves of a flowering plant? The phytochrome in leaves absorb less light, auxin production drops, and the production of ethylene increases.

17. The layer of cells at the petiole that seals off a leaf from the vascular system is called the _____abscission layer_____.

18. Why doesn't a tree's sap freeze during a cold winter? At the onset of winter, xylem and phloem tissues pump themselves full of ions and organic compounds. These molecules act like antifreeze in a car, preventing the sap from freezing.

Reading Skill Practice

A flowchart can help you remember the order in which events occur. On a separate sheet of paper, create a flowchart that describes the steps that take place when flowering plants lose their leaves as winter approaches. This process is explained in the subsection Winter Dormancy. For more information about flowcharts, see Organizing Information in Appendix A at the back of your textbook.

Students' flowcharts should begin with the shortening of days, which causes the phytochrome in leaves to absorb less light, and should end with leaves falling to the ground.

Section 25–3 Plant Adaptations (pages 643–646)

👉 **Key Concepts**
- How are plants adapted to different environments?
- How do plants obtain nutrients from sources other than photosynthesis?
- How do plants defend themselves from insects?

Aquatic Plants (page 643)

1. What adaptation do aquatic plants have that allows them to grow in mud that is saturated with water and nearly devoid of oxygen? Aquatic plants have tissues with large air-filled spaces through which oxygen can diffuse.

2. How do waterlilies get oxygen to their roots? There are large open spaces in the long petioles that reach from the leaves down to the roots. Oxygen diffuses from these open spaces into the roots.

3. Circle the letter of each sentence that is true about the adaptations of aquatic plants.
   a. All aquatic plants grow very slowly after germination.
   b. In waterlilies, oxygen diffuses from open spaces in petioles into the roots.
   c. The knees of mangrove trees bring oxygen-rich air down to the roots.
   d. The seeds of some aquatic plants can float in water.

Salt-Tolerant Plants (page 644)

4. What adaptation do the leaves of salt-tolerant plants have that protects them against high salt concentration? The leaves have specialized cells that pump salt out of the plant tissues and onto leaf surfaces, where it is washed off by rain.

Desert Plants (pages 644–645)

5. What are three plant adaptations to a desert climate?
   a. Extensive roots
   b. Reduced leaves
   c. Thick stems that can store water

6. What are xerophytes? They are desert plants.

7. Why do the roots of xerophytes have many hairs? The hairs quickly absorb water after a rainstorm, before the water sinks too deeply into the soil.

8. Where is most of a desert plant's photosynthesis carried out? It is carried out in the plant's fleshy stem.

9. Why do cactuses have small leaves or no leaves at all? _____
That adaptation reduces water loss due to transpiration.

Name_____ Class _____ Date _____

10. What is the advantage for many desert plants that have seeds that can remain dormant for years? They germinate only when sufficient moisture guarantees them a chance for survival.

Nutritional Specialists (page 645)

11. The Venus' flytrap is an example of what kind of nutritional specialist?
It is a carnivorous plant.

12. What nutrient do carnivorous plants need to obtain from insects that they can't otherwise get from the environment? They need nitrogen.

13. How does a Venus' flytrap obtain the nutrient it needs from an insect it catches?
Over a period of several days, the leaf of the plant secretes enzymes that digest the insect and release nitrogen for the plant to use.

14. What common plant grows as a parasite on conifers in the western United States?
Mistletoe

Epiphytes (page 645)

15. What are epiphytes? They are plants that are not rooted in soil but instead grow directly on the bodies of other plants.

16. Why aren't epiphytes considered to be plant parasites? Unlike parasites, epiphytes gather their own moisture, generally from rainfall, and produce their own food.

Chemical Defenses (page 646)

17. How do many plants defend themselves against insect attack? They manufacture compounds that have powerful effects on animals.

18. How does nicotine protect a tobacco plant from potential predators? Biologists hypothesize that nicotine is a natural insecticide that disrupts the nervous system of many insects.

Chapter 25 Plant Responses and Adaptations

Vocabulary Review

True or False *In the space, write* true *if the statement is true. If the statement is false, write the term that makes the statement true.*

__true__ **1.** <u>Auxins</u> are plant hormones that stimulate cell elongation.

__lateral bud__ **2.** A(An) <u>abscission layer</u> is a meristematic area on the side of a stem that gives rise to side branches.

__Gibberellins__ **3.** <u>Cytokinins</u> are plant hormones that increase the overall size of plants.

__true__ **4.** <u>Tropisms</u> are the responses of plants to external stimuli.

__Short__ **5.** <u>Long</u>-day plants flower when days are short.

__true__ **6.** In <u>dormancy,</u> plant growth and activity decrease or stop.

__Epiphytes__ **7.** <u>Xerophytes</u> are plants that are not rooted in soil and grow directly on other plants.

Matching *In the space provided, write the letter that best matches each term.*

__d__ **8.** hormone

__h__ **9.** phototropism

__c__ **10.** gravitropism

__a__ **11.** apical dominance

__f__ **12.** herbicide

__b__ **13.** thigmotropism

__g__ **14.** photoperiodism

__e__ **15.** phytochrome

a. inhibition of lateral bud growth near stem tips

b. response of a plant to touch

c. response of a plant to the force of gravity

d. substance produced in one part of an organism that affects another part of the organism

e. plant pigment that responds to periods of light and darkness

f. compound that is toxic to plants

g. response of a plant to periods of light and darkness

h. response of a plant to light

Summary

26–1 Introduction to the Animal Kingdom

All members of the kingdom Animalia share certain characteristics. Animals are multicellular, eukaryotic heterotrophs whose cells lack cell walls. The bodies of most animals contain tissues. Over 95 percent of all animal species are often grouped in a single, informal category: invertebrates. Invertebrates are animals that do not have a backbone, or vertebral column. The other 5 percent of animals are called vertebrates, because they have a backbone.

Animals carry out the following essential functions: feeding, respiration, circulation, excretion, response, movement, and reproduction. The study of the functions of organisms is called physiology. The structure, or anatomy, of an animal's body enables it to carry out physiological functions.

Many body functions help animals maintain homeostasis. Homeostasis is often maintained by internal feedback mechanisms. Most of these mechanisms involve feedback inhibition, in which the product or result of a process stops or limits the process.

Complex animals tend to have high levels of cell specialization and internal body organization, bilateral symmetry, a front end or head with sense organs, and a body cavity.

Animals that reproduce sexually begin life as zygotes. The zygote undergoes a series of divisions to form a blastula, a hollow ball of cells. The blastula folds in on itself, forming a single opening called a blastopore. The blastopore leads to a central tube that becomes the digestive tract. A protostome is an animal whose mouth is formed from the blastopore. A deuterstome is an animal whose anus is formed from the blastopore. The anus is the opening through which wastes leave the digestive tract.

During early development, the cells of most animal embryos differentiate into three layers, called germ layers. The endoderm is the innermost germ layer; the mesoderm is the middle germ layer; and the ectoderm is the outermost germ layer.

With the exception of sponges, every kind of animal exhibits some type of body symmetry. Some animals exhibit radial symmetry, in which any number of imaginary planes can be drawn through the center, each dividing the body into equal halves. More complex animals have bilateral symmetry, in which only a single imaginary plane can divide the body into two equal halves. Animals with bilateral symmetry usually exhibit cephalization, which is the concentration of sense organs and nerve cells at the front of the body. Most animals have a body cavity, which is a fluid-filled space that lies between the digestive tract and the body wall.

26–2 Sponges

Sponges make up the phylum Porifera. Sponges are sessile, meaning that they live their entire adult lives attached to a single spot. Sponges are classified as animals because they are multicellular, are heterotrophic, have no cell walls, and contain a few specialized cells.

Sponges are asymmetrical—they have no front or back ends. Sponges have specialized cells, called choanocytes, that move a steady current of water through the body. This water enters through pores in the body wall and leaves through the osculum, a large hole at the top of the central cavity. The movement of water through the sponge provides a simple mechanism for feeding, respiration, circulation, and excretion.

Sponges are filter feeders that sift microscopic food particles from the water. Digestion is intracellular, meaning that it takes place inside cells. Sponges can reproduce either sexually or asexually. In sexual reproduction, eggs are fertilized inside the sponge's body, a process called internal fertilization. After fertilization occurs, the resulting zygote develops into a larva. A larva is an immature stage of an organism that looks different from the adult form.

Sponges provide habitats for marine animals such as snails and sea stars. Sponges also form partnerships with photosynthetic organisms.

26–3 Cnidarians

Cnidarians are soft-bodied, carnivorous animals. They have stinging tentacles arranged around their mouths. Cnidarians are the simplest animals to have body symmetry and specialized tissues. Cnidarians get their name from cnidocytes, which are stinging cells on their tentacles.

Cnidarians exhibit radial symmetry. They have a central mouth surrounded by numerous tentacles. Cnidarians typically have a life cycle that includes two different-looking stages: a polyp and a medusa. A polyp has a cylindrical body with armlike tentacles. In a polyp, the mouth points upward. A medusa has a bell-shaped body with the mouth at the bottom. Polyps are usually sessile, while medusas are motile.

A cnidarian has a gastrovascular cavity, which is a digestive chamber with one opening. Food enters and wastes leave the same opening. Digestion is extracellular, meaning that it takes place outside of cells. For gathering information from the environment, cnidarians have a nerve net. A nerve net is a loosely organized network of nerve cells that together allow cnidarians to detect stimuli. Some cnidarians have a hydrostatic skeleton. In most cnidarians, sexual reproduction takes place with external fertilization in the water. External fertilization takes place outside the female's body.

Cnidarians include jellyfishes, hydras and their relatives, and sea anemones and corals. The class Scyphozoa contains the jellyfishes. Scyphozoans live their lives primarily as medusas. The class Hydrozoa contains hydras and related animals. The polyps of most hydrozoans grow in branching colonies. The Portuguese man-of-war is a colonial hydrozoan composed of many specialized polyps. The class Anthozoa contains sea anemones and corals. Anthozoans have only the polyp stage in their life cycles. Most corals are colonial, and their polyps grow together in large numbers. As the colonies grow, they secrete an underlying skeleton of calcium carbonate (limestone). Coral colonies produce the structures called coral reefs. Many coral reefs are now suffering from the effects of human activity.

Section 26–1 Introduction to the Animal Kingdom (pages 657–663)

🔑 Key Concepts
- What characteristics do all animals share?
- What essential functions do animals carry out?
- What are the important trends in animal evolution?

What Is an Animal? (page 657)

1. Is the following sentence true or false? The cells that make up animal bodies are eukaryotic. _____true_____

2. What characteristics do all animals share? _Animals are multicellular, eukaryotic heterotrophs_ _whose cells lack cell walls._

3. Complete the table about animals.

CATEGORIES OF ANIMALS

Category	Percentage of Species	Description	Examples
Invertebrates	95%	Animals without backbones	Sea stars, worms, insects
Vertebrates	5%	Animals with backbones	Fishes, amphibians, reptiles, birds, mammals

What Animals Do to Survive (pages 658–659)

4. What are seven essential functions that animals carry out?

a. Feeding

b. Respiration

c. Circulation

d. Excretion

e. Response

f. Movement

g. Reproduction

5. Complete the table about types of feeders.

TYPES OF FEEDERS

Type of Feeder	Description
Herbivore	Feeds on plants
Carnivore	Feeds on other animals
Filter feeder	Strains tiny floating organisms from water
Detritivore	Feeds on decaying plant and animal material

6. Explain the difference between a parasite and a host. A parasite is a type of symbiont that lives within or on another organism, the host. The parasite feeds on the host, harming it.

7. What does an animal do when it respires? It takes in oxygen and gives off carbon dioxide.

8. What does the excretory system of most animals do? It either eliminates ammonia quickly or converts it to a less toxic substance that is removed from the body.

9. Animals respond to events in their environment using specialized cells called nerve cells .

10. What are receptors, and what is their function? They are nerve cells that respond to sound, light, and other stimuli.

11. What does it mean that an animal is motile? A motile animal is one that can move.

12. What enables motile animals to move around? Muscle contraction enables animals to move around, usually by working in combination with a skeleton.

13. Circle the letter of the process that helps a species maintain genetic diversity.

    a. asexual reproduction   **c.** response

    b. movement   **d.** sexual reproduction

14. What does asexual reproduction allow animals to do? It allows animals to increase their numbers rapidly.

Trends in Animal Evolution (pages 660–663)

15. What are four characteristics that complex animals tend to have?

    a. High levels of cell specialization and internal body organization

    b. Bilateral body symmetry

    c. A front end or head with sense organs, or cephalization

    d. A body cavity

16. How have the cells of animals changed as animals have evolved? Their cells have become specialized to carry out different functions, such as movement and response.

17. Groups of specialized cells form _____tissues_____, which form organs, which form _____organ systems_____.

18. After a zygote undergoes a series of divisions, it becomes a(an) blastula.

19. What is a protostome? It is an animal whose mouth is formed from the blastopore.

20. What is a deuterostome? It is an animal whose anus is formed from the blastopore.

21. Is the following sentence true or false? Most invertebrates are deuterostomes. _____false_____

22. In the development of a deuterostome, when is the mouth formed? The mouth is formed second, after the anus.

23. Complete the table about germ layers.

GERM LAYERS

Germ Layer	Location	Develops Into These Body Structures
Endoderm	Innermost layer	Digestive tract, respiratory system
Mesoderm	Middle layer	Muscles and circulatory, reproductive, and excretory systems
Ectoderm	Outermost layer	Skin, sense organs, nerves

24. Complete the table about body symmetry.

BODY SYMMETRY

Type of Symmetry	Description	Examples
Radial symmetry	Body parts that repeat around the center	Sea anemones, sea stars
Bilateral symmetry	A single plane divides the body into two equal halves	Worms, arthropods, vertebrates

25. In an animal with radial symmetry, how many imaginary planes can be drawn through the center of the animal that would divide the animal in half? Any number of imaginary planes would divide the animal in half.

Match the term with its meaning.

	Term		Meaning
c	26. anterior	a.	Upper side
b	27. posterior	b.	Back end
a	28. dorsal	c.	Front end
d	29. ventral	d.	Lower side

30. A body that is constructed of many repeated and similar parts, or segments, exhibits _____ segmentation _____.

31. What is cephalization? It is the concentration of sense organs and nerve cells at the front end of the body.

32. How do animals with cephalization respond differently to the environment than animals without cephalization? Animals with cephalization respond to the environment more quickly and in more complex ways than simpler animals can.

33. What is a body cavity? It is a fluid-filled space that lies between the digestive tract and the body wall.

34. Why is having a body cavity important? It provides a space in which internal organs can be suspended so that they are not pressed on by muscles or twisted out of shape by body movements.

Reading Skill Practice

An outline can help you remember the main points of a section. Write an outline of Section 26–1. Use the section's blue headings for the first level of your outline and the section's green headings for the second level. Support your headings with details from the section. Do your work on a separate sheet of paper.

Students' outlines should match the headings of Section 26–1. Under each subhead, students should list two or three important details.

Section 26–2 Sponges (pages 664–667)

🔑 **Key Concepts**
- Why are sponges classified as animals?
- How do sponges carry out essential functions?

What Is a Sponge? (page 664)

1. Sponges are placed in the phylum _____Porifera_____.

2. What are pores, and where are pores on a sponge's body? Pores are tiny openings found all over a sponge's body.

3. What does it mean that sponges are sessile? They live their entire adult life attached to a single spot and do not move.

4. Why are sponges classified as animals? They are classified as animals because they are multicellular, are heterotrophic, have no cell walls, and contain a few specialized cells.

Form and Function in Sponges (pages 664–667)

5. Is the following sentence true or false? Sponges have no tissues. _____true_____

6. What does the movement of water through a sponge provide? It provides a simple mechanism for feeding, respiration, circulation, and excretion.

Match the body part with its description.

	Body Part	Description
b	7. Choanocyte	a. Cell that makes spicules
d	8. Spicule	b. Cell that uses flagella to move water through the sponge
c	9. Osculum	c. A large hole at the top of the sponge
a	10. Archaeocyte	d. A spike-shaped structure

11. Where does digestion take place in sponges? Digestion is intracellular. It takes place inside cells.

12. Circle the letter of each sentence that is true about sponges.
    (a.) Sponges are filter feeders.
    b. Sponges reproduce only asexually.
    (c.) Sponges rely on water movement to carry out body functions.
    (d.) Sponges do not have a nervous system.

13. How do many sponges protect themselves from predators? <u>Many produce toxins that</u>
<u>make them unpalatable or poisonous to potential predators.</u>

14. An immature stage of an organism that looks different from the adult form is
called a(an) _____ <u>larva</u> _____.

15. How is a sponge larva different from the adult form? <u>The larvae of sponges are motile</u>
<u>and are usually carried by currents before they settle to the sea floor.</u>

16. What are gemmules, and what is their role in sponge reproduction? <u>Gemmules are</u>
<u>groups of archaeocytes surrounded by a tough layer of spicules that can survive freezing</u>
<u>temperatures and drought conditions that would kill adult sponges. Sponges reproduce asexually</u>
<u>by producing gemmules.</u>

Ecology of Sponges (page 667)

17. Why do you think many sponges are colored green? <u>They are green because symbiotic</u>
<u>bacteria, algae, or plantlike protists are living in the sponges.</u>

18. What adaptation may allow sponges to survive in a wide range of habitats?
<u>The spicules of some sponges focus and direct sunlight to cells lying below the</u>
<u>surface of the sponge, where symbiotic organisms carry out photosynthesis.</u>

Name_____ Class_____ Date_____

Section 26–3 Cnidarians (pages 669–675)

🔑 **Key Concepts**
- What is a cnidarian?
- What two body plans exist in the cnidarian life cycle?
- What are the three groups of cnidarians?

Introduction (page 669)

1. Cnidarians are members of the phylum _____Cnidaria_____.

What Is a Cnidarian? (page 669)

2. What important features unite the cnidarians as a group? _Cnidarians are soft-bodied,_ _carnivorous animals that have stinging tentacles arranged in circles around their mouths. They_ _have body symmetry and specialized tissues._

3. What are cnidocytes? _They are stinging cells that are located along cnidarians' tentacles._
_____

4. A poison-filled, stinging structure within a cnidocyte that contains a tightly coiled dart is called a(an) _____nematocyst_____.

Form and Function in Cnidarians (pages 670–672)

5. Is the following sentence true or false? Cnidarians have bilateral symmetry.
_____false_____

6. What are the two stages in the cnidarian life cycle?

    a. _Polyp_____ b. _Medusa_____

7. Write labels on each illustration below to identify the life-cycle stage and to name the different body parts.

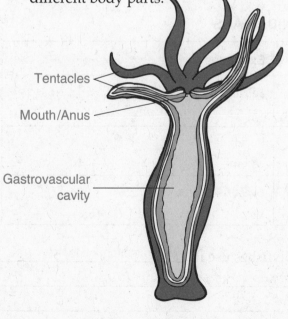

Tentacles

Mouth/Anus

Gastrovascular cavity

_____Polyp_____

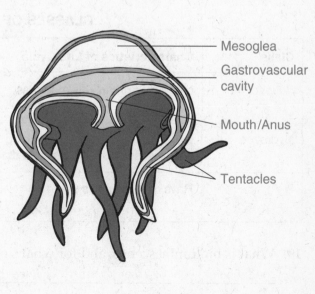

Mesoglea

Gastrovascular cavity

Mouth/Anus

Tentacles

_____Medusa_____

Match the cnidarian structure with its description.

Structure	Description
__c__ **8.** Gastroderm	**a.** Digestive chamber with single opening
__e__ **9.** Mesoglea	**b.** Sensory cells that help determine direction of gravity
__a__ **10.** Gastrovascular cavity	
__d__ **11.** Nerve net	**c.** Inner lining of the gastrovascular cavity
__b__ **12.** Statocysts	**d.** Loosely organized network of nerve cells
__f__ **13.** Ocelli	**e.** Layer that lies between gastroderm and epidermis
	f. Eyespots that detect light

14. Circle the letter of each sentence that is true about form and function in cnidarians.

   a. In a polyp, the mouth points downward.

   (**b.**) Materials that cannot be digested are passed out of the body through the mouth.

   (**c.**) Cnidarians respire by diffusion through their body walls.

   (**d.**) Most cnidarians reproduce sexually and asexually.

15. What does a cnidarian's hydrostatic skeleton consist of? It consists of a layer of circular muscles and a layer of longitudinal muscles, as well as the water in the gastrovascular cavity.

16. Cnidarian polyps can reproduce asexually by _____budding_____.

17. In the *Aurelia* life cycle, how are young medusas released? An *Aurelia* polyp buds to release medusas.

Groups of Cnidarians (pages 672–674)

18. Complete the table about classes of cnidarians.

CLASSES OF CNIDARIANS

Class	Characteristics of Life Cycle	Examples
Scyphozoa	Live lives primarily as medusas	Jellyfishes
Hydrozoa	Polyps of most grow in branching colonies; some lack a medusa stage	Portuguese men-of-war, hydras
Anthozoa	Have only the polyp stage	Sea anemones, corals

19. What is bioluminescence, and for what do jellyfishes use it? Bioluminescence is the production of light by an organism. Jellyfishes use it to ward off predators.

20. How do hydras differ from other cnidarians in the class Hydrozoa?
They lack a medusa stage.

21. Circle the letter of each sentence that is true about corals.

(a.) Corals secrete an underlying skeleton of calcium carbonate.

b. Corals are solitary polyps that live at all depths of the ocean.

(c.) Coral colonies growing near one another produce coral reefs.

(d.) Most corals are colonial.

22. Is the following sentence true or false? Sea anemones are solitary polyps.
_____ true _____

23. How are coral reefs produced? As colonies grow, they secrete an underlying skeleton of
calcium carbonate. Many coral colonies growing near one another produce coral reefs.

Ecology of Corals (page 675)

24. What variables determine the worldwide distribution of corals?

a. Temperature

b. Water depth

c. Light intensity

25. What do corals depend on to capture solar energy, recycle nutrients, and help lay
down their skeletons? They depend on symbioses with algae.

26. Circle the letter of each way that coral reefs can be harmed.

(a.) Sediments from logging can smother corals.

(b.) Overfishing can upset the ecological balance of coral reefs.

c. Algae can remove energy from corals.

(d.) Industrial pollutants can poison corals.

27. What is coral bleaching? High temperatures can cause symbiotic algae to be lost from the
tissues of corals, leaving behind only transparent cells atop ghostly white skeletons.

© Pearson Education, Inc., publishing as Pearson Prentice Hall.

Name_____ Class_____ Date _____

Vocabulary Review

Completion   *Fill in the blanks with terms from Chapter 26.*

1. An animal without a backbone is called a(an) _____invertebrate_____.

2. In sexual reproduction, the zygote undergoes a series of divisions to form a(an) _____blastula_____, a hollow ball of cells.

3. A(An) _____protostome_____ is an animal whose mouth is formed from the blastopore.

4. In _____bilateral_____ symmetry, only a single imaginary plane can divide the body into two equal halves.

5. The concentration of sense organs and nerve cells at the front end of the body is called _____cephalization_____.

6. A(An) _____larva_____ is an immature stage of an organism that looks different from the adult form.

7. Sponges are placed in the phylum _____Porifera_____.

8. A(An) _____polyp_____ is a stage in the cnidarian life cycle in which the mouth points upward.

9. A digestive chamber with one opening is called a(an) _____gastrovascular_____ cavity.

Answering Questions   *In the space provided, write an answer to each question.*

10. What are the names of an animal's three germ layers? They are endoderm, mesoderm, and ectoderm.

11. What is a body cavity? A body cavity is a fluid-filled space that lies between the digestive tract and the body wall.

12. What does the movement of water through a sponge provide for the sponge?
    It provides a simple mechanism for feeding, respiration, circulation, and excretion.

13. What kind of fertilization do sponges use? They use internal fertilization.

14. Which way does the mouth point in a medusa? It points down.

15. What structures do coral colonies produce? They produce coral reefs.

Summary

27–1 Flatworms

The phylum Platyhelminthes consists of the flatworms. Flatworms are soft, flattened worms that have tissues and internal organ systems. They are the simplest animals to have three embryonic germ layers, bilateral symmetry, and cephalization. Flatworms are known as acoelomates, which means that there is no coelom between the tissues of flatworms. A coelom is a fluid-filled body cavity that is lined with tissue derived from mesoderm.

All flatworms rely on diffusion for some essential body functions, such as respiration, excretion, and circulation. Flatworms have a digestive cavity with a single opening, or mouth. Near the mouth is a muscular tube called a pharynx that pumps food into the digestive cavity. In free-living flatworms, several ganglia, or groups of nerve cells, control the nervous system. Many free-living flatworms have eyespots that detect changes in light. Asexual reproduction in free-living flatworms takes place by fission, in which an organism splits in two.

Turbellarians are free-living flatworms. Most live in marine or fresh water. Flukes are parasitic flatworms. Most flukes infect the internal organs of their hosts. Flukes reproduce sexually in the primary host and reproduce asexually in the intermediate host. Tapeworms are long, flat, parasitic worms that are adapted to life inside the intestines of their hosts.

27–2 Roundworms

The phylum Nematoda consists of the roundworms. Roundworms are slender, unsegmented worms. Most species are free-living. Roundworms have a body cavity between the endoderm and mesoderm tissues. This body cavity is called a pseudocoelom, because it is only partially lined with mesoderm tissue. Roundworms have a digestive tract with two openings—a mouth and an anus.

Roundworms depend on diffusion for respiration, circulation, and excretion. In roundworms, the muscles and fluid in the pseudocoelom function as a hydrostatic skeleton. Roundworms reproduce sexually by internal fertilization.

Parasitic roundworms include trichinosis-causing worms, filarial worms, ascarid worms, and hookworms. Trichinosis is a disease caused by the roundworm *Trichinella*. Adult worms live and mate in the intestines of their hosts, including humans and pigs. *Trichinella* larvae form cysts. The roundworm completes its life cycle only when another animal eats muscle tissue containing these cysts.

Filarial worms are transmitted from host to host through biting insects. Filarial worms cause elephantiasis. Ascarid worms are serious parasites of humans and other animals. Hookworms infect one quarter of the people in the world.

27–3 Annelids

The phylum Annelida consists of earthworms and other annelids. The body of an annelid is divided into segments that are separated by septa, which are internal walls. Most segments are similar to one another. Some segments may be modified to perform special functions, including segments with eyes or antennae. In many annelids, bristles called setae are attached to each segment. Annelids are worms with segmented bodies. They have a true coelom that is lined with tissue derived from mesoderm.

Annelids have complex organ systems. Many annelids get their food using a pharynx. In earthworms, food moves through the crop, where it can be stored. Then, food moves through the gizzard, where it is ground into smaller pieces. Annelids typically have a closed circulatory system, in which blood is contained in a network of blood vessels.

Aquatic annelids often breathe through gills. A gill is an organ specialized for the exchange of gases underwater. Most annelids reproduce sexually. Some annelids, including earthworms, are hermaphroditic. When eggs are ready to be fertilized, a clitellum—a band of thickened segments—secretes a mucus ring in which fertilization takes place.

There are three classes of annelids: oligochaetes, leeches, and polychaetes. The oligochaetes are annelids that typically have streamlined bodies and relatively few setae. Most oligochaetes, including earthworms, live in soil or fresh water. The class Hirudinea includes the leeches. Leeches are typically external parasites that suck the blood and body fluids of their hosts. The polychaetes are marine annelids that have paired, paddlelike appendages tipped with setae.

Earthworms mix and aerate soil. Their tunnels provide passageways for plants. Their feces enrich the soil.

27–4 Mollusks

Mollusks—phylum Mollusca—are soft-bodied animals that usually have an internal or external shell. Many mollusks share similar developmental stages. Many aquatic mollusks have a free-swimming larval stage called a trochophore.

The body plan of most mollusks has four parts. The muscular foot is used for crawling, burrowing, or catching prey. The mantle is a thin layer of tissue that covers most of the mollusk's body. The shell is made by glands in the mantle that secrete calcium carbonate (limestone). Just beneath the mantle is the visceral mass, which consists of the internal organs.

Mollusks can be herbivores, carnivores, filter feeders, detritivores, or parasites. Snails and slugs feed using a flexible, tongue-shaped structure called a radula. Mollusks have an open circulatory system, in which blood is pumped through vessels and through sinuses.

There are three major classes of mollusks. The gastropods include pond snails, land slugs, and nudibranchs. Gastropods are shell-less or single-shelled mollusks that move by using a muscular foot located on the ventral (lower) side. The bivalves include clams, oysters, mussels, and scallops. Bivalves have two shells that are held together by one of two powerful muscles. Cephalopods include octopi, squids, cuttlefishes, and nautiluses. Cephalopods are typically soft-bodied mollusks in which the head is attached to a single foot. The foot is divided into tentacles. Most cephalopods have only small internal shells or no shells at all. Cephalopods have numerous complex sense organs.

Chapter 27 Worms and Mollusks

Section 27–1 Flatworms (pages 683–688)

Key Concepts
- What are the defining features of flatworms?
- What are the characteristics of the three groups of flatworms?

What Is a Flatworm? (page 683)
1. Flatworms make up the phylum _____Platyhelminthes_____.
2. What are the defining features of flatworms? _Flatworms are soft, flattened worms that have_ tissues and internal organ systems. They are the simplest animals to have three embryonic germ layers, bilateral symmetry, and cephalization.

3. A fluid-filled body cavity that is lined with tissue derived from mesoderm is called a(an) _____coelom_____.
4. Why are flatworms known as acoelomates? _No coelom forms between the tissues of_ flatworms.

5. Is the following sentence true or false? Flatworms are the simplest animals to have three germ layers. _____true_____

Form and Function in Flatworms (pages 684–686)
6. Circle the letter of each sentence that is true about flatworms.
   - **(a.)** Parasitic species are typically simpler in structure than free-living species.
   - **(b.)** Free-living flatworms have organ systems for digestion, excretion, response, and reproduction.
   - **c.** Free-living species probably evolved from parasitic ancestors.
   - **(d.)** All flatworms rely on diffusion for some essential functions.
7. What do free-living flatworms feed on? _They can be carnivores that feed on tiny aquatic_ animals or scavengers that feed on recently dead animals.

8. A muscular tube near the mouth at the end of the gastrovascular cavity is called a(an) _____pharynx_____.
9. What is the function of the pharynx? _Flatworms use a pharynx to suck food into the_ gastrovascular cavity.

10. What are flame cells, and what is their function? _Flame cells are specialized cells that_ remove excess water from the body. They may also filter and remove metabolic wastes such as ammonia and urea.

11. What are ganglia, and what do they do in flatworms? <u>Ganglia are groups of nerve cells,</u>
<u>and they control the nervous system in flatworms.</u>
_____

12. A group of cells that can detect changes in the amount of light in a flatworm's environment is called a(an) _____<u>eyespot</u>_____.

13. How do cilia help flatworms move, and what do muscle cells allow them to do?
<u>Cilia help flatworms glide through the water over the bottom of a stream or pond.</u>
<u>Muscle cells allow them to twist and turn in reaction to environmental stimuli.</u>
_____

14. What is a hermaphrodite? <u>A hermaphrodite is an individual that has both male and female</u>
<u>reproductive organs.</u>
_____

15. What occurs during fission? <u>An organism splits in two, and each half grows new parts to</u>
<u>become a complete organism.</u>
_____

16. Is the following sentence true or false? Free-living flatworms often have complex life cycles that involve both sexual and asexual reproduction. _____<u>false</u>_____

Groups of Flatworms (pages 686–688)

17. Complete the table about the main groups of flatworms.

GROUPS OF FLATWORMS

Common Name	Class	Description
Turbellarians	Turbellaria	Free-living bottom dwellers
Flukes	Trematoda	Parasitic flatworms that infect hosts' internal organs or outside parts
Tapeworms	Cestoda	Long, flat, parasitic worms that live in hosts' intestines

18. Circle the letter of each sentence that is true of turbellarians.

(**a.**) Most live in marine or fresh water.

b. Most are the same color, form, and size.

(**c.**) Most are bottom dwellers.

(**d.**) The most familiar are the planarians.

© Pearson Education, Inc., publishing as Pearson Prentice Hall.

19. How does the blood fluke *Schistosoma mansoni* infect humans? It burrows through
exposed skin.

20. In which host do blood flukes reproduce sexually, and in which do they reproduce
asexually? Blood flukes reproduce sexually in the primary host and asexually in the intermediate
host.

21. On the illustration of the blood fluke's life cycle, label the primary host and the
intermediate host.

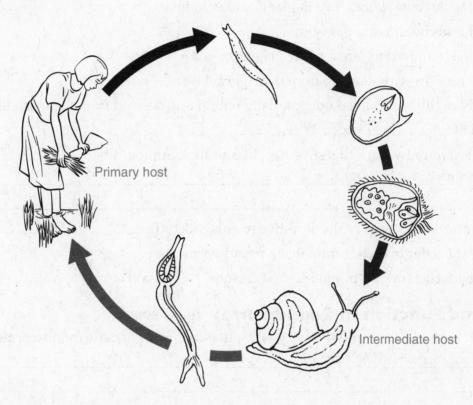

Primary host

Intermediate host

22. In what areas is schistosomiasis particularly widespread? It is widespread in
tropical areas that lack proper sewage systems, where human wastes are tossed into streams
or used as fertilizer.

23. The head of an adult tapeworm is called a(an) _____scolex_____.

24. What does a tapeworm use its scolex for? A tapeworm uses its scolex to attach to the
intestinal wall of its host, where it absorbs nutrients.

25. What are proglottids? They are the segments that make up most of a tapeworm's body.

26. Sperm are produced by male reproductive organs, called _____testes_____.

27. Is the following sentence true or false? Sperm produced by a tapeworm's testes can
fertilize the eggs of the same individual. _____true_____

Section 27–2 Roundworms (pages 689–693)

⊂━ Key Concepts
- What are the defining features of roundworms?
- What roundworms are important in human disease?

What Is a Roundworm? (page 689)

1. Circle the letter of each sentence that is true about roundworms.

   (a.) Parasitic roundworms live in plants and in animals.

   b. All roundworms are parasitic.

   (c.) Some roundworms are a meter in length.

   (d.) All roundworms develop from three germ layers.

2. A body cavity that is lined only partially with tissue derived from the mesoderm is called a(an) _____pseudocoelom_____.

3. How is a roundworm's digestive tract like a tube-within-a-tube? The inner tube is the digestive tract, and the outer tube is the body wall.

4. The posterior opening of the digestive tract is called the _____anus_____.

5. Circle the letter of each feature that a roundworm has.

   (a.) pseudocoelom   (b.) mouth   (c.) anus   d. coelom

Form and Function in Roundworms (page 690)

6. Which have more complex body systems, free-living or parasitic roundworms?
   Free-living roundworms have more complex body systems.

7. Is the following sentence true or false? Many free-living roundworms are predators.
   _____true_____

8. Roundworms exchange gases and excrete metabolic wastes through their
   _____body walls_____.

9. What can roundworms' sense organs detect? They detect chemicals given off by prey or hosts.

10. Do roundworms reproduce sexually or asexually? They reproduce sexually.

Roundworms and Human Disease (pages 690–692)

11. How do *Trichinella* roundworms cause pain in their hosts? They travel through the bloodstream and burrow into organs and tissues.

12. Complete the table about roundworms and human disease.

DISEASE-CAUSING ROUNDWORMS

Roundworm	Disease or Condition Caused	How Disease Is Spread
Trichinella	Trichinosis	By eating muscle tissue of infected animal
Filarial worms	Elephantiasis	Through biting insects, especially mosquitoes
Ascarid worms	Malnutrition	In the feces of the host
Hookworms	Weakness and poor growth	Burrowing through an unprotected foot

13. What is elephantiasis? It is a condition in which a part of the body swells enormously. The swelling is caused by large numbers of filarial worms blocking the passage of fluids within the lymph vessels.

14. Circle the letter of each sentence that is true about the life cycle of *Ascaris*.

(**a.**) Larvae in the lungs are coughed up and swallowed.

b. The eggs develop into larvae in the lungs.

(**c.**) Fertilized eggs leave the host's body in feces.

(**d.**) The host ingests *Ascaris* eggs in contaminated food or water.

15. How are ascarid worms commonly spread? They are spread by eating vegetables or other foods that are not washed properly.

16. Where do hookworm eggs hatch and develop? They hatch outside the body of a host and develop in the soil.

Research on C. *elegans* (page 693)

17. Circle the letter of each sentence that is true about C. *elegans*.

(**a.**) It is a free-living roundworm.

(**b.**) Its DNA was the first of any multicellular animal's to be sequenced completely.

(**c.**) It feeds on rotting vegetation.

d. Its DNA has 30 times the number of base pairs that human DNA has.

Name_____ Class_____ Date _____

Section 27–3 Annelids (pages 694–699)

🔑 **Key Concepts**
- What are the defining features of annelids?
- What are the characteristics of the three classes of annelids?

Introduction (page 694)

1. Of what phylum are earthworms a member? _____Annelida_____

2. What evidence is there that annelids are more closely related to clams and snails than to flatworms or roundworms? _Annelids, clams, and snails all share a similar larval stage._

_____

What Is an Annelid? (page 694)

3. What is a septum? _A septum is an internal wall between two segments of an annelid's body._

_____

4. Attached to each annelid segment are bristles called _____setae_____.

5. Annelids are among the simplest animals to have a true _____coelom_____.

Form and Function in Annelids (pages 695–696)

6. How is the pharynx used differently in carnivorous species than in annelids that feed on decaying vegetation? _In carnivores, the pharynx usually holds two or more sharp jaws that are used to attack prey. In worms that eat vegetation, the worm collects food by extending a pharynx covered with sticky mucus and pressing it against the surrounding sediments._

_____

7. What is a closed circulatory system? _It is a system in which blood is contained within a network of blood vessels._

_____

8. What is a gill? _A gill is an organ specialized for the exchange of gases underwater._

_____

9. How do aquatic annelids respire differently than land-dwelling annelids? _Aquatic annelids often breathe through gills, while land-dwelling annelids respire through their moist skin._

_____

10. How do annelids keep their skins moist? _They secrete a thin protective coating called a cuticle._

11. What are the two major groups of body muscles in annelids called?
   a. _Longitudinal muscles_
   b. _Circular muscles_

12. Marine annelids have paddlelike appendages called _____parapodia_____.

Name_____ Class_____ Date _____

13. What is a clitellum, and what is its function? A clitellum is a band of thickened, specialized
segments that secrete a mucous ring into which eggs and sperm are released.

_____

14. Write labels on the illustration of the annelid for each of the features pointed to.

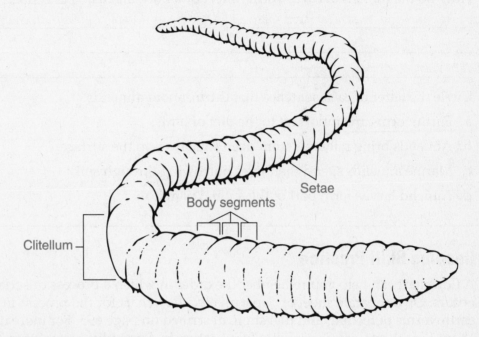

Setae

Body segments

Clitellum –

Groups of Annelids (pages 697–698)

15. Complete the table about common types of oligochaetes.

OLIGOCHAETES

Type of Oligochaete	Description	Habitat
Earthworms	Long, pinkish-brown worms with few setae	Woods, fields, and gardens
Tubifex worms	Red, threadlike worms with few setae	Aquatic environments

16. Circle the letter of each sentence that is true about leeches.

   (a.) They suck blood and body fluids from their hosts.

   (b.) Most live in moist, tropical habitats.

   (c.) They are typically external parasites.

   d. All are carnivores that feed on snails.

17. Circle the letter of each sentence that is true about polychaetes.

   a. They typically have only a few setae.

   (b.) They have paired, paddlelike appendages tipped with setae.

   c. They suck the blood of their host.

   (d.) They are marine annelids.

Reading and Study Workbook **327**

© Pearson Education, Inc., publishing as Pearson Prentice Hall.

18. What annelids do polychaetes include? _They include sandworms, bloodworms, and their_ relatives.

Ecology of Annelids (page 699)

19. How do the tunnels of earthworms affect other organisms? _Earthworm tunnels provide_ passageways for plant roots and water and allow the growth of beneficial, oxygen-requiring soil bacteria.

_____

20. Circle the letter of each sentence that is true about annelids.

(a.) Earthworms are important to the diet of birds.

(b.) Annelids bring minerals from deep soil layers to the surface.

c. Marine annelids spend their lives burrowing through soil.

(d.) Annelid larvae form part of the animal plankton.

Reading Skill Practice

A flowchart can help you remember the order in which a process or series of events occurs. On a separate sheet of paper, make a flowchart for the process in earthworms of feeding and digestion, described on page 695. For more information about flowcharts, see Organizing Information in Appendix A of your textbook.

Students should describe food pumped into the esophagus by the pharynx and then moving through the crop, gizzard, and intestine.

© Pearson Education, Inc., publishing as Pearson Prentice Hall.

Section 27–4 Mollusks (pages 701–708)

⊂⊃ **Key Concepts**
- What are the defining features of mollusks?
- What is the basic body plan of mollusks?
- What are the characteristics of the three main classes of mollusks?

What Is a Mollusk? (page 701)

1. Mollusks are members of the phylum _____Mollusca_____.

2. Circle the letter of each sentence that is true about mollusks.

   (a.) They share similar developmental stages.

   (b.) They usually have an internal or external shell.

   c. They are the ancestors of annelids.

   (d.) They are soft-bodied animals.

3. What is a trochophore? __It is a larval stage of a mollusk.__

Form and Function in Mollusks (pages 702–704)

4. What are the four parts of the body plan of most mollusks?

   a. Foot _____   c. Shell _____

   b. Mantle _____   d. Visceral mass _____

5. What forms does the muscular mollusk foot take? __Flat structures for crawling, spade-__ __shaped structures for burrowing, and tentacles for capturing prey__

6. The thin layer of tissue that covers most of the mollusk's body is called the _____mantle_____.

7. How is the mollusk shell made? __It is made by glands in the mantle that secrete calcium__ __carbonate.__

8. Snails and slugs feed using a tongue-shaped structure known as a(an) _____radula_____.

9. What is a siphon? __A siphon is a tubelike structure through which water enters and leaves the body.__

10. Why do land snails and slugs typically live only in moist places? __They respire using a__ __mantle cavity that has a large surface area lined with blood vessels, and the lining must be kept__ __moist so that oxygen can diffuse across its surface.__

11. How does an open circulatory system carry blood to all parts of a mollusk's body? __Blood is pumped through vessels by a simple heart. Blood eventually leaves__ __the vessels and works its way through different sinuses.__

12. A large saclike space in the body is called a(an) _____sinus_____.

13. Ammonia is removed from the blood and released out of the body by tube-shaped _____nephridia_____.

14. Circle the letter of each sentence that is true about mollusk response.

    (a.) Clams have a simple nervous system.

    (b.) Octopi and their relatives have the most highly developed nervous system of all invertebrates.

    c. Clams have well-developed brains.

    d. Vertebrates are more intelligent than octopi.

15. Where does fertilization take place in tentacled mollusks and certain snails?
    It takes place inside the body of the female.

Groups of Mollusks (pages 705–707)

16. Complete the table about groups of mollusks.

GROUPS OF MOLLUSKS

Class	Common Name	Description of Shell	Examples
Gastropoda	Gastropods	Shell-less or single-shelled	Pond snails, land slugs, sea butterflies, sea hares, nudibranchs
Bivalvia	Bivalves	Two shells that are held together by one or two powerful muscles	Clams, oysters, mussels, scallops
Cephalopoda	Cephalopods	Only small internal shells or no shells	Octopi, squids, cuttlefishes, nautiluses

17. Circle the letter of each sentence that is true about bivalves.

    (a.) Mussels use sticky threads to attach themselves to rocks.

    (b.) Some bivalves feed on material deposited in sand or mud.

    c. Clams move by flapping their shells rapidly when threatened.

    d. Scallops sting predators with recycled cnidarian nematocysts.

18. How do gastropods move? __They move by using a muscular foot located on the ventral side.__
    _____

19. The cephalopod head is attached to a single _____foot_____.

20. What is a cephalopod's foot divided into? __Tentacles, or arms__

21. What allows squids to locate a wide variety of prey? __They have large, complex eyes that__ can distinguish objects as small as 0.5 centimeters from a meter away. _____

22. The only present-day cephalopods with external shells are _____nautiluses_____.

Ecology of Mollusks (page 708)

23. What allows mollusks to inhabit the extreme environment around deep-sea volcanic vents? __Within the bivalves around these vents are symbiotic bacteria that extract chemical__ energy from compounds in the water. From that energy, the bacteria produce food molecules that the mollusks can use. _____

24. Why can careful checks of bivalves warn public health officials of possible health problems to come? __Filter-feeding bivalves concentrate dangerous pollutants__ and microorganisms in their tissues. Therefore if certain bivalves contain high levels of pollutants, people are warned not to eat them. _____

Vocabulary Review

Crossword Puzzle   *Use the clues below to fill in the spaces of the puzzle with the correct words.*

Across

3. process of asexual reproduction in free-living flatworms
6. annelid that sucks blood
7. structure in mollusks made of calcium carbonate
8. mollusk with tentacles
10. organism that has no coelom
12. type of annelid that includes the earthworm
14. thin layer of tissue that covers most of a mollusk's body
15. body cavity only partially lined with mesoderm

Down

1. soft-bodied invertebrate with an internal or external shell
2. structure in mollusks that contains the internal organs
4. marine annelid with appendages
5. fluid-filled body cavity lined with mesoderm tissue
9. structure used for respiration in mollusks
11. groups of nerve cells that control the nervous system in free-living flatworms
13. single-shelled mollusk that moves using its muscular foot

Summary

28–1 Introduction to the Arthropods

Phylum Arthropoda includes animals such as crabs, spiders, and insects. Arthropods have a segmented body, a tough exoskeleton, and jointed appendages. An exoskeleton is an external body covering. An arthropod exoskeleton is made from protein and a carbohydrate called chitin. All arthropods have jointed appendages. Appendages are structures such as legs and antennae that extend from the body wall.

The evolution of arthropods—by natural selection and other processes—has led to fewer body segments and highly specialized appendages for feeding, movement, and other functions. Most living arthropods have only two or three segments. Living arthropods have specialized appendages such as antennae, walking legs, wings, and mouthparts.

Arthropods include herbivores, carnivores, and omnivores. Most terrestrial arthropods breathe through a network of branching tracheal tubes that extend throughout the body. Air enters and leaves the tracheal tubes through small openings called spiracles. Other terrestrial arthropods, such as spiders, respire using book lungs. Most aquatic arthropods have gills. Arthropods have an open circulatory system. Most terrestrial arthropods dispose of nitrogen-containing wastes using saclike organs called Malpighian tubules. Terrestrial arthropods have internal fertilization. Aquatic arthropods have internal or external fertilization.

When arthropods outgrow their exoskeltons, they undergo periods of molting. During molting, an arthropod sheds its entire exoskeleton and manufactures a larger one to take its place.

28–2 Groups of Arthropods

Arthropods are classified based on the number and structure of their body segments and appendages—particularly their mouthparts.

Crustaceans—subphylum Crustacea—include crabs, shrimps, lobsters, crayfishes, and barnacles. Crustaceans typically have two pairs of antennae, two or three body sections, and chewing mouthparts called mandibles. Crustaceans with three body sections have a head, a thorax, and an abdomen. The thorax lies just behind the head and houses most of the internal organs. In crustaceans with two sections, the head and thorax are fused, forming a cephalothorax.

Chelicerates—subphylum Chelicerata—include horseshoe crabs, spiders, ticks, and scorpions. Chelicerates have mouthparts called chelicerae and two body sections. Nearly all chelicerates have four pairs of walking legs. Chelicerates are divided into two main classes—Merostomata and Arachnida. Class Merostomata includes horseshoe crabs. Horseshoe crabs are the oldest living arthropods. Class Arachnida includes spiders, mites, ticks, and scorpions. Spiders are the largest group of arachnids. Spiders spin strong webs by forcing liquid silk through spinnerets, organs that contain silk glands.

Uniramians—subphylum Uniramia—include centipedes, millipedes, and insects. Uniramians have jaws, one pair of antennae, and unbranched appendages. Centipedes have a few to more than 100 pairs of legs. Most body segments have one pair of legs each. Centipedes are carnivores. Millipedes have two, not one, pairs of legs per segment. Millipedes feed on dead or decaying plant material.

28–3 Insects

Insects have a body divided into three parts—head, thorax, and abdomen. Three pairs of legs are attached to the thorax. A typical insect has a pair of antennae, a pair of compound eyes, and two pairs of wings. Compound eyes are made of many lenses, and they detect minute changes in color and movement.

Insects have three pairs of appendages used as mouthparts, including a pair of mandibles. Insect mouthparts are a variety of shapes.

The growth and development of insects usually involve metamorphosis, which is a process of changing shape and form. In incomplete metamorphosis, the immature forms of insects look very much like adults. The immature forms are called nymphs. Nymphs gradually acquire adult structures, such as wings, and functional sex organs. Insects such as bees, moths, and beetles undergo complete metamorphosis. These insects hatch into larvae that look and act nothing like adults. A larva changes into a pupa, the stage in which an insect changes from larva to adult.

Insects are known for their destructive effects. Termites destroy wood, and mosquitoes bite humans. Yet, insects are also beneficial to humans. For example, insects pollinate many crops.

Insects communicate using sound, chemical, and other types of signals. Pheromones are specific chemical messengers that affect behavior or development in other individuals of the same species.

Ants, bees, termites, and some of their relatives form complex associations called societies. A society is a group of animals of the same species that work together for the benefit of the whole group.

28–4 Echinoderms

Phylum Echinodermata consists of animals such as sea stars, sea urchins, and sand dollars. Echinoderms are characterized by spiny skin, a water vascular system, and suction-cuplike structures called tube feet. Echinoderms have an endoskeleton, which is an internal skeleton. Most adult echinoderms exhibit five-part radial symmetry. Echinoderm larvae exhibit bilateral symmetry. Echinoderms are deuterostomes—an indication that echinoderms and vertebrates are closely related.

Echinoderms have a system of internal tubes called a water vascular system. The water vascular system is filled with fluid. It carries out many essential body functions in echinoderms, including respiration, circulation, and movement. It opens to the outside through a sievelike structure called a madreporite. In sea stars, the madreporite connects to a ring canal. From the ring canal, five radial canals extend along body segments. Attached to each radial canal are hundreds of tube feet. A tube foot is a structure that operates much like a suction cup. In most echinoderms, waste is released as feces through the anus. Most echinoderms move using their tube feet. Echinoderms reproduce by external fertilization.

Classes of echinoderms include sea urchins and sand dollars, brittle stars, sea cucumbers, sea stars, and sea lilies and feather stars. Echinoderms are common in a variety of marine habitats. Sea urchins help control the distribution of algae and other forms of marine life. Sea stars are important predators that help control the numbers of clams and corals.

Section 28–1 Introduction to the Arthropods
(pages 715–719)

🔑 Key Concepts
- What are the main features of arthropods?
- What are the important trends in arthropod evolution?
- What happens when an arthropod outgrows its exoskeleton?

What Is an Arthropod? (page 715)

1. What is the basic body plan of all arthropods? _Arthropods have a segmented body, a tough_ _exoskeleton, and jointed appendages._

2. A tough body wall that protects and supports the body of arthropods is called a(an) _____exoskeleton_____.

3. What is chitin? _Chitin is made from protein and a carbohydrate and makes up the arthropod_ _exoskeleton._

4. Circle the letter of each sentence that is true about arthropod exoskeletons.

   (**a.**) The exoskeletons of many land-dwelling species have a waxy covering.

   b. All arthropod exoskeletons are the same shape.

   (**c.**) Lobster exoskeletons cannot be crushed by hand.

   (**d.**) An exoskeleton is an external covering.

5. What are appendages? _Appendages are structures such as legs and antennae that extend from_ _the arthropod's body wall._

6. Is the following sentence true or false? The appendages of arthropods are jointed. _____true_____

Evolution of Arthropods (page 716)

7. Where did the first arthropods appear more than 600 million years ago? _They appeared in the sea._

8. What are two ways in which arthropods have evolved since they first appeared?

   a. _Fewer body segments_

   b. _More specialized appendages for feeding, movement, and other functions_

9. Circle the letter of each sentence that is true about arthropod evolution.

    a. Most primitive arthropods had only one or two body segments.

    (b.) Arthropod appendages evolved into different forms.

    (c.) The early body plan was modified gradually.

    (d.) Appendages of living arthropods include wings, flippers, and mouthparts.

Form and Function in Arthropods (pages 716–719)

10. Is the following sentence true or false? Arthropods include herbivores, carnivores, and omnivores. _____true_____

Match the arthropod structure with its description.

	Structure	Description
b	**11.** Tracheal tubes	**a.** Saclike organs that extract wastes from the blood and add them to feces
e	**12.** Spiracles	
d	**13.** Book lungs	**b.** Network of branching tubes through which arthropods breathe
c	**14.** Book gills	
a	**15.** Malpighian tubules	**c.** Organs through which horseshoe crabs respire
		d. Layers of respiratory tissue stacked like the pages of a book through which spiders respire
		e. Small openings on the side of the body through which air enters and leaves tracheal tubes

16. Complete the concept map about arthropod respiration.

17. Circle the letter of each sentence that is true about the response to the environment by arthropods.

(a.) Most arthropods have sophisticated sense organs.

(b.) All arthropods have a brain.

(c.) Ganglia along a ventral nerve cord coordinate the movements of individual legs.

d. Very few arthropods have a well-developed nervous system.

18. How do aquatic arthropods carry out excretion? In aquatic arthropods, diffusion moves cellular wastes from the arthropods' bodies into the surrounding water.

19. How do arthropods move? Arthropods move using well-developed groups of muscles that are coordinated by the nervous system.

20. Circle the letter of each sentence that is true about arthropod reproduction.

a. Aquatic arthropods have only internal fertilization.

(b.) In some species, males have an organ that places sperm inside females.

c. Terrestrial arthropods may have internal or external fertilization.

(d.) In some aquatic species, males shed sperm around eggs released into the environment.

Growth and Development in Arthropods (page 719)

21. When do arthropods undergo periods of molting? They molt when they become too large for their exoskeletons.

22. What occurs in arthropods during molting? An arthropod sheds its entire exoskeleton and manufactures a larger one to take its place.

© Pearson Education, Inc., publishing as Pearson Prentice Hall.

Section 28–2 Groups of Arthropods
(pages 720–725)

⊂⊃ Key Concepts
- How are arthropods classified?
- What are the distinguishing features of the three major groups of arthropods?

Introduction (page 720)

1. What characteristics do biologists use to classify arthropods? Arthropods are classified based on the number and structure of their body segments and appendages—particularly their mouthparts.

2. What are the three major groups of arthropods?

   a. Crustaceans

   b. Spiders and their relatives

   c. Insects and their relatives

Crustaceans (pages 720–721)

3. Circle the letter of each description of structures that crustaceans typically have.

   (a.) two pairs of branched antennae

   b. four or five body sections

   (c.) chewing mouthparts called mandibles

   (d.) two or three body sections

4. Label the two body sections of a typical crustacean.

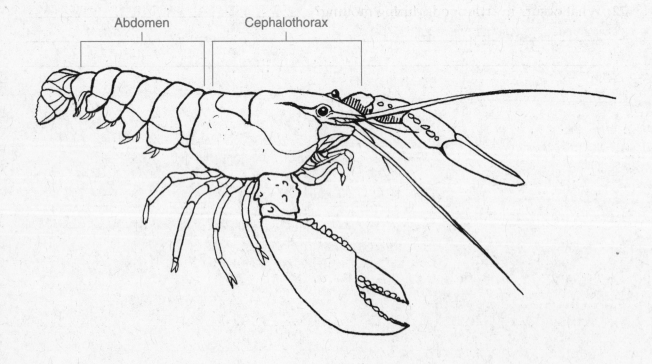

Abdomen   Cephalothorax

5. The largest group of crustaceans is the _____decapods_____.

6. Complete the table about crustacean body parts.

CRUSTACEAN BODY PARTS

Body Part	Description
Thorax	Section just behind the head that houses most of the internal organs
Cephalothorax	Fusion of the head with the thorax
Abdomen	The posterior part of the body
Carapace	The part of the exoskeleton that covers the cephalothorax
Mandible	A mouthpart adapted to biting and grinding food
Chelipeds	First pair of legs in decapods, which bear large claws
Swimmerets	Flipperlike appendages used for swimming

7. Circle the letter of each sentence that is true about barnacles.

a. They are sessile.

b. They have an outer, shell-like covering.

c. They move backward by snapping a tail.

d. They attach themselves to rocks and marine animals.

Spiders and Their Relatives (pages 722–724)

8. Horseshoe crabs, spiders, ticks, and scorpions are grouped as _____chelicerates_____.

9. Circle the letter of each description of structures that chelicerates have.

a. four or five pairs of legs

b. three or four body sections

c. two pairs of branched antennae

d. mouthparts called chelicerae

10. What is the function of the chelicerae? Chelicerae contain fangs and are used to stab and paralyze prey.

11. The appendages near the mouth that are usually modified to grab prey are called _____pedipalps_____.

12. How do spiders respire? Air enters through spiracles and then circulates across the surfaces of the book lung.

13. What arthropods do arachnids include? They include spiders, mites, ticks, and scorpions.
_____

14. How are horseshoe crabs like and unlike crabs? They are heavily armored like crabs, but
they have an anatomy closer to that of spiders.
_____

15. Why must spiders liquefy their food to swallow it? Spiders do not have jaws for chewing.
_____

16. Circle the letter of each sentence that is true about spiders and silk.

(**a.**) Spiders spin silk into cocoons for eggs.

(**b.**) Spinning webs seems to be a programmed behavior.

(**c.**) Spinnerets are organs that contain silk glands.

d. Tarantulas cannot produce silk.

17. Is the following sentence true or false? Mites and ticks are often parasitic.
___true___

18. Scorpions have pedipalps that are enlarged into _____claws_____.

19. What do ticks transmit that cause Rocky Mountain spotted fever and Lyme disease?
They carry bacteria that cause these diseases.
_____

Insects and Their Relatives (page 725)

20. Centipedes, millipedes, and insects are all grouped as _____uniramians_____.

21. Circle the letter of each description of structures that uniramians have.

(**a.**) one pair of antennae

b. unbranched appendages

c. mouthparts called chelicerae

(**d.**) jaws

22. Why are centipedes restricted to moist or humid areas? Their spiracles cannot close, and
they lack a waterproof coating on their exoskeleton. As a result, their bodies lose water easily.
_____

23. How many pairs of legs does each body segment of most centipedes have? Most
body segments of centipedes bear one pair of legs each.
_____

24. How many pairs per segment do millipedes have?
Each millipede segment bears two pairs of legs.
_____

Name_____ Class_____ Date_____

Section 28–3 Insects (pages 726–733)

🔑 **Key Concepts**
- What are the distinguishing features of insects?
- What two types of development can insects undergo?
- What types of insects form societies?

Introduction (page 726)

1. What are three characteristics of insects that have contributed to their evolutionary success?

    a. Different ways of responding to stimuli _____

    b. The evolution of flight _____

    c. A life cycle in which the young differ from adults _____

What Is an Insect? (pages 727–729)

2. Label the three body parts of an insect.

3. How many pairs of legs does an insect have, and where are they attached?

    An insect has three pairs of legs, attached to the thorax.

4. Circle the letter of each sentence that is true about a typical insect.

    ⓐ It has tracheal tubes used for respiration.

    ⓑ It has a pair of compound eyes on the head.

    c. It has two pairs of wings on the abdomen.

    ⓓ It has a pair of antennae on the head.

5. What is the multiple-lens structure of the compound eye better at detecting than the human eye? _____ Movement _____

6. Where do insects have chemical receptors for taste and smell? These receptors are located on their mouthparts and also on their antennae and legs. _____

_____

Name_____ Class_____ Date _____

7. Is the following sentence true or false? Many insects have well-developed ears.
   _____true_____

8. Why do insect mouthparts take on a variety of shapes? Insect mouthparts are specialized
   for a variety of functions.
   _____

9. How many pairs of wings does a flying insect typically have, and what are they
   made of? A flying insect typically has two pairs of wings that are made of chitin.
   _____
   _____

10. What has the evolution of flight allowed insects to do? It has allowed insects to disperse
    long distances and to colonize a wide variety of habitats.
    _____
    _____

11. What is metamorphosis? Metamorphosis is a process of changing shape and form.
    _____

12. What is the main difference between complete metamorphosis and incomplete
    metamorphosis? Insects that undergo incomplete metamorphosis gradually acquire
    adult structures. Insects that undergo complete metamorphosis change in body form more
    dramatically.
    _____

13. The immature forms of an insect that undergo incomplete metamorphosis are
    called _____nymphs_____.

14. Circle the letter of each type of insect that undergoes complete metamorphosis.
    (a.) moths
    (b.) bees
    c. chinch bugs
    (d.) beetles

15. What do the insects that undergo complete metamorphosis hatch into?
    _____Larvae_____

16. The stage in which an insect changes from larva to adult is called a(an)
    _____pupa_____.

17. Circle the letter of each sentence that is true about complete metamorphosis.
    a. The nymphs gradually acquire adult structures.
    (b.) During the pupal stage, the body is completely remodeled
         inside and out.
    (c.) The larva molts a few times but changes little in appearance.
    (d.) The adult that emerges seems like a completely different
         animal from the larva.

342 Chapter 28

© Pearson Education, Inc., publishing as Pearson Prentice Hall.

Name_____ Class_____ Date _____

Insects and Humans (page 730)

18. Is the following sentence true or false? Only male mosquitoes bite humans and
other animals to get a blood meal. _____false_____

19. How do insects contribute beneficially to agriculture? Insects such as bees, butterflies,
wasps, moths, and flies pollinate many crops. About one third of the food you eat depends on
plants pollinated by animals.

Insect Communication (page 731)

20. Circle the letter of each sentence that is true about insect communication.

(a.) To attract females, male crickets chirp.

(b.) Much of an insect's communication involves finding a mate.

(c.) Insects communicate using visual signals.

d. Fireflies use sound cues to communicate with potential mates.

21. What are pheromones? Pheromones are specific chemical messengers that affect the
behavior or development of other individuals of the same species.

Insect Societies (pages 732–733)

22. What is a society? A society is a group of closely related animals of the same species that
work together for the benefit of the whole group.

23. Circle the letter of each sentence that is true about castes.

(a.) Each caste has a body form specialized for its role.

b. Most insect societies have multiple queens.

(c.) Groups of individuals in a society are specialized to perform
particular tasks.

(d.) The queen is typically the largest individual in the colony.

24. What does a honeybee's round dance tell the other bees? There is food within a relatively
short distance from the hive.

25. What does a honeybee's waggle dance tell the other bees? The food is a longer distance
away.

Reading Skill Practice

By looking carefully at illustrations in textbooks, you can help yourself understand
better what you have read. Look carefully at Figure 28–16 on page 728. What important
idea do these illustrations communicate? Do your work on a separate sheet of paper.
Insect mouthparts are adapted for a variety of functions and therefore take on a variety of shapes.

© Pearson Education, Inc., publishing as Pearson Prentice Hall.

Name_____ Class_____ Date _____

Section 28–4 Echinoderms (pages 734–738)

Key Concepts
- What are the distinguishing features of echinoderms?
- What functions are carried out by the water vascular system of echinoderms?
- What are the different classes of echinoderms?

Introduction (page 734)

1. An internal skeleton is called a(an) _____endoskeleton_____.

2. What forms an echinoderm's endoskeleton? Hardened plates of calcium carbonate form its endoskeleton.

3. In what environment do all echinoderms live? They live in the sea.

What Is an Echinoderm? (page 734)

4. Is the following sentence true or false? The bodies of most echinoderms are two-sided. ____true____

5. What are five features that characterize echinoderms?
   a. Spiny skin
   b. Radial symmetry
   c. An internal skeleton
   d. A water-vascular system
   e. Tube feet

6. What characteristic of echinoderms indicates that they are closely related to vertebrates? Both echinoderms and vertebrates are deuterostomes.

Form and Function in Echinoderms (pages 735–736)

7. What functions does the water vascular system carry out in echinoderms? It carries out respiration, circulation, and movement.

8. The water vascular system opens to the outside through a sievelike structure called a(an) ____madreporite____.

9. What is a tube foot? A tube foot is a structure that operates much like a living suction cup.

10. Is the following sentence true or false? Sea stars usually feed on mollusks. ____true____

11. In most echinoderms, how are solid wastes released? They are released as feces through the anus.

12. What is the structure of the nervous system in most echinoderms? Most have a nerve ring that surrounds the mouth and radial nerves that connect the ring with the body sections.

13. What do most echinoderms use to move? Most echinoderms move using tube feet.

14. Is the following sentence true or false? Echinoderms reproduce by internal fertilization. ____false____

Groups of Echinoderms (pages 737–738)

15. Complete the table about groups of echinoderms.

GROUPS OF ECHINODERMS

Group	Description of Feeding	Description of Body
Sea urchins and sand dollars	Many are detritivores or grazers	Disk-shaped
Brittle stars	Filter feeders and detritivores	Star-shaped with slender, flexible arms
Sea cucumbers	Most are detritus feeders	Look like warty, moving pickles
Sea stars	Carnivores	Star-shaped
Sea lilies and feather stars	Filter feeders	Long, feathery arms and attached to the ocean bottom by a stalk

16. How do sand dollars defend themselves? They often burrow under layers of sand or mud.

17. When a brittle star is attacked, it sheds one or more arms. How does this help the echinoderm? The detached arm keeps moving, distracting the predator while the brittle star escapes.

18. Where are most sea cucumbers found? On the deep-sea floor

19. What happens if a sea star is pulled into pieces? Each piece will grow into a new animal, as long as it contains a portion of the central part of the body.

20. Where do many feather stars live? They live on coral reefs.

Ecology of Echinoderms (page 738)

21. What is the effect of a sudden rise or fall in the number of echinoderms in a marine habitat? It can cause major changes to populations of other marine organisms.

22. Circle the letter of each sentence that is true about the ecology of echinoderms.

(**a.**) The crown-of-thorns sea star is a major threat to coral reefs.

(**b.**) Sea urchins help control the distribution of algae.

c. Echinoderms feed almost exclusively on coral.

(**d.**) Sea stars help control the number of clams and corals.

Vocabulary Review

Labeling Diagrams *Use terms from Chapter 28 to label the diagram below.*

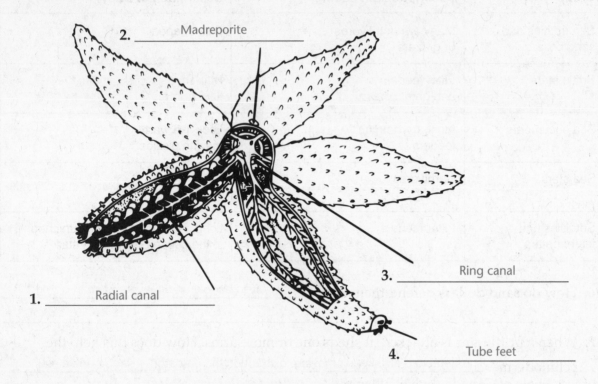

2. _____ Madreporite _____

3. _____ Ring canal _____

1. _____ Radial canal _____

4. _____ Tube feet _____

Completion *Fill in the blanks with terms from Chapter 28.*

5. A(An) _____ exoskeleton _____ is a tough external covering of the body.

6. A structure that extends from the body wall of an arthropod is called a(an)
   _____ appendage _____.

7. The chewing mouthparts of crustaceans are called _____ mandibles _____.

8. Chelicerates have _____ four _____ pairs of walking legs.

9. Arachnids include mites, ticks, scorpions, and _____ spiders _____.

10. Insects have a body divided into three parts—a head, a(an) _____ thorax _____,
    and an abdomen.

11. In complete metamorphosis, the stage in which an insect changes from larva to adult is
    called a(an) _____ pupa _____.

12. Specific chemical messengers that affect the behavior or development of individuals of
    the same insect species are called _____ pheromones _____.

13. A(An) _____ endoskeleton _____ is an internal skeleton.

14. Most echinoderms exhibit five-part _____ radial _____ symmetry.

© Pearson Education, Inc., publishing as Pearson Prentice Hall.

Summary

29–1 Invertebrate Evolution

Paleontologists have identified microscopic fossils from between 610 and 570 million years ago. From the same time period, they have identified trace fossils, which are tracks and burrows made by soft-bodied animals. The fossils of some of the earliest and most primitive animals known were discovered in the Ediacara Hills of Australia. The Ediacaran animals, which lived between 575 and 543 million years ago, were flat and plate-shaped. They lived on the bottom of shallow seas and were made of soft tissues. They were segmented and had bilateral symmetry. However, the fossils show little evidence of cell specialization or a front and back end.

The Cambrian Period, which began 544 million years ago, is marked by the abundance of different fossils. One of the best-known sites of Cambrian fossils is the Burgess Shale of Canada. In just a few million years, animals had evolved complex body plans. Because of the extraordinary growth in animal diversity, events of the early Cambrian Period are called the Cambrian Explosion. The anatomies of Burgess Shale animals typically had body symmetry, segmentation, some type of skeleton, a front and a back end, and appendages adapted for many functions.

The appearance of each animal phylum in the fossil record represents the evolution of a successful and unique body plan. Modern sponges and cnidarians have little internal specialization. As larger and more complex animals have evolved, specialized cells join together to form tissues, organs, and organ systems.

All invertebrates except sponges exhibit some type of body symmetry. Cnidarians and echinoderms exhibit radial symmetry—body parts extend from the center of the body. Worms, mollusks, and arthropods exhibit bilateral symmetry—they have mirror-image right and left sides. The evolution of bilateral symmetry was accompanied by the trend toward cephalization, which is the concentration of sense organs and nerve cells in the front of the body. Invertebrates with cephalization can respond to the environment in more sophisticated ways than can simpler invertebrates.

Most complex animals are coelomates, with a true coelom that is lined with tissue derived from mesoderm. A coelom is a body cavity. Flatworms are acoelomates—they don't have a coelom. Roundworms are pseudocoelomates—their coelom is only partially lined with mesoderm. Annelids, mollusks, arthropods, and echinoderms have true coeloms.

In most invertebrates, the zygote divides to form a blastula. In protostomes, the blastopore develops into a mouth. In deuterostomes, the blastopore develops into an anus. Worms, arthropods, and mollusks are protostomes. Echinoderms (and chordates) are deuterostomes.

29–2 Form and Function in Invertebrates

In many ways, each animal phylum represents an "experiment" in the adaptation of body structures to carry out the essential functions of life. Biologists can learn a great deal about the nature of life by comparing body systems among the various living invertebrates.

The simplest animals—sponges—break down food primarily through intracellular digestion, which is the process of digesting food inside cells. More complex animals—mollusks, annelids, arthropods, and echinoderms—use extracellular digestion, which is the process of breaking down food outside the cells in a digestive cavity or tract. Complex animals digest food in a tube called the digestive tract. Food enters the body through the mouth and leaves the body through the anus.

All respiratory systems share two basic features: (1) Respiratory organs have large surface areas that are in contact with the air or water. (2) For diffusion to occur, the respiratory surfaces must be moist. Aquatic animals naturally have moist respiratory surfaces. Aquatic mollusks, arthropods, and many annelids exchange gases through gills. In terrestrial animals, surfaces are covered with water or mucus. Such covering prevents water loss from the body and also moistens air as it travels through the body to the respiratory surface.

All cells require a constant supply of oxygen and nutrients. Also, cells must remove wastes. The smallest and thinnest animals accomplish these tasks by diffusion between their bodies and the environment. Most complex animals move blood through their bodies using one or more hearts. Some animals use an open circulatory system, in which blood is only partially contained within blood vessels. The blood moves through vessels into a system of sinuses, where the blood directly contacts tissues. Other animals have a closed circulatory system. In a closed circulatory system, a heart or heartlike organ forces blood through vessels that extend throughout the body.

Multicellular animals must control the amount of water in their tissues. But they also have to get rid of ammonia, a poisonous nitrogen-containing waste produced as a result of metabolism. Most animals have an excretory system that rids the body of metabolic wastes while controlling the amount of water in the tissues. Many land animals convert ammonia into a compound called urea, which is eliminated from the body through urine.

Invertebrates show three trends in the evolution of the nervous system: centralization, cephalization, and specialization. The more complex an animal's nervous system is, the more developed its sense organs are.

Invertebrates have one of three main kinds of skeletal systems: hydrostatic skeletons, exoskeletons, or endoskeletons. Annelids and certain cnidarians have a hydrostatic skeleton, in which muscles surround a fluid-filled body cavity that supports the muscles. Arthropods have an exoskeleton, which is an external skeleton. Echinoderms have an endoskeleton, which is structural support located inside the body.

Most invertebrates reproduce sexually during at least part of their life cycle. Depending on environmental conditions, however, many invertebrates may also reproduce asexually. In external fertilization, eggs are fertilized outside the female's body. In internal fertilization, eggs are fertilized inside the female's body.

Chapter 29 Comparing Invertebrates

Section 29–1 Invertebrate Evolution
(pages 745–750)

🔑 **Key Concept**
- What are the major trends in invertebrate evolution?

Introduction (page 745)

1. What are three places where fossils have been found that shed light on the origins of invertebrates?

   a. Ediacara Hills, Australia

   b. Chengjiang, China

   c. Burgess Shale deposits in the Canadian Rockies

Origin of the Invertebrates (pages 745–747)

2. What are trace fossils? They are tracks and burrows made by soft-bodied animals whose bodies were not fossilized.

3. Circle the letter of how old the fossils of the Ediacaran fauna are.

   a. 700–600 years old

   b. 6500–7500 years old

   c. 60–75 million years old

   (d.) 610–570 million years old

4. Is the following sentence true or false? Most fossils of Ediacaran fauna show little evidence of cell specialization. _____false_____

5. What is the best known site of Cambrian fossils? The Burgess Shale of western Canada

6. Circle the letter of each sentence that is true about animals of the Burgess Shale.

   (a.) They were ancestors of most modern animal phyla.

   (b.) They had features that are characteristic of most invertebrates living today.

   (c.) They had specialized cells, tissues, and organs.

   d. They were far less diverse than animals that lived earlier.

7. What features of the Burgess Shale animals made them so successful? The anatomies of Burgess Shale animals typically had body symmetry, segmentation, some type of skeleton, a front and a back end, and appendages adapted for many functions.

Invertebrate Phylogeny (page 747)

8. To which group of invertebrates are chordates most closely related?

____Echinoderms____

9. Number the features below according to the sequence in which they evolved. Number the feature that evolved first *1*.

___4___ **a.** Deuterostome development

___1___ **b.** Tissues

___3___ **c.** Coelom

___2___ **d.** Protostome development

Evolutionary Trends (pages 748–750)

10. What does the appearance of each phylum in the fossil record represent in terms of evolution? Each represents the evolution of a successful and unique body plan.
_____

11. As larger and more complex animals evolved, in what ways did specialized cells join together? Specialized cells joined together to form tissues, organs, and organ systems that work together to carry out complex functions.
_____

12. Circle the letter of each animal group that has organ systems.

a. flatworms

b. cnidarians

(**c.**) mollusks

(**d.**) arthropods

13. What are the two kinds of symmetry that invertebrates exhibit? Bilateral symmetry and radial symmetry

14. What is cephalization? It is the concentration of sense organs and nerve cells in the front of the body.
_____

15. What body plan and lifestyle characterize invertebrates that have evolved cephalization? They exhibit bilateral symmetry and rely on movement for feeding, defense, and other functions.
_____

16. What are the three germ layers that most invertebrates develop from?

a. Endoderm

b. Mesoderm

c. Ectoderm

17. What is a coelom? <u>It is a body cavity.</u>

18. Label each of the cross sections of the acoelomate, pseudocoelomate, and coelomate.

Pseudocoelomate

Digestive tract

Body cavity

Endoderm

Mesoderm

Ectoderm

Coelomate

Endoderm

Digestive tract

Ectoderm

Body cavity

Mesoderm

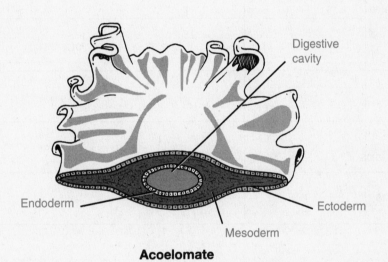

Acoelomate

Digestive cavity

Endoderm

Mesoderm

Ectoderm

19. What does segmentation allow an animal to do with a minimum of new genetic material?
<u>It allows an animal to increase in body size.</u>

20. Most complex animal phyla have a true coelom that is lined completely with
<u>mesoderm</u>.

21. In most invertebrates, the zygote divides repeatedly to form a(an)
<u>blastula</u>.

22. What is the difference in early development between a protostome and a deuterostome? <u>In protostomes, the blastopore develops into a mouth. In deuterostomes,</u>
<u>the blastopore develops into an anus.</u>

23. Which groups of invertebrates are protostomes? <u>Flatworms, roundworms, annelids,</u>
mollusks, and arthropods are protostomes.

24. Complete the table that shows the general characteristics of the main groups of invertebrates.

Invertebrate	Germ Layer	Body Symmetry	Cephalization	Coelom
Sponges	absent	absent	absent	absent
Cnidarians	two	radial	absent	absent
Flatworms	three	bilateral	present	absent
Roundworms	three	bilateral	present	pseudocoelom
Annelids	three	bilateral	present	true coelom
Mollusks	three	bilateral	present	true coelom
Arthropods	three	bilateral	present	true coelom
Echinoderms	three	bilateral	present	true coelom

Reading Skill Practice

A good way to show similarities and differences between items is with a Venn diagram, which consists of two or more circles that overlap. Create Venn diagrams that compare these groups of invertebrates: (1) cnidarians and roundworms, (2) annelids and mollusks, and (3) arthropods and echinoderms. Use the table in Figure 29–5 for the information to be contained in your diagrams. For more information about Venn diagrams, see Organizing Information in Appendix A of your textbook.

Students should make three Venn diagrams, each reflecting differences and similarities in germ layers, body symmetry, cephalization, coelom presence, and early development.

Section 29–2 Form and Function in Invertebrates (pages 751–758)

🔑 **Key Concept**
* How do different invertebrate phyla carry out life functions?

Introduction (page 751)

1. What are seven essential tasks all animals perform to survive? <u>The seven are feeding</u>
<u>and digestion, respiration, circulation, excretion, response, movement, and reproduction.</u>
_____

2. Why aren't more complicated systems in living animals necessarily better than simpler

systems in other living animals? <u>The fact that any system is found in living animals testifies</u>
<u>to its success in performing functions.</u>
_____

Feeding and Digestion (pages 751–752)

3. How is the digestion of food different in simple animals compared to that in more

complex animals? <u>Simple animals break down food primarily through intracellular digestion,</u>
<u>but more complex animals use extracellular digestion.</u>
_____

4. Complete the table about types of digestion.

TYPES OF DIGESTION

Type	Definition
Intracellular digestion	Digestion of food inside cells
Extracellular digestion	Digestion of food outside the cells in a digestive tract

5. More-complex animals digest food in a tube called a(an) _____ digestive tract _____.

Respiration (pages 752–753)

6. Why do respiratory organs have large surface areas? <u>The more surface area that is</u>
<u>exposed to the environment, the greater the amount of gas exchange that can occur.</u>
_____

7. Why are respiratory surfaces kept moist? <u>Gases diffuse most efficiently across a moist</u>
<u>membrane.</u>

8. What are gills? <u>They are feathery structures that expose a large surface area to the</u>
<u>environment.</u>

9. What are book lungs made of? <u>They are made of parallel, sheetlike layers of thin tissues that</u>
<u>contain blood vessels.</u>

Name_____ Class _____ Date _____

Circulation (page 754)

10. How do the smallest and thinnest animals meet the requirement of supplying oxygen and nutrients to cells and removing metabolic wastes? <u>They meet the requirement by</u> <u>simple diffusion between their body surface and the environment.</u>

_____

11. Complex animals move fluid through their bodies using one or more
<u>hearts</u> .

12. Label each of the organisms below according to which has a closed circulatory system and which has an open circulatory system.

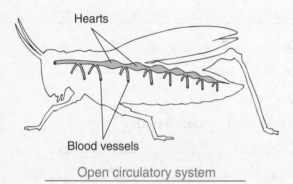

Hearts

Blood vessels

<u>Open circulatory system</u>

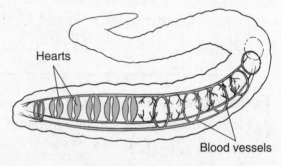

Hearts

Blood vessels

<u>Closed circulatory system</u>

13. Closed circulatory systems are characteristic of what kinds of animals? <u>They are</u> <u>characteristic of larger, more active animals.</u>

_____

Excretion (pages 754–755)

14. What does the excretory system of most animals do? <u>It rids the body of metabolic wastes</u> <u>and controls the amount of water in their tissues.</u>

_____

15. How do aquatic invertebrates rid their bodies of ammonia? <u>Ammonia diffuses from their</u> <u>body tissues into the surrounding water.</u>

_____

16. Circle the letter of each way that terrestrial invertebrates eliminate nitrogenous wastes from their bodies.

   a. Ammonia diffuses from body tissues into the surrounding water.

   (b.) They convert ammonia into urea.

   (c.) They convert ammonia into uric acid.

   (d.) They form a thick paste that leaves the body through the rectum.

© Pearson Education, Inc., publishing as Pearson Prentice Hall.

Response (page 756)

17. What three trends do invertebrates show in the evolution of the nervous system?

a. Centralization

b. Cephalization

c. Specialization

18. Number the following groups of invertebrates according to how centralized their nervous system is. Number the group with the simplest nervous system *1*.

___2___ **a.** Flatworms

___1___ **b.** Cnidarians

___3___ **c.** Arthropods

19. What is cephalization? It is the concentration of nerve tissue and organs in one end of the body.

20. Is the following sentence true or false? The more complex an animal's nervous system, the more developed its sense organs are. _____true_____

Movement and Support (pages 756–757)

21. What are the three main kinds of skeletal systems among invertebrates?

a. Hydrostatic skeletons

b. Exoskeletons

c. Endoskeletons

22. What invertebrates have endoskeletons? Echinoderms

Sexual and Asexual Reproduction (pages 757–758)

23. What is the difference between external and internal fertilization? In external fertilization, eggs are fertilized outside the female's body. In internal fertilization, eggs are fertilized inside the female's body.

24. Circle the letter of each sentence that is true about invertebrate reproduction.

(a.) Most invertebrates reproduce sexually in one part of their life cycle.

b. Asexual reproduction maintains genetic diversity in a population.

(c.) Asexual reproduction includes budding and division in two.

(d.) Most invertebrates have separate sexes.

Chapter 29   Comparing Invertebrates

Vocabulary Review

Answering Questions   *In the space provided, write an answer to each question.*

1. Why are events of the early Cambrian Period called the Cambrian Explosion? _____
   Because of the extraordinary growth in animal diversity
   _____

   _____

2. What is the advantage of cephalization? Invertebrates with cephalization can respond to the
   environment in more sophisticated ways than can simpler invertebrates.
   _____

   _____

3. What are the two basic features that all respiratory systems share? Respiratory organs have
   large surface areas that are in contact with air or water. For diffusion to occur, the
   respiratory surfaces must be moist.
   _____

   _____

Matching   *In the space provided, write the letter of the definition that best matches each term.*

g	4. acoelomate	a. fertilization inside the body of the female
c	5. hydrostatic skeleton	b. animal whose blastopore develops into its mouth
l	6. intracellular digestion	c. fluid-filled body cavity surrounded and supported by muscles
a	7. internal fertilization	d. fertilization outside the body of the female
e	8. deuterostome	e. animal whose blastopore develops into its anus
h	9. extracellular digestion	f. animal whose body cavity is fully lined with mesoderm
k	10. pseudocoelomate	g. animal with no body cavity
b	11. protostome	h. food is broken down in a digestive cavity or tract
d	12. external fertilization	i. hard body covering
i	13. exoskeleton	j. structural support inside the body
f	14. coelomate	k. animal whose body cavity is partly lined with mesoderm
j	15. endoskeleton	l. food is broken down within cells

Summary

30–1 The Chordates

A chordate is an animal that has, for at least some stage of its life, a hollow nerve cord, a notochord, pharyngeal pouches, and a tail.

The hollow nerve cord runs along the back of the body. Nerves branch from it and connect to organs and muscles.

The notochord is a long supporting rod that runs just below the nerve cord. Most chordates have a notochord only as embryos.

Pharyngeal pouches are paired structures in the throat. In some chordates, they develop into gills.

Most chordates are vertebrates. Vertebrates have a backbone made of segments called vertebrae. The backbone replaces the notochord. The backbone gives support and protects the spinal cord. It also gives the muscles a place to attach.

Two groups of chordates do not have backbones. Tunicates are filter feeders that live in the ocean. Adult tunicates have neither a notochord nor a tail. Larval tunicates have the chordate characteristics.

The other group of chordates without a backbone is the lancelet. Lancelets are small, fishlike animals. Adult lancelets have all four chordate characteristics. They also have a definite head region.

30–2 Fishes

Fishes are animals with backbones that live in water. They usually have paired fins, scales, and gills.

Fishes were the first vertebrates to evolve. The evolution of jaws and paired fins was the most important development in fish evolution. Jaws improved defense and expanded food choices. Paired fins gave more control of body movement.

Fishes have various modes of feeding. Fishes are herbivores, carnivores, parasites, filter feeders, and detritus feeders. One fish may even have several different modes of feeding, depending on the food available.

Most fishes breathe with gills. Gills have many tiny blood vessels. This provides a large surface area for oxygen and carbon to be exchanged. Most fishes breathe by pulling water through the mouth and pumping it over the gills and out through openings in the sides of the pharynx.

Fishes have a closed circulatory system that pumps blood in a single loop—from the heart to the gills, from the gills to the body, and back to the heart. The heart is made up of four parts: the sinus venosus, atrium, ventricle, and bulbus arteriosus. The ventricle is the actual pumping portion of the heart. The atrium is a one-way compartment for blood that is going to enter the ventricle.

Most fishes get rid of wastes as ammonia. Some wastes pass through the gills into the water. Other wastes are removed from the blood by the kidneys. Kidneys also help fishes control the amount of water in their bodies.

Fishes have well-developed nervous systems. The brain has several parts. The olfactory bulbs and cerebrum are involved with the sense of smell. The optic lobes process information from the eyes. The cerebellum coordinates body movements. Most fishes have a lateral line system that senses currents and vibrations in the water.

Most fishes move by contracting muscles on either side of the backbone. Fins propel the fish forward and help it steer. Many fishes have a gas-filled swim bladder that keeps them from sinking.

Fishes reproduce in a number of ways. Their eggs are fertilized either externally or internally, depending on the species. Some lay eggs. They are called oviparous. In ovoviviparous fishes, the eggs develop inside the female. The embryos are fed by an attached yolk sac. In viviparous fishes, the embryos get their food from the mother's body, not from an egg.

All fishes can be classified into three groups: jawless fishes, cartilaginous fishes, and bony fishes. Lampreys and hagfishes are jawless fishes. Their bodies are supported by a notochord. They do not have true teeth or jaws. They are parasites and scavengers.

The cartilaginous fishes include sharks, rays, and skates. All members of this group of fishes have a skeleton made of cartilage. Most also have toothlike scales covering their skin.

Bony fishes have skeletons made of bone. Almost all bony fishes belong to the group known as the ray-finned fishes. Their fins have thin, bony spines that are joined together by a thin layer of skin.

30–3 Amphibians

Amphibians have some—but not all—of the adaptations necessary to live on land. As larvae, they live in water. As adults, they live on land. Adult amphibians breathe with lungs and have moist skin that has mucus glands. They do not have scales and claws.

Early amphibians had several adaptations that helped them live on land. Leg bones became stronger to hold weight and allow movement. Lungs and moist skin allowed them to get oxygen from air. The breastbone supported and protected internal organs.

Amphibian larvae are filter feeders or herbivores. They have long, coiled intestines. This helps them break down plant material. Adults have a much shorter intestine because they are carnivores.

In most larvae, gas exchange occurs through the skin as well as lungs. Lungs usually replace gills when an amphibian becomes an adult. However, some gas exchange occurs through the skin and the lining of the mouth.

In adult amphibians, the circulatory system forms a double loop. The first loop carries oxygen-poor blood from the heart to the lungs. It returns oxygen-rich blood to the heart from the lungs. The second loop carries oxygen-rich blood from the heart to the body and returns to the heart with oxygen-poor blood. The amphibian heart has three separate chambers: left atrium, right atrium, and ventricle.

Kidneys remove wastes from blood. Urine passes to the cloaca. From there, it either passes directly to the outside or is stored in a small bladder.

Amphibian eggs do not have shells. The female usually lays eggs in water. The male fertilizes them externally. The eggs hatch into larvae, which are often called tadpoles. Tadpoles gradually change into adults that live on land.

Amphibians have well-developed nervous systems and sense organs. Frogs have keen vision to spot and respond to moving insects. Tympanic membranes, or eardrums, receive sound vibrations.

The amphibian groups are salamanders, frogs and toads, and caecilians. Salamanders have long bodies, legs, and tails. Frogs and toads do not have tails and can jump. Caecilians do not have legs.

Chapter 30   Nonvertebrate Chordates, Fishes, and Amphibians

Section 30–1 The Chordates (pages 767–770)

🗝 Key Concepts
- What characteristics do all chordates share?
- What are the two groups of nonvertebrate chordates?

What Is a Chordate? (page 767)

1. List the four key characteristics of a chordate.

   a. Dorsal, hollow nerve cord

   b. Notochord

   c. Pharyngeal pouches

   d. Tail that extends beyond the anus

Use the diagram below to match the description of the chordate characteristic with its structure.

Structure

a. Notochord   d. Hollow nerve cord

b. Tail

c. Pharyngeal pouches

Description

___d___ 2. Connects nerves to internal organs, muscles, and sense organs

___a___ 3. Long supporting rod located just below the nerve cord

___c___ 4. Paired structures in the throat region

___b___ 5. Contains bone and muscle

Most Chordates Are Vertebrates (page 768)

6. What structure do most vertebrates have? A backbone

7. What chordate structure becomes the spinal cord in vertebrates? Hollow nerve cord

8. The backbone is made of individual segments called _____vertebrae_____ that enclose and protect the spinal cord.

9. Circle the letter of each sentence that is true about vertebrates.

   (a.) A vertebrate's backbone is part of an endoskeleton.

   (b.) The endoskeleton supports and protects the animal's body.

   c. The endoskeleton must be shed as the animal grows.

   d. The endoskeleton is made entirely of nonliving material.

Nonvertebrate Chordates (pages 769–770)

10. How are tunicates and lancelets similar to each other? Both are soft-bodied marine organisms.

11. What evidence indicates that vertebrates and nonvertebrate chordates evolved from a common ancestor? Similarities in structure and embryological development, as well as the fossil record, indicate that nonvertebrate chordates and vertebrates are related.

12. Circle the letter of each characteristic found only in tunicate larvae and not in tunicate adults.

   a. tunic   (c.) hollow nerve cord

   (b.) tail   (d.) notochord

13. Is the following sentence true or false? Both larval and adult tunicates are filter feeders. _____true_____

14. Circle the letter of each characteristic found in lancelets.

   (a.) definite head region   (c.) notochord

   b. jaws   d. fins

15. Is the following sentence true or false? Lancelets use the pharynx for feeding and gas exchange. _____true_____

16. How is blood moved through the body of a lancelet? The walls of the major blood vessels contract to push blood through the body.

Reading Skill Practice

A Venn diagram is a useful tool to compare and contrast two things. Construct a Venn diagram to compare and contrast the characteristics of tunicates and lancelets. See Appendix A for more information about Venn diagrams. Do your work on a separate sheet of paper.

Venn diagrams should include information about tunicates and lancelets as given on pages 769–770.

Section 30–2 Fishes (pages 771–781)

🔑 Key Concepts

- What are the basic characteristics of fishes?
- What were the important developments during the evolution of fishes?
- How are fishes adapted for life in water?
- What are the three main groups of fishes?

What Is a Fish? (page 771)

1. Write the function of each characteristic of fishes.

   a. Paired fins _____ Movement _____

   b. Scales _____ Protection _____

   c. Gills _____ Gas exchange _____

2. Is the following sentence true or false? The characteristics of living fishes are very uniform and almost no diversity exists among fishes. _____ false _____

Evolution of Fishes (pages 772–773)

3. Circle the letter of each sentence that is true about the evolution of fishes.

   (a.) Fishes were the first vertebrates to evolve.

   b. Fishes arose directly from tunicates and lancelets.

   c. Fishes changed little during the course of their evolution.

   (d.) Early fishes were jawless and covered with bony plates.

4. Which period is known as the Age of Fishes?

   a. Cambrian   c. Silurian

   b. Ordovician   (d.) Devonian

5. Jawless fishes with little armor of the Devonian Period were the ancestors of modern
   _____ hagfishes _____ and _____ lampreys _____.

6. Why were jaws an extremely useful adaptation? Jaws can hold teeth and muscles, making it possible for vertebrates to eat a wider variety of food. Jaws can also be used for defense by biting.

7. A strong tissue that supports the body and is more flexible than bone is _____ cartilage _____.

8. Is the following sentence true or false? Paired fins gave fishes less control over their movement. _____ false _____

Form and Function in Fishes (pages 774–778)

9. What are the different modes of feeding found in fishes? Fishes can be herbivores, carnivores, parasites, and filter feeders.

Name_____ Class_____ Date _____

10. Is the following sentence true or false? A single fish may exhibit only one mode of feeding. _____false_____

Match the internal organ with its function.

	Internal Organ	**Function**
c	**11.** Pyloric ceca	**a.** Short tube connecting the fish's mouth to the stomach
e	**12.** Intestine	
d	**13.** Pancreas	**b.** Where food is first partially broken down
a	**14.** Esophagus	**c.** Fingerlike pouches in which food is processed and nutrients absorbed
f	**15.** Anus	
b	**16.** Stomach	**d.** Adds digestive enzymes and other substances to food as it moves through the gut

e. Completes the process of digestion and nutrient absorption

f. Opening through which undigested material is eliminated

17. What does the capillary network in each gill filament provide? It provides a large surface area for the exchange of oxygen and carbon dioxide.

18. Describe how fishes with gills exchange gases. They pull oxygen-rich water in through their mouths, pump it over the gill filaments, then push oxygen-poor water out through slits in the sides of the pharynx.

19. The protective bony cover over the gill slit from which water is pumped out of a fish's body is called a(an) _____operculum_____.

20. How do lungfishes survive in oxygen-poor water? They have specialized organs that serve as lungs. A tube brings oxygen from the air to this organ through the fish's mouth.

21. Is the following sentence true or false? Fishes have an open circulatory system. _____false_____

Match each chamber of the heart in fishes with its function.

	Heart Chamber	**Function**
c	**22.** Ventricle	**a.** Collects oxygen-poor blood from the veins
a	**23.** Sinus venosus	**b.** Large muscular cavity that serves as a one-way compartment for blood entering the ventricle
d	**24.** Bulbus arteriosus	
b	**25.** Atrium	**c.** Thick-walled, muscular chamber that is the actual pumping portion of the heart

d. Large, muscular tube that connects to the ventricle and moves blood through the aorta toward the gills

26. What form of nitrogenous waste do most fishes excrete?
Ammonia

27. How does the function of kidneys in saltwater fishes differ from their function in freshwater fishes? In saltwater fishes, the kidneys concentrate wastes and return as much water as possible to the body. In freshwater fishes, they pump out dilute urine.

Match the structures of the fish's brain with their functions.

	Structure	Function
d	**28.** Olfactory bulb	**a.** Controls the functioning of many internal organs
b	**29.** Cerebrum	**b.** Primarily processes the sense of smell in fishes
e	**30.** Optic lobe	**c.** Coordinates body movements
c	**31.** Cerebellum	**d.** Involved with the sense of smell, or olfaction
a	**32.** Medulla oblongata	**e.** Processes information from the eyes

33. Circle the letter of each sentence that is true about the sense organs of fishes.

   a. Fishes have poorly developed sense organs.

   (**b.**) Many fishes have chemoreceptors that sense tastes and smells.

   c. Fishes have a lateral line system used for sensing sounds.

   (**d.**) Some fishes can sense low levels of electric current.

34. What are two ways that fins help fish to move?

   a. Fins keep the fish on course and adjust direction.

   b. Fins give an extra boost of speed.

35. The streamlined body shapes of most fishes help reduce the amount of
_____drag or friction_____ as they move through the water.

36. What is the function of the swim bladder? It adjusts a fish's buoyancy to prevent it from sinking.

37. In which mode of fish reproduction do the embryos develop inside the mother's body using the egg yolk for nourishment?

   a. oviparous   **c.** viviparous

   (**b.**) ovoviviparous   **d.** herbivorous

Groups of Fishes (pages 778–780)

38. Fishes are divided into groups according to _____body_____ structure.

39. Complete the table about the groups of fishes.

GROUPS OF FISHES

Type	Description	Examples
Jawless fishes	No true teeth; skeletons made of fibers and cartilage; keep their notochord as adults	Lampreys and hagfishes
Cartilaginous fishes	Skeletons made entirely of cartilage; toothlike scales covering skin	Sharks, rays, skates
Bony fishes	Skeletons made of hard, calcified tissue called bone	Ray-finned fishes, such as flounder, angelfish, and flying fish and lobe-finned fishes, such as lungfishes and the coelacanth

40. Is the following sentence true or false? Hagfishes are filter feeders as larvae and parasites as adults. _____ false _____

41. Circle the letter of each characteristic of a shark.

   a. torpedo-shaped body

   b. secretes slime

   c. many teeth

   d. winglike fins

42. Is the following sentence true or false? Lobe-finned fishes have fleshy fins supported by bones that are sometimes jointed. _____ true _____

Ecology of Fishes (page 781)

43. Fishes that spend most of their lives in the ocean but migrate to fresh water to breed are called _____ anadromous _____.

44. Fishes that live in fresh water but migrate to the ocean to breed are called _____ catadromous _____.

Section 30–3 Amphibians (pages 782–789)

🔑 **Key Concepts**
- What is an amphibian?
- How are amphibians adapted for life on land?
- What are the main groups of living amphibians?

What Is an Amphibian? (page 782)

1. Is the following sentence true or false? Amphibian adults are fishlike aquatic animals that respire using gills. _____false_____

2. Circle the letter of each characteristic of amphibians.

   a. scales   b. claws   (c.) moist skin   (d.) mucus glands

Evolution of Amphibians (pages 782–783)

3. List three challenges that had to be overcome by vertebrates colonizing land habitats.

   a. Breathe air

   b. Protect themselves and their eggs from drying out

   c. Support themselves against the pull of gravity

4. List three adaptations that evolved in amphibians that helped them live at least part of their lives out of water.

   a. Stronger bones in the limbs and limb girdles

   b. Set of lungs and breathing tubes

   c. Ribs that form a bony cage around the internal organs

5. Amphibians became the dominant form of animal life during the ____Carboniferous____ Period, also known as the Age of Amphibians.

6. Why did most amphibian groups become extinct by the end of the Permian Period?
   Climate changes caused the low, swampy habitats to disappear, and many amphibian groups
   became extinct.

   _____

7. What three orders of amphibians survive today?

   a. Frogs and toads

   b. Salamanders

   c. Caecilians

Form and Function in Amphibians (pages 784–787)

8. Circle the letter of each characteristic of a tadpole.

   a. carnivore

   (b.) herbivore

   (c.) long intestines

   d. short intestines

Name_____ Class_____ Date _____

9. Circle the letter of each characteristic of an adult amphibian.

    a. carnivore   **c.** sticky tongue

    b. herbivore   **d.** long intestines

10. Briefly describe the path of food in a frog's digestive system.

Food moves from the mouth through the esophagus into the stomach, and then through the small

intestine, the large intestine, or colon, with wastes exiting the cloaca.

_____

11. Circle the letter of each sentence that is true about respiration.

    a. In tadpoles, gas exchange occurs only through the skin.

    b. Lungs replace gills when an amphibian becomes an adult.

    c. Gas exchange in adults can also occur through the skin.

    d. All adult amphibians have lungs.

12. Amphibians have _____kidneys_____ that filter wastes from the blood.

13. Complete the captions in the diagram about the stages in the life cycle of a frog.

Adult Frog

Frog eggs are laid in water and undergo _____external_____ fertilization.

Fertilized Eggs

The eggs hatch into _____tadpoles_____ a few days to several weeks later.

Tadpoles gradually grow limbs, lose their _____tails_____ and _____gills_____, and develop into terrestrial adults.

14. How is the first loop in the circulatory system of an adult amphibian different from the second loop? The first loop carries blood between the heart and the lungs. The second loop carries blood between the heart and the rest of the body.

_____

_____

Match the type of amphibian with its method of movement.

Amphibian	Method of Movement
_a_ **15.** Tadpoles	**a.** Flattened tail for propulsion
_c_ **16.** Adult salamanders	**b.** Well-developed hind limbs for jumping
_b_ **17.** Frogs and toads	**c.** Legs push backward against the ground

18. Circle the letter of each sentence that is true about response in amphibians.

a. An amphibian's brain is structured very differently from a fish's.

(**b.**) An amphibian's eye is protected from damage and kept moist by the nictitating membrane.

(**c.**) Frogs probably do not see color as well as fishes.

(**d.**) Amphibians hear through tympanic membranes, or eardrums.

Groups of Amphibians (page 788)

19. Circle the letter of each characteristic of salamanders.

(**a.**) tail   **c.** herbivore

(**b.**) carnivore   **d.** short body

20. Circle the letter of each characteristic of frogs and toads.

a. tail   (**c.**) able to jump

(**b.**) no tail   **d.** adults have gills

21. Circle the letter of each characteristic of caecilians.

(**a.**) legless   **c.** able to jump

b. long legs   (**d.**) some scales

Ecology of Amphibians (page 789)

22. What are two ways in which amphibians protect themselves from predators?

a. Skin colors and markings that camouflage or serve as a warning

b. Skin glands that release unpleasant-tasting toxins

23. Is the following sentence true or false? For the past several decades, the number of living species of amphibians has been increasing. _____false_____

Vocabulary Review

Labeling Diagrams   *Use the following words to label the structures of the animal below:* nerve cord, notochord, pharyngeal pouches, *and* tail. *Then, complete the sentence.*

1. _____notochord_____

2. _____nerve cord_____

4. _____tail_____

3. _____pharyngeal pouches_____

5. The animal diagrammed above is an example of a(an) _____chordate_____.

Matching   *In the space provided, write the letter of the definition that best matches each term.*

_g_	**6.** vertebrae	**a.** part of the brain responsible for voluntary activities
_f_	**7.** cartilage	**b.** part of the brain that controls many internal organs
_c_	**8.** atrium	**c.** chamber of the heart into which blood enters from the body
_i_	**9.** ventricle	**d.** method of development in which eggs hatch outside the mother's body
_a_	**10.** cerebrum	
_h_	**11.** cerebellum	**e.** receptors in fishes that sense motion and vibrations in water
_b_	**12.** medulla oblongata	**f.** tissue that is softer and more flexible than bone
_e_	**13.** lateral line system	**g.** individual segments that make up the backbone
_j_	**14.** swim bladder	**h.** part of the brain that coordinates body movements
_d_	**15.** oviparous	**i.** the actual pumping portion of the heart
		j. gas-filled organ in fishes that adjusts buoyancy

Completion   *Fill in the blanks with terms from Chapter 30.*

16. In _____ovoviviparous_____ animals, the eggs develop inside the mother's body, and the embryo uses the yolk for nourishment.

17. In _____viviparous_____ animals, the embryos develop inside the mother's body and obtain their nourishment from their mother, not the egg.

18. The muscular cavity at the end of the large intestine in amphibians is called the _____cloaca_____.

19. Transparent eyelids, called _____nictitating_____ membranes, protect an amphibian's eyes underwater and keep them moist in air.

20. Amphibians hear through _____tympanic_____ membranes, or eardrums.

Summary

31–1 Reptiles

Reptiles are vertebrates that are adapted to live entirely on land. They have dry skin that is covered with protective scales. This helps hold water in their bodies. They have efficient lungs that get oxygen from air. Reptiles also have eggs with a shell and several membranes.

As the climate became drier at the end of the Carboniferous Period, amphibians began dying out. This opened up many new habitats for reptiles. The Mesozoic Era is often called the Age of Reptiles because of the diversity and large numbers of reptiles that lived. Dinosaurs were everywhere. The Age of Reptiles ended with a mass extinction at the end of the Cretaceous Period.

Reptiles are ectotherms. They control their body temperature by their behavior. To warm up, they bask in the sun. To cool down, they move into shade, go for a swim, or move to an underground burrow.

Reptiles eat a wide range of foods. They also have many different ways of eating.

Reptile lungs have more gas-exchange area than amphibian lungs. Reptiles also have muscles around their ribs. They are able to expand their chest to inhale and collapse it to exhale.

Reptiles have a double-loop circulatory system. One loop carries blood to and from the lungs. The other loop carries blood to and from the rest of the body. Most reptiles have a three-chambered heart with a partially separated ventricle. Crocodiles have two atria and two ventricles.

Reptiles get rid of liquid wastes as urine. The urine contains either ammonia or uric acid. Reptiles that live in water excrete ammonia. Reptiles that live on land convert ammonia to uric acid. Uric acid is less toxic and requires less water to dilute it.

The reptilian brain is similar to the amphibian brain. However, the cerebrum and cerebellum are larger. Reptiles have well-developed sense organs.

Reptiles have larger and stronger limbs than amphibians. Their legs are rotated further under the body than those of amphibians. In this position, the legs can carry more body weight.

Reptiles have internal fertilization. Most are oviparous, laying eggs that develop outside the mother's body. The embryos are covered with membranes and a protective shell. This amniotic egg keeps the embryo from drying out. Some snakes and lizards are ovoviviparous, and the young are born alive.

Four groups of reptiles survive today. Lizards and snakes (order Squamata) have legs, clawed toes, external ears, and movable eyelids. Snakes are lizards that have lost their legs during their evolution.

Crocodilians (order Crocodilia) have long, broad snouts and a squat appearance. They are fierce carnivores that live only in tropical climates. Crocodilians include alligators, crocodiles, caimans, and gavials.

Turtles and tortoises (order Testudines) have backbones fused to a shell, which provides protection. Turtles usually live in water. Tortoises usually live on land. Instead of teeth, these reptiles have horny ridges on their jaws.

The tuatara (order Sphenodonta) is found only on a few islands near New Zealand. They look somewhat like lizards, but do not have external ears and have primitive scales. They also have a "third eye," which is part of a sense organ on the top of the brain.

31–2 Birds

Birds are reptilelike animals that have a constant internal body temperature. They have two legs that are covered with scales. Their front legs are modified into wings. Birds are covered with feathers. Feathers help birds fly and keep them warm. Birds have different kinds of feathers.

Paleontologists agree that birds evolved from extinct reptiles. Some think that birds evolved directly from dinosaurs. Others think that birds and dinosaurs evolved from an earlier common ancestor.

Birds have many adaptations that enable them to fly. Birds are endotherms. They produce their own body heat. Their high metabolic rate produces heat. Feathers help conserve this heat.

Birds need to eat large amounts of food to maintain their high metabolic rate. Birds have bills adapted to the type of food they eat. Some birds have digestive organs called a crop and a gizzard. The crop is located at the end of the esophagus. Food is stored and moistened in the crop. The gizzard is part of the stomach. It grinds and crushes food so that it is easier to digest.

Birds have a very efficient respiratory system. A system of air sacs and breathing tubes ensures that air flows into the air sacs and out through the lungs in one direction.

The lungs are constantly exposed to oxygen-rich air. This helps birds maintain their high metabolic rate.

Birds have a four-chambered heart and two circulatory loops. A bird's heart has two separate ventricles. Oxygen-rich blood and oxygen-poor blood are completely separated.

Birds have an excretory system similar to that of reptiles. Nitrogenous wastes are converted to uric acid and sent to the cloaca. The cloaca reabsorbs most of the water from the wastes before they are expelled.

Birds have a well-developed brain and sense organs. The cerebrum and cerebellum are large in relation to body size. These adaptations enable birds to respond quickly to stimuli and coordinate the movements for flight. Birds have well-developed sight and hearing but do not sense smells or tastes very well.

The bodies, wings, legs, and feet of birds are adapted to many different habitats and lifestyles. Some of these adaptations, like air spaces in bones, help birds fly. All birds, however, do not fly.

Birds have internal fertilization. They lay amniotic eggs that have a hard shell. Most birds keep their eggs warm until they hatch. One or both parents may care for the offspring.

Chapter 31 Reptiles and Birds

Section 31–1 Reptiles (pages 797–805)

🔑 Key Concepts
- What are the characteristics of reptiles?
- How are reptiles adapted to life on land?
- What are the four living orders of reptiles?

What Is a Reptile? (page 797)

1. List three characteristics shared by all reptiles.

    a. Scaly skin

    b. Lungs

    c. Eggs with several protective membranes

2. What is the disadvantage of reptilian scaly skin? It does not grow as the reptile grows and must be shed periodically.

Evolution of Reptiles (pages 798–799)

3. Circle the letter of each sentence that is true about the evolution of reptiles.

    a. Reptiles evolved rapidly in the warm, humid climate of the Carboniferous Period.

    (b.) Mammal-like reptiles dominated many land habitats until near the end of the Triassic Period.

    c. All dinosaurs were enormous.

    (d.) Some dinosaurs may have had feathers.

4. Is the following sentence true or false? The extinction of dinosaurs opened up new niches on land and in the sea, providing opportunities for other kinds of organisms to evolve. _____true_____

Form and Function in Reptiles (pages 800–802)

5. How do ectotherms control their body temperature? They rely on interactions with the environment.

6. Is the following sentence true or false? All reptiles are herbivores. _____false_____

7. Circle the letter of each adaptation reptiles have for respiration.

    (a.) lungs   (c.) strong rib muscles

    b. moist skin   d. gill slits

8. Circle the letter of each sentence that is true about circulation in reptiles.

    (a.) Reptiles have a double-loop circulatory system.

    b. All reptile hearts have only one atrium.

    (c.) Most reptiles have one ventricle with partial internal walls.

    d. Crocodiles have the least developed heart of living reptiles.

9. What is the advantage of uric acid to terrestrial reptiles? _Uric acid is much less toxic than_
ammonia and is excreted as a pasty solid that helps conserve water.
_____

10. Circle the letter of each sentence that is true about response in reptiles.

   a. The reptilian cerebrum is smaller than that of amphibians.

   (b.) Reptiles that are active during the day tend to have complex eyes.

   c. Reptiles do not have ears.

   (d.) Snakes sense vibrations in the ground through bones in their skulls.

11. Explain why reptiles are able to carry more body weight than amphibians.
Reptilian legs are rotated further under the body than those of amphibians.
_____

12. All reptiles reproduce by ____internal____ fertilization in which the male deposits
sperm inside the body of the female.

13. In the diagram below, label the four membranes in the amniotic egg that surround the
developing embryo.

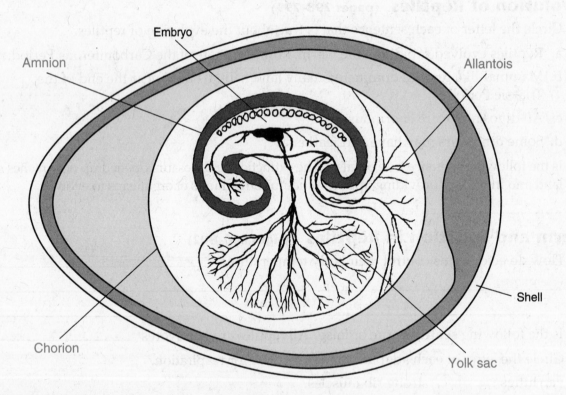

Groups of Reptiles (pages 803–805)

14. List the four living orders of reptiles.

   a. Lizards and snakes

   b. Crocodilians

   c. Turtles and tortoises

   d. Tuataras

15. Is the following sentence true or false? Both snakes and lizards have scaly skin and clawed toes. _____false_____

16. Circle the letter of each characteristic of crocodilians.
    a. long snout   c. herbivore
    b. long legs   d. protective of young

17. Members of the order Testudines that live on land are referred to as
    _____tortoises_____.

18. How do most turtles and tortoises protect themselves? _They pull into their shells._

19. Circle the letter of each characteristic of turtles and tortoises.
    a. teeth   c. strong limbs
    b. strong jaws   d. long, broad snout

20. Describe how tuataras differ from lizards. _Tuataras lack external ears, retain primitive_ scales, and have a "third eye," which is part of a complex organ on top of the brain.

Ecology of Reptiles (page 805)

21. Circle the letter of each sentence that is true about the ecology of reptiles.
    a. Reptiles are in no danger of disappearing.
    b. Reptilian habitats have been expanding.
    c. Humans hunt reptiles for food, to sell as pets, and for their skins.
    d. Conservation programs are in place to help reptiles survive.

Reading Skill Practice

Flowcharts can help you to order the steps in a process or the stages in a series of events. Construct a flowchart that shows the stages in the evolution of reptiles, beginning at the end of the Carboniferous Period and ending with the extinction of dinosaurs at the end of the Cretaceous Period. See Appendix A for more information about flowcharts. Do your work on a separate sheet of paper.

Students should include the major events in the evolution of reptiles as described on pages 798–799.

© Pearson Education, Inc., publishing as Pearson Prentice Hall.

Name_____ Class_____ Date _____

Section 31–2 Birds (pages 806–814)

👄 **Key Concepts**
- What characteristics do birds have in common?
- How are birds adapted for flight?

What Is a Bird? (page 806)

1. Circle the letter of each characteristic of birds.
   - (a.) feathers
   - b. four legs
   - (c.) wings
   - d. scales

2. The single most important characteristic that separates birds from all other living animals is _____feathers_____.

3. List two functions of feathers.
   a. Help birds fly _____
   b. Keep birds warm _____

4. Identify each type of feather diagrammed below.

Contour feather

Down feather

Evolution of Birds (page 807)

5. In what ways is the early bird *Archaeopteryx* different from modern birds?
   Archaeopteryx had teeth in its beak, a bony tail, and toes and claws on its wings.

_____

6. Is the following sentence true or false? Scientists know for certain that birds evolved directly from dinosaurs. _____false_____

© Pearson Education, Inc., publishing as Pearson Prentice Hall.

Form, Function, and Flight (pages 808–812)

7. What adaptations do birds have that enable them to fly? The adaptations include highly efficient digestive, respiratory, and circulatory systems; aerodynamic feathers and wings; strong, lightweight bones; and strong chest muscles.

8. For what two things do birds require energy?

a. Flight

b. Maintaining body temperature

9. Is the following sentence true or false? Birds have a low metabolic rate compared to reptiles. __false__

Match the type of bird bill with the type of food it is adapted to eat.

Bird Bill   **Food**

___c___ **10.** Short and fine   **a.** Flower nectar

___b___ **11.** Short and thick   **b.** Seeds

___d___ **12.** Strong and hooked   **c.** Insects

___a___ **13.** Long and thin   **d.** Animal prey

14. What is the main function of the crop? The crop is where food is stored and moistened before it moves further in the digestive tract.

15. Why might a bird swallow gravel or small stones? Small stones or gravel help a bird to grind and crush food particles together, making them easier to digest.

16. What is an advantage of the one-way airflow through a bird's lungs? One-way airflow constantly exposes the lungs to oxygen-rich air. In other vertebrates, the lungs are exposed to oxygen-rich air only during inhalation.

17. What type of circulatory system do birds have? Birds have a double-loop circulatory system with a four-chambered heart.

18. Circle the letter of the form of nitrogenous waste excreted by birds.

a. ammonia

b. urea

(c.) uric acid

d. nitrate

19. Circle the letter of each sentence that is true about response in birds.

(a.) Birds have brains that quickly interpret and respond to signals.

(b.) The cerebrum controls behaviors, such as nest building.

c. The cerebellum in birds is much like that in reptiles.

d. Birds can sense tastes and smells quite well.

20. What are two ways in which the skeleton of a flying bird is strengthened for flight?

a. Many large bones are fused together.

b. The bones are strengthened by internal struts.

21. How are the amniotic eggs of birds different from the eggs of reptiles? Bird eggs have hard outer shells.

22. Is the following sentence true or false? Bird parents do not ever care for their offspring. false

Groups of Birds (pages 812–813)

Match the bird group with its characteristics. Use Figure 31–19 as a guide.

Bird Groups

b **23.** Birds of prey

c **24.** Ostriches and their relatives

e **25.** Parrots

a **26.** Perching birds

d **27.** Herons and their relatives

g **28.** Cavity-nesting birds

f **29.** Pelicans and their relatives

Characteristics

a. Largest order of birds, which includes songbirds

b. Fierce predators with hooked bills, large wingspans, and sharp talons

c. Flightless birds that move by running

d. Adapted to wading in aquatic habitats

e. Colorful, noisy birds that use their feet to hold up food

f. Birds found in all types of aquatic ecosystems; have four toes connected by a web

g. Multicolored birds that live in holes made in trees, mounds, or underground tunnels

Ecology of Birds (page 814)

30. Circle the letter of each way in which birds interact with natural ecosystems.

(a.) pollinate flowers

(b.) disperse seeds

(c.) control insects

d. produce toxic wastes

31. Is the following sentence true or false? Some species of migrating birds use stars and other celestial bodies as guides. _____true_____

32. Is the following sentence true or false? Birds are not affected by changes in the environment. _____false_____

Reading Skill Practice

By looking at illustrations in textbooks, you can help yourself remember better what you have read. Look carefully at Figure 31–14 on page 809. What important information does the illustration communicate? Do your work on a separate sheet of paper.

Students' answers should correctly identify and describe the stages of digestion in birds.

Chapter 31   Reptiles and Birds

Vocabulary Review

Matching   *In the space provided, write the letter of the definition that best matches each term.*

___c___ **1.** ectotherms

___b___ **2.** endotherms

___e___ **3.** carapace

___d___ **4.** plastron

___f___ **5.** crop

___a___ **6.** gizzard

a. digestive structure that grinds and crushes food

b. animals that can generate their own body heat

c. animals that rely on behavior to control body temperature

d. ventral part of a turtle shell

e. dorsal part of a turtle shell

f. digestive structure that stores and moistens food

Completion   *Fill in the blanks with terms from Chapter 31.*

7. One of the most important adaptations to life on land is the _____amniotic egg_____, which protects the growing embryo and keeps it from drying out.

8. An outer covering of _____feathers_____ helps birds fly and keeps them warm.

9. In birds, _____air sacs_____ direct air through the lungs in an efficient, one-way flow.

Labeling Diagrams   *Use the following words to label the amniotic egg:* allantois, amnion, chorion, embryo, shell, *and* yolk sac.

10. _____embryo_____

15. _____amnion_____

11. _____allantois_____

14. _____shell_____

12. _____chorion_____

13. _____yolk sac_____

Summary

32–1 Introduction to the Mammals

All mammals have hair and mammary glands. In females, mammary glands produce milk to nourish the young. In addition to hair and mammary glands, all mammals breathe air, have four-chambered hearts, and can generate their body heat internally.

Mammals descended from ancient reptiles. Early mammals, which lived during the time of dinosaurs, were small and active only at night. When the dinosaurs became extinct, mammals evolved to fill many different niches.

Mammals have many different adaptations that allow them to live in diverse habitats. Like birds, mammals are endotherms. Their metabolism creates their body heat. They have body fat and fur or hair to prevent heat loss. Many have sweat glands to conserve body heat.

Mammals must eat a lot of food to maintain their high metabolic rate. Mammals have specialized teeth, jaws, and digestive systems for eating plants or animals or both.

All mammals use lungs to breathe. Well-developed muscles in the chest, including the diaphragm, help pull air into the lungs and push air out.

Mammals have a four-chambered heart and a double-loop circulatory system. One loop brings blood to and from the lungs, and the other loop brings blood to and from the rest of the body. Each side of the heart has an atrium and a ventricle. Oxygen-rich blood is completely separated from oxygen-poor blood.

Highly developed kidneys help control the amount of water in the body. This enables mammals to live in many different habitats. The kidneys filter nitrogenous wastes from the blood, forming urine.

Mammals have the most highly developed brains of any animals. Mammalian brains consist of a cerebrum, cerebellum, and medulla oblongata. The cerebrum contains a well-developed outer layer called the cerebral cortex. It is the center of thinking and other complex behaviors.

Mammals, like other vertebrates, have endocrine glands that are part of an endocrine system. Endocrine glands regulate body activities by releasing hormones that affect other organs and tissues.

Mammals have many different adaptations for movement. Variations in the structure of limb bones allow mammals to run, walk, climb, burrow, hop, fly, and swim.

Mammals reproduce by internal fertilization. All newborn mammals feed on the mother's milk. Most mammal parents care for their young for a certain amount of time after birth. The length of care varies among species.

32–2 Diversity of Mammals

The three groups of living mammals are the monotremes, marsupials, and placentals. They differ in their means of reproduction and development. Monotremes lay eggs. They also have a cloaca, similar to the cloaca of reptiles. When the soft-shelled monotreme eggs hatch, the young are nourished by the mother's milk.

Marsupials bear live young that complete their development in an external pouch. The young are born at a very early stage of development. They crawl across the mother's fur and attach to a nipple. They continue to drink milk until they are large enough to survive on their own.

Placental mammals are the most familiar. Placental mammals are named for the placenta—an internal structure that is formed when the embryo's tissues join with tissues from within the mother's body. Nutrients, oxygen, carbon dioxide, and wastes are passed between the embryo and mother through the placenta. After birth, most placental mammals care for their offspring.

32–3 Primates and Human Origins

All primates share several important adaptations. Many of these adaptations are useful for a life spent mainly in trees. These adaptations include binocular vision, a well-developed cerebrum, flexible fingers and toes, and arms that rotate in broad circles.

Very early in evolutionary history, primates split into several groups. Prosimians are small, nocturnal primates with large eyes adapted for seeing in the dark. Anthropoids include monkeys, apes, and humans.

Very early in their evolutionary history, anthropoids split into two major groups. One group evolved into the monkeys found today in Central and South America. This group is called the New World monkeys. All New World monkeys have a prehensile tale. A prehensile tail is a tail that can coil tightly around a branch to serve as a "fifth hand." The other group of anthropoids includes the Old World monkeys and the great apes. Old World monkeys do not have prehensile tails. Great apes, which are also called hominoids, include gorillas, chimpanzees, and humans.

The hominoid line gave rise to the branch that leads to modern humans. This group, called the hominids, evolved adaptations for upright walking, thumbs adapted for grasping, and larger brains.

Many recent fossil finds have changed the way paleontologists think about hominid evolution. Now researchers think that hominid evolution occurred in a series of complex adaptive radiations. This produced a large number of different species rather than one species that led directly to the next.

Researchers agree that our genus, *Homo*, first appeared in Africa. However, researchers do not agree when the first hominids began migrating from Africa. They are also not sure when and where *Homo sapiens* arose. The multiregional model suggests that modern humans evolved independently in several parts of the world. The out-of-Africa model proposes that modern humans arose in Africa and then migrated out.

About 500,000 years ago, two main groups of hominids are known to have existed. *Homo neanderthalensis* lived in Europe and western Asia. Fossil evidence suggests that they used stone tools and lived in organized groups. The other group is the first *Homo sapiens*. Researchers think that they lived side by side with Neanderthals.

According to one hypothesis, around 50,000–40,000 years ago, *H. sapiens* dramatically changed their way of life. They made more sophisticated tools. They produced cave paintings. They also began burying their dead with elaborate rituals. In other words, they began to behave more like modern humans. The Neanderthals disappeared about 30,000 years ago. It is not yet known why. Since then, *H. sapiens* has been the only hominid on Earth.

Section 32–1 Introduction to the Mammals
(pages 821–827)

⟜ **Key Concepts**

- What are the characteristics of mammals?
- When did mammals evolve?
- How do mammals maintain homeostasis?

Introduction (page 821)

1. List the two notable features of mammals.

   a. Hair

   b. Mammary glands

2. Circle the letter of each characteristic of mammals.

   (a.) breathe air   **c.** ectotherm

   b. three-chambered heart   **(d.)** endotherm

Evolution of Mammals (page 821)

3. What three characteristics help scientists identify mammalian fossils?

   a. Lower jaw consisting of a large, teeth-bearing bone connected by a joint directly to the skull

   b. Complex teeth

   c. Certain features of the limbs and the backbone

4. The ancestors of mammals diverged from ancient _____reptiles_____ during the
   Permian Period.

5. Circle the letter of each sentence that is true about the evolution of mammals.

   a. The first true mammals were as large as dinosaurs.

   (b.) During the Cretaceous Period, mammals were probably nocturnal.

   (c.) After dinosaurs disappeared, mammals increased in size and filled many
   new niches.

   d. The Permian Period is usually called the Age of Mammals.

Form and Function in Mammals (pages 822–827)

6. List two ways in which mammals conserve body heat.

   a. External body hair

   b. Subcutaneous fat

© Pearson Education, Inc., publishing as Pearson Prentice Hall.

7. Is the following sentence true or false? Mammals have a low rate of metabolism. _____ false

8. Circle the letter of each way mammals are able to rid themselves of excess heat.
   a. fat   (c.) sweat glands
   b. hair   (d.) panting

9. The ability of mammals to regulate their body heat from within is an example of _____ homeostasis .

10. Is the following sentence true or false? Animals that are omnivores consume only meat. _____ false

11. As mammals evolved, the form and function of their _____ jaws _____ and _____ teeth _____ became adapted to eat foods other than insects.

12. Complete the table about the different kinds of teeth found in mammals.

TEETH ADAPTATIONS IN MAMMALS

Type	Description
Canines	Pointed teeth; used for piercing, gripping, and tearing
Incisors	Chisellike incisors used for cutting, gnawing, and grooming
Molars and premolars	Used for crushing and grinding food

13. In which type of animal would you expect to find sharp canine teeth? _____ Carnivores _____

14. How are herbivores' molars adapted for their diet? Herbivores have broad, flat molars and premolars, which are adapted for grinding plants.

15. Is the following sentence true or false? Carnivores have a shorter intestine than herbivores. _____ true _____

16. Complete the flowchart to show how cows digest their food.

```
┌─────────────────────────────────────────────────────────────────┐
│ Newly swallowed food is stored and processed in the ___rumen___.  │
└─────────────────────────────────────────────────────────────────┘
                              │
                              ▼
┌─────────────────────────────────────────────────────────────────┐
│ Symbiotic bacteria in the rumen digest the ___cellulose___ of most │
│ plant tissues.                                                     │
└─────────────────────────────────────────────────────────────────┘
                              │
                              ▼
┌─────────────────────────────────────────────────────────────────┐
│ The cow ___regurgitates___ the food from the rumen into its mouth, and │
│ food is chewed and swallowed again.                                │
└─────────────────────────────────────────────────────────────────┘
                              │
                              ▼
┌─────────────────────────────────────────────────────────────────┐
│ The food is swallowed again and moves through the rest of the      │
│ ___stomach___ and ___intestine___.                                 │
└─────────────────────────────────────────────────────────────────┘
```

17. How does the diaphragm work to help move air into and out of the lungs?

The diaphragm is a powerful muscle that pulls the bottom of the chest cavity downward, which
increases its volume, and air is pulled into the lungs. When it relaxes, the volume of the chest
decreases and air is pushed out.

18. Is the following sentence true or false? Mammals have a four-chambered heart that
pumps blood into two separate circuits around the body. ___true___

19. Where does the right side of the heart pump oxygen-poor blood? To the lungs

20. After blood picks up oxygen in the lungs, where does it go? The blood returns to
the left side of the heart, where it is then pumped to the rest of the body.

21. How do mammalian kidneys help to maintain homeostasis? The kidneys excrete or retain excess liquid. They also retain salts, sugars, and other compounds the body cannot afford to lose.

Match each part of the mammalian brain with its function.

	Part of the brain	Function
c	**22.** medulla oblongata	**a.** Involved in thinking and learning
d	**23.** cerebral cortex	**b.** Controls muscular coordination
a	**24.** cerebrum	**c.** Regulates involuntary body functions
b	**25.** cerebellum	**d.** Part of the cerebrum that is the center of thinking and other complex behaviors

26. What are endocrine glands? Endocrine glands are part of the endocrine system. They regulate body activities by releasing chemicals called hormones that affect other organs and tissues.

27. What body system helps to protect mammals from disease? The immune system

28. Is the following sentence true or false? Mammals have a rigid backbone, as well as rigid shoulder and pelvic girdles for extra stability. _____false_____

29. Mammals reproduce by _____internal_____ fertilization.

30. Is the following sentence true or false? All mammals are viviparous, or live-bearing. _____false_____

31. What do young mammals learn from their parents? The young learn the behaviors they need to survive in their particular environment.

Section 32–2 Diversity of Mammals (pages 828–832)

🔑 Key Concepts
- How do the three groups of living mammals differ from one another?
- How did convergent evolution cause mammals on different continents to be similar in form and function?

Introduction (page 828)

1. List the three groups of living mammals.

   a. Monotremes   **b.** Marsupials   **c.** Placentals

2. The three groups of mammals differ greatly in their means of __reproduction__ and development.

Monotremes and Marsupials (pages 828–829)

3. The mammals that lay eggs are __monotremes__. Those that bear live young at a very early stage of development are __marsupials__.

4. What two characteristics do monotremes share with reptiles?

   a. The reproductive, digestive, and urinary systems all open into a cloaca.

   b. They lay soft-shelled eggs that are incubated outside the body.

5. How do monotremes differ from reptiles? Young monotremes are nourished by the mother's milk, which they lick from pores on the surface of her abdomen.

6. Circle the letter of each mammal that is a marsupial.

   (a.) koala   **c.** platypus

   b. echidna   **(d.)** kangaroo

7. Describe how marsupial embryos develop. The embryo develops inside the mother's reproductive tract, where it is nourished by a small yolk sac. When the food is used up, the embryo leaves its mother's body and crawls across its mother's fur into the marsupium, where it is nourished by its mother's milk and finishes developing.

Placental Mammals (pages 829–831)

8. What is the placenta? The placenta is an internal structure that is formed when the embryo's tissues join with tissues from within the mother's body.

9. What four substances are exchanged between the embryo and the mother through the placenta?

a. Nutrients

c. Carbon dioxide

b. Oxygen

d. Wastes

10. Is the following sentence true or false? After birth, most placental mammals care for their young and provide them with nourishment by nursing. _____true_____

Match the main order of placental mammal with its description. Use Figure 32–12 on pages 830–831.

Order	Description
e 11. Insectivores	a. Hoofed mammals with an even number of digits on each foot
c 12. Sirenians	b. Herbivores with two pairs of incisors in the upper jaw and hind legs adapted for leaping
d 13. Chiropterans	c. Herbivores that live in rivers, bays, and warm coastal waters
a 14. Artiodactyls	d. The only mammals capable of true flight
f 15. Proboscideans	e. Insect eaters with long, narrow snouts and sharp claws
b 16. Lagomorphs	f. Mammals that have trunks

Biogeography of Mammals (page 832)

17. Is the following sentence true or false? During the Paleozoic Era, the continents were one large landmass. _____true_____

18. What effect on the evolution of mammals was caused when the continents drifted apart? Different mammal groups were isolated from one another, and each landmass took with it a unique array of species. Similar ecological opportunities on the different continents have produced some striking examples of convergent evolution.

Reading Skill Practice

A compare-and-contrast table is a useful tool for organizing similarities and differences. Make a table to compare the three groups of living mammals. Include information about the reproduction and development of each group. For more information about compare-and-contrast tables, look in Appendix A of your textbook. Do your work on a separate sheet of paper.

Tables should include information from pages 828–829 in the textbook.

Section 32–3 Primates and Human Origins
(pages 833–841)

🔑 Key Concepts
- What characteristics do all primates share?
- What are the major evolutionary groups of primates?
- What is the current scientific thinking about hominid evolution?

What Is a Primate? (pages 833–834)

1. What characteristic distinguished the first primates from other mammals? <u>They had an</u>
<u>increased ability to use their eyes and front limbs together to perform certain tasks.</u>
_____

2. List four adaptations that are shared by primates.
   a. <u>Binocular vision</u>
   b. <u>Relatively long fingers and toes</u>
   c. <u>Well-developed cerebrum</u>
   d. <u>Arms that can rotate in their shoulder joints</u>

3. Circle the letter of each sentence that is true about primates.
   a. Primates are well adapted to a life of running on the ground.
   (b.) Many primates can hold objects firmly in their hands.
   (c.) A well-developed cerebrum enables primates to display elaborate social behaviors.
   d. Because primates have a flat face, both eyes point to the sides.

4. What is binocular vision? <u>It is the ability to merge visual images from both eyes, which</u>
<u>provides depth perception and a three-dimensional view.</u>
_____
_____

Evolution of Primates (pages 834–835)

5. Circle the letter of each characteristic of prosimians.
   (a.) nocturnal   b. diurnal   (c.) small in size   d. small eyes

Match the characteristics to the anthropoid group. Each anthropoid group may be used more than once.

	Characteristic	Anthropoid Group
<u>a</u>	**6.** Found today in Central and South America	**a.** New World monkeys
<u>b</u>	**7.** Found today in Africa and Asia	**b.** Old World monkeys
<u>b</u>	**8.** Includes baboons and macaques	
<u>a</u>	**9.** Includes squirrel monkeys and spider monkeys	
<u>b</u>	**10.** Lack prehensile tails	
<u>a</u>	**11.** Long, prehensile tails and long, flexible arms	

12. Complete the concept map to show the evolution of primates.

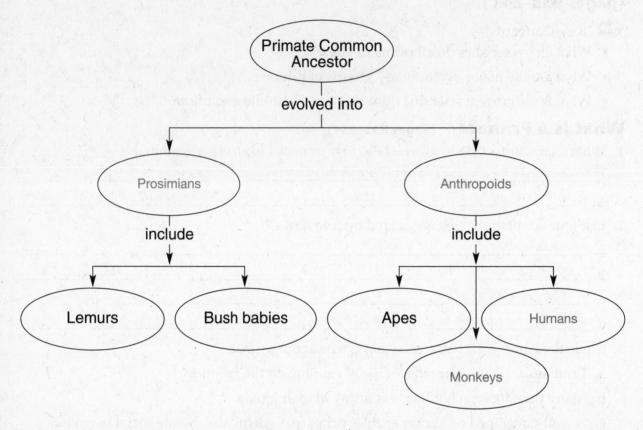

13. The anthropoid group that includes Old World monkeys also includes the great apes, or _____hominoids_____.

Hominid Evolution (pages 835–838)

14. What was the importance of bipedal locomotion that evolved in the hominid family?
Bipedal locomotion freed both hands to use tools.
_____

15. The hominid hand evolved a(an) _____opposable_____ thumb that enabled grasping objects and using tools.

16. Is the following sentence true or false? Hominids have a much larger brain than the other hominoids, such as chimpanzees. _____true_____.

17. Is the following sentence true or false? Only one fossil species exists that links humans with their nonhuman primate ancestors. _____false_____

18. Circle the letter of each characteristic of the hominid genus *Australopithecus*.

    (a.) bipedal apes

    b. never lived in trees

    (c.) fruit eaters

    d. very large brains

© Pearson Education, Inc., publishing as Pearson Prentice Hall.

19. Is the following sentence true or false? Fossil evidence shows that hominids walked bipedally long before they had large brains. _____true_____

20. Based on their teeth, what kind of diet did the known *Paranthropus* species probably eat?
Their diet probably included coarse and fibrous plant foods like those eaten by modern gorillas.

21. Is the following sentence true or false? Currently, researchers completely understand the evolution of the hominid species. _____false_____

The Road to Modern Humans (pages 839–840)

22. *Homo habilis* was found with tools made of _____stone and bone_____.

23. Describe the two hypotheses that explain how modern *Homo sapiens* might have evolved from earlier members of the genus *Homo*.

   a. Multiregional model; *Homo sapiens* could have evolved independently in several places around the world.

   b. Out-of-Africa model; the first true *Homo sapiens* evolved in Africa, and then left Africa in one or more recent waves of migration.

Modern *Homo sapiens* (page 841)

24. Circle the letter of each characteristic of Neanderthals.

   (**a.**) stone tools

   (**b.**) lived in social groups

   c. gave rise to *H. sapiens*

   d. made cave paintings

25. Is the following sentence true or false? Neanderthals and *Homo sapiens* lived side by side for around 50,000 years. _____true_____

26. What fundamental changes did some populations of *H. sapiens* make to their way of life around 50,000–40,000 years ago? They used new technology to make more sophisticated tools, produced spectacular cave paintings, and began burying their dead with elaborate rituals.

Vocabulary Review

Multiple Choice   *In the space provided, write the letter of the answer that best completes each sentence.*

____b____ 1. Mammals are characterized by hair and
     a. lungs.
     b. mammary glands.
     c. four-chambered hearts.
     d. prehensile tails.

____c____ 2. The outer layer of the cerebrum that is the center of thinking is the
     a. cerebellum.
     b. medulla oblongata.
     c. cerebral cortex.
     d. subcutaneous fat.

____a____ 3. Mammals that lay eggs are
     a. monotremes.
     b. placental mammals.
     c. marsupials.
     d. primates.

____a____ 4. Small, nocturnal primates with large eyes adapted to seeing in the dark belong to the primate group called
     a. prosimians.
     b. hominoids.
     c. anthropoids.
     d. hominids.

____d____ 5. Members of the primate group in which the only living members are humans are called
     a. prosimians.
     b. hominoids.
     c. anthropoids.
     d. hominids.

Completion   *Fill in the blanks with terms from Chapter 32.*

6. The layer of fat located beneath the skin is called _____subcutaneous fat_____.

7. The _____rumen_____ is a stomach chamber in which newly swallowed plant food is stored and processed.

8. A powerful muscle called the _____diaphragm_____ pulls the bottom of the chest cavity downward, pulling air into the lungs.

9. Mammals bearing live young that complete their development in a pouch are called _____marsupials_____.

10. A structure called a(an) _____placenta_____ forms when an embryo's tissues join with tissues from the mother's body.

11. The ability to merge visual images from both eyes is called _____binocular vision_____.

12. Members of the primate group that includes monkeys, apes, and humans are called _____anthropoids_____.

13. A tail that can coil tightly around a branch is called a(an) _____prehensile_____ tail.

14. The evolution of _____bipedal_____, or two-foot, locomotion freed the hands to use tools.

15. The hominid hand evolved a(an) _____opposable thumb_____ that enabled grasping objects and using tools.

Summary

33–1 Chordate Evolution

Scientists have learned the most about chordates by studying the embryos of living organisms. Scientists have found evidence of early chordates in the fossilized remains of *Pikaia*. *Pikaia* had a notochord and paired muscles. On the basis of this early evidence, scientists classify *Pikaia* as an early chordate.

Chordates include both vertebrates and nonvertebrates. These two groups share a common invertebrate ancestor. Modern amphibians, reptiles, birds, and mammals share more recent common ancestors.

Scientists infer how vertebrates have evolved by studying fossils and the characteristics of living chordates. Scientists believe that the appearance of new adaptations, such as jaws and paired appendages, has led to adaptive radiations. Adaptive radiation results in many new species with different adaptations. Even though these species might look different, they are related.

Another trend in evolution, called convergent evolution, occurs when unrelated species adapt to similar environments. Convergent evolution produces species that look and behave alike even though they are not related.

33–2 Controlling Body Temperature

Controlling body temperature is important for maintaining homeostasis. The chemical reactions that carry out life functions can occur only within a certain temperature range. Vertebrates have different ways to control body temperature. These ways depend on a source of body heat, a way to conserve heat, and a way to get rid of excess heat.

In terms of how they generate and control their body heat, vertebrates are classified into two basic groups: ectotherms and endotherms. Ectotherms rely on the temperature of the environment for body heat. Ectotherms have low rates of metabolism. They do not have good insulation and easily lose heat to the environment.

Endotherms generate their own body heat. They have high metabolic rates. They conserve heat within their bodies with outer coverings, such as feathers, fat, and fur or hair. They get rid of excess heat by sweating or panting.

Endotherms can survive in cool temperatures. However, they require a lot of food. Ectotherms need much less food. However, they cannot survive in very cold environments.

The first land vertebrates were most likely ectotherms. Scientists do not know exactly when endothermy evolved. Some scientists think that dinosaurs were endotherms; others do not. Evidence suggests that endothermy might have evolved more than once.

33–3 Form and Function in Chordates

Organ systems of different vertebrates are specialized to perform specific functions. The complexity of these systems increases from fishes to mammals.

The skulls and teeth of vertebrates are adapted for feeding on a wide variety of foods. For example, the hummingbird's long bill and the narrow snout of the honey possum are adaptations for feeding on nectar. Invertebrates' digestive systems are also adapted for different feeding habits. Carnivores have shorter digestive tracts than herbivores. Herbivores often house bacteria to help break down plant fibers.

Chordates have two basic structures for respiration. Animals that live in water use gills for respiration. Animals that live on land use lungs. As you move from amphibians to mammals, the surface area of the lungs increases. Birds have the most efficient gas exchange. The combination of air sacs and tubes ensures that oxygen-rich air is always in the lungs.

Vertebrates with gills have a single-loop circulatory system. Blood travels from the heart to the gills, then to the rest of the body, and back to the heart. Vertebrates with lungs have a double-loop circulatory system. The first loop carries blood between the heart and the lungs. The second loop carries blood between the heart and the body.

As chordates evolved, the heart developed chambers to separate oxygen-rich blood from oxygen-poor blood. Fish have two chambers: an atrium to receive blood from the body and a ventricle to pump blood. Amphibians have three chambers: two atria and one ventricle. Most reptiles also have a three-chambered heart, but the ventricle has a partial partition. Birds, mammals, and crocodiles have a four-chambered heart. Oxygen-rich blood is completely separated from oxygen-poor blood.

The excretory system removes nitrogenous wastes from the body. It also controls the amount of water in the body. In nonvertebrate chordates and fishes, wastes leave the body through gills and gill slits. These wastes are in the form of ammonia. In most other vertebrates, the kidneys filter out wastes. Vertebrates that live on land excrete wastes in less toxic forms such as urea or uric acid. This enables land vertebrates to conserve water.

Nonvertebrate chordates have a relatively simple nervous system. They do not have specialized sense organs. Vertebrates have a much more complex brain. Each region of the brain is distinct and has a different function. The sense organs and nerve cells in vertebrates are concentrated at the front of the body. From fishes to mammals, the size and complexity of the cerebrum and cerebellum increase.

Vertebrates are much more mobile than nonvertebrate chordates. All vertebrates, except jawless fishes, have an internal skeleton of bone, or in some fishes, cartilage. The bones are held together with tough, flexible tissues that allow movement and keep the bones in place. Body muscles and limb placement help vertebrates move. Amphibians have limbs that stick out sideways. Reptiles, birds, and mammals have limbs directly under the body. This supports more body weight.

Almost all chordates reproduce sexually. Fishes and amphibians have external fertilization. The eggs of reptiles, birds, and mammals are fertilized internally.

Chordates may be oviparous, ovoviviparous, or viviparous. In oviparous species, the eggs develop outside the mother's body. Most fishes, amphibians, reptiles, and all birds are oviparous. In ovoviviparous species like sharks, the eggs develop inside the mother's body. The embryo gets nutrients from the egg yolk. The young are born alive. In viviparous species like most mammals, the embryos get nutrients directly from the mother. Like ovoviviparous species, the young of viviparous animals are born alive.

Section 33–1 Chordate Evolution (pages 849–852)

Key Concepts
- What are the roots of the chordate family tree?
- What is a main trend in the evolution of chordates?

Chordate Origins (page 849)

1. Studies of embryos of living organisms suggest that the most ancient chordates were closely related to _____ echinoderms _____.

2. Why do scientists consider *Pikaia* to be an early chordate and not a worm?
   Pikaia had a notochord and muscles arranged like those of nonvertebrate chordates.

   _____

3. In the diagram below, label the notochord, head region, paired muscle blocks, tentacle, and tail fin of *Pikaia*.

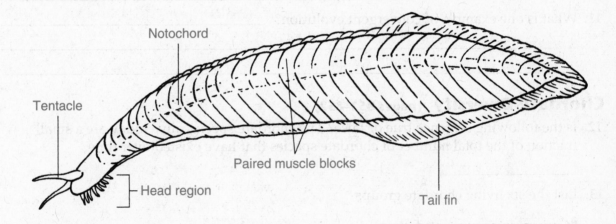

Notochord

Tentacle

Paired muscle blocks

Head region

Tail fin

4. A flexible, supporting structure found only in chordates is a(an) _____ notochord _____.

5. Is the following question true or false? Scientists study tunicate larvae to better understand the early evolution of chordates. _____ true _____

The Chordate Family Tree (page 850)

6. Circle the letter of each sentence that is true about the chordate family tree. See Figure 33–2 on page 850.

   (a.) Vertebrates share a common invertebrate ancestor with tunicates and lancelets.

   b. Mammals and fishes share a more recent common ancestor than mammals and birds.

   c. Lungs evolved before paired appendages.

   (d.) Endothermy evolved after the amniotic egg.

Evolutionary Trends in Vertebrates (page 851)

7. What two things do scientists use to study the evolutionary trends in vertebrates?

   a. Fossil record

   b. Characteristics of chordates living today

8. What effect has the appearance of new adaptations had on the evolution of vertebrates? The appearance of new adaptations has launched adaptive radiations, or the rapid growth in the diversity of a group of organisms.

9. What is convergent evolution? It is the evolution of species that are similar in appearance and behavior, even though they are not related.

10. When does convergent evolution occur? It occurs when unrelated species encounter similar ecological conditions and evolve similar adaptations.

11. What is one example of convergent evolution? Flying vertebrates, such as birds and bats, are an example of convergent evolution.

Chordate Diversity (pages 851–852)

12. Is the following sentence true or false? The chordate species alive today are a small fraction of the total number of chordate species that have existed over time.
    true

13. List the six living chordate groups.

    a. Fishes

    b. Birds

    c. Reptiles

    d. Amphibians

    e. Mammals

    f. Nonvertebrate chordates

Reading Skill Practice

By looking carefully at photographs and illustrations in textbooks, you can help yourself better understand what you have read. Look carefully at Figure 33–3 on page 851. What idea does the photograph communicate?

This photograph shows that the evolution of four limbs allowed animals to move more easily on land.

Section 33–2 Controlling Body Temperature
(pages 854–856)

🔑 **Key Concepts**
- How is the control of body temperature an important aspect of vertebrate life?
- What is the difference between ectotherms and endotherms?

Body Temperature and Homeostasis (pages 854–855)

1. Circle the letter of each sentence that is true about body temperature.

   a. Essential life functions in animals can be carried out most efficiently at any temperature.

   b. If muscles are too cold, they may contract slowly.

   c. If an animal gets too hot, its muscles will work more efficiently.

   d. The control of body temperature is important for maintaining homeostasis.

2. List three features that vertebrates need in order to control their body temperature.

   a. A source of body heat for the body

   b. A way to conserve heat

   c. A method of eliminating excess heat

Match each description with the method of controlling body heat. Methods may be used more than once.

	Description	Method
b	**3.** An animal whose body temperature is controlled from within	**a.** Ectotherm
a	**4.** Examples include reptiles, fishes, and amphibians	**b.** Endotherm
a	**5.** Warm up by basking in the sun	
b	**6.** High metabolic rates that generate a significant amount of heat	
a	**7.** An animal whose body temperature is mainly determined by the temperature of its environment	
b	**8.** Have feathers, body fat, or hair for insulation	
a	**9.** Easily lose heat to the environment	
a	**10.** Low metabolic rate	
b	**11.** Cools off by panting or sweating	

Comparing Ectotherms and Endotherms (page 856)

12. Name one advantage and one disadvantage of endothermy.

Advantage: _Endotherms can move around easily during cool nights or in cold weather._

_____

Disadvantage: _Endotherms require a lot of fuel in the form of food._

_____

13. Is the following sentence true or false? Ectothermy is a more energy-efficient way to live in cold environments. _____false_____

Evolution of Temperature Control (page 856)

14. Circle the letter of each sentence that is true about the evolution of temperature control.

   (a.) The first land vertebrates were ectotherms.

   b. Scientists know when endothermy evolved.

   (c.) Some biologists hypothesize that dinosaurs were endotherms.

   (d.) Evidence suggests that endothermy evolved more than once.

Name_____ Class_____ Date _____

Section 33–3 Form and Function in Chordates
(pages 857–864)

⊂⊃ Key Concept
- How do the organ systems of the different groups of chordates carry out essential life functions?

Feeding (pages 857–858)

1. Most tunicates and all lancelets are _____filter feeders_____. They remove plankton from the water that passes through their _____pharynx_____.

2. Circle the letter of the vertebrates that are filter feeders.
   (a.) tunicates   (b.) flamingoes   (c.) manta rays   d. crocodiles

3. What adaptations do vertebrates have to feed on nectar? _They have long bills or narrow snouts._

4. Is the following sentence true or false? Mammals with sharp canine teeth and incisors are filter feeders. _____false_____

5. Circle the letter of the vertebrates that typically have short digestive tracts that produce enzymes.
   a. herbivores   b. endotherms   (c.) carnivores   d. ectotherms

Respiration (pages 858–859)

6. Is the following sentence true or false? Generally, aquatic chordates use lungs for respiration. _____false_____

7. List three examples of respiratory adaptations or structures used by chordates in addition to gills and lungs.
   a. _Many bony fish have air sacs that are derived from the gut._
   b. _Lancelets and some sea snakes respire by the diffusion of oxygen across their body surfaces._
   c. _Many adult amphibians use their moist skin and the linings of their mouths and pharynxes to respire by diffusion._

8. Describe the basic process of breathing among land vertebrates. _Inhaling brings oxygen-rich air into the trachea and into the lungs. The oxygen diffuses into the blood, and carbon dioxide diffuses out of the capillaries into the air. Oxygen-poor air is then exhaled._

9. Is the following sentence true or false? Mammals typically have more surface area in their lungs than amphibians. _____true_____

10. Bubblelike structures in the lungs that provide an enormous surface area for gas exchange are called _____alveoli_____.

11. Complete the flowchart that describes the path of water as it moves through a fish. See Figure 33–9 on page 859.

Water flows in through the fish's _____mouth_____, where muscles pump the water across the _____gills_____.

↓

As water passes over the gill filaments, _____oxygen_____ molecules diffuse into blood in the capillaries. At the same time, _____carbon dioxide_____ diffuses from blood into water.

↓

Water and carbon dioxide are pumped out through the _____operculum_____.

12. Why do mammals need large amounts of oxygen? They require oxygen for their endothermic metabolism.

13. Why are the lungs of birds most efficient? Air flows through bird lungs in only one direction. Thus, gas-exchange surfaces are constantly in contact with oxygen-rich air.

Circulation (pages 860–861)

14. Is the following sentence true or false? Chordates that use gills for respiration have a single-loop circulatory system. _____true_____

15. Identify where the blood is carried in each loop of a double-loop circulatory system.
First loop: Carries blood between the heart and the lungs
Second loop: Carries blood between the heart and the body

16. Is the following sentence true or false? In a double-loop system, oxygen-poor blood from the heart is carried to the body. _____false_____

17. In vertebrates with gills, the heart consists of _____two_____ chambers.

18. What is the advantage of the reptilian heart over the amphibian heart? The reptilian heart has a partial partition in the ventricle that reduces the mixing of oxygen-rich and oxygen-poor blood.

19. Why is a four-chambered heart sometimes described as a double pump? One pump moves blood through the lung loop, and the other moves blood through the body loop.

Excretion (page 861)

20. In nonvertebrate chordates and fishes, _____gills_____ play an important role in excretion. However, most vertebrates rely on _____kidneys_____.

21. Circle the letter of each chordate that eliminates nitrogenous wastes as urea.

    a. tunicates   c. birds

    b. reptiles   (d.) mammals

22. How do vertebrate kidneys help maintain homeostasis? _The kidneys regulate the_ _amounts of water, salt, and other substances dissolved in body fluids._ _____

Response (page 862)

23. Is the following sentence true or false? Nonvertebrate chordates have a complex brain with distinct regions. _____false_____

24. Circle the letter of the part of the brain that controls the function of many internal organs.

    (a.) medulla oblongata   c. olfactory bulbs

    b. optic lobes   d. cerebrum

25. Is the following sentence true or false? The cerebrum and cerebellum are most developed in birds and mammals. _____true_____

Movement (page 863)

26. Although nonvertebrate chordates lack bones, they do have _____muscles_____.

27. What structures make it possible for vertebrates to control movement? _Along with_ _muscles, the backbone and ligaments support the body, making it possible to control movement._ _____

Reproduction (page 864)

28. Is the following sentence true or false? Vertebrate evolution shows a general trend from internal to external fertilization. _____false_____

29. Circle the letter of development in which the eggs develop internally and the embryos receive nutrients from the yolk surrounding them.

    a. oviparous   c. viviparous

    (b.) ovoviviparous   d. asexual

Name_____ Class_____ Date _____

Vocabulary Review

Labeling Diagrams   *Study the diagrams of the vertebrate brains below. Then, write the vertebrate group to which each brain belongs.*

| Amphibian | Bird | Bony Fish | Mammal | Reptile |

Multiple Choice   *In the space provided, write the letter of the answer that best completes each sentence or answers the question.*

__b__   **6.** Which of the following best describes a notochord?
    a. develops into gills in fishes   **c.** is dorsal and hollow
    b. is a flexible, supporting structure   **d.** extends posterior to the anus

__a__   **7.** The rapid diversification of species as they adapt to new conditions is
    a. adaptive radiation.   **c.** convergent evolution.
    b. divergent evolution.   **d.** homeostasis.

__c__   **8.** Which of the following is NOT true about ectotherms?
    a. The environment determines their body temperature.
    b. These animals have low metabolic rates.
    c. Examples include birds and mammals.
    d. Examples include reptiles, fishes, and amphibians.

__d__   **9.** Endotherms get rid of excess heat by
    a. seeking shelter in underground burrows.
    b. basking in the sun.
    c. fluffing up feathers.
    d. panting or sweating.

__d__   **10.** Alveoli are located in the
    a. digestive system.   **c.** circulatory system.
    b. brain.   **d.** lungs.

Summary

34–1 Elements of Behavior

Behavior is the way an organism reacts to changes within its body or in its environment. Behaviors usually occur when an animal reacts to a stimulus. The single, specific reaction to a stimulus is a response. Animals detect stimuli with their sense organs. When an animal responds, the nervous system and the muscles work together to produce the behavior.

Animal behavior is important to survival and reproduction. Some behaviors are controlled by genes. They are influenced by natural selection. Organisms with a certain behavior may survive and reproduce better than organisms without the behavior. Over time, most individuals in the population will have that behavior.

Some behaviors are innate. These behaviors are fully functional the first time they are performed, even though the animal may have had no previous experience with the stimuli to which it responds. Examples of innate behaviors are the suckling of a newborn mammal and the weaving of a spider web.

Learning is the way animals change their behavior as a result of experience. Acquired behavior is another name for learning, because these behaviors develop over time. Animals learn in different ways. These include habituation, classical conditioning, operant conditioning, and insight learning.

Habituation is the simplest way in which animals learn. In habituation, an animal's response to a stimulus decreases or stops when the animal is neither rewarded nor harmed for responding.

Classical conditioning occurs when an animal makes a mental connection between a stimulus and a good or bad event. One famous example was described by Ivan Pavlov. Pavlov discovered that if he rang a bell when he fed his dog, the dog would begin to salivate whenever he rang the bell.

In operant conditioning, an animal learns to behave in a certain way in order to receive a reward or to avoid punishment. Operant conditioning is also called trial-and-error learning because it begins with a random behavior that is rewarded.

Insight learning, or reasoning, is the most complicated form of learning. In insight learning, an animal applies something it has already learned to a new situation. Insight learning is found most often in humans.

Most behaviors are the result of innate behavior and learning combined. One example of this is imprinting. Newborn ducks and geese have an innate urge to follow the first moving object they see. They are not born knowing what that object will look like. The newborn must learn from experience what object to follow.

34–2 Patterns of Behavior

Many animal behaviors occur in patterns. These patterns often follow the natural cycles of day and night, seasonal changes, or moon phases. Examples of cycles of behavior include dormancy, migration, and circadian rhythms. Dormancy allows an animal to survive periods when food and other resources may not be available. Migration is the periodic movement from one place to another and then back again. Circadian rhythms occur in a daily pattern, like sleeping at night and going to school during the day.

© Pearson Education, Inc., publishing as Pearson Prentice Hall.

Animal behaviors also help animals reproduce. Courtship behaviors help an animal find a healthy mate. Some courtship behaviors involve an elaborate series of rituals. Most rituals have specific signals and responses.

Animals have social behavior whenever they interact with members of their own species. Many animals form societies. A society is a group of related animals of the same species that interact closely and often cooperate with one another. Termites form societies. So do zebras, wild dogs, and primates. Animal societies use their strength in numbers to improve their ability to hunt, protect their territory, guard their young, and fight rivals.

Some animal behaviors help prevent others from using limited resources. These behaviors help protect territories. A territory is the area occupied and protected by an animal or group of animals. Territories contain resources, such as food, water, and shelter, that an animal needs to survive and reproduce.

Competition occurs when two or more animals claim the same territory. During competition, an animal may use threatening behavior, or aggression, to gain control over the other animal.

Communication is the passing of information from one animal to another. Animals use many different ways to communicate. Animals with good eyesight often use visual signals such as movement and color to communicate.

Animals with a well-developed sense of smell produce chemicals called pheromones. These chemicals affect the behavior of other members of the species, to mark a territory, for example.

Animals with strong vocal abilities communicate with sound. Birds, toads, crickets, and dolphins use sound to communicate.

Language is the most complicated form of communication. Language combines sounds, symbols, and gestures according to sets of rules about word order and meaning. Only humans are known to use language.

Section 34–1 Elements of Behavior (pages 871–876)

🔑 Key Concepts
- What produces behavior in animals?
- What is an innate behavior?
- What are the major types of learning?

Stimulus and Response (pages 871–872)

1. How do biologists define behavior? Behavior is the way an organism reacts to changes in
its internal condition or external environment.

2. Behaviors are usually performed when an animal reacts to a(an) _____stimulus_____.

3. What is a response? A response is a single, specific reaction to a stimulus.

4. Circle the letter of each response.
   a. alarm ringing
   c. answering the phone
   b. hunger pangs
   d. swimming toward moving prey

5. Circle the letter of each stimulus.
   a. light
   c. heat
   b. sound
   d. odors

6. Is the following sentence true or false? All animals can detect all types of stimuli.
   _____false_____

7. What body systems interact to produce a behavior in response to a stimulus?
   The sense organs, nervous system, and muscles interact to produce the behavior.

8. Is the following sentence true or false? Animals with more complex nervous systems can respond to stimuli with more complicated and precise behaviors. _____true_____

Behavior and Evolution (page 872)

9. Is the following sentence true or false? Animal behaviors are not influenced by genes.
   _____false_____

10. Explain how natural selection works in the evolution of behaviors in a population.
    Organisms with an adaptive behavior will survive and reproduce better than organisms that lack the
    behavior. After many generations, most individuals in the population will exhibit the adaptive
    behavior.

Innate Behavior (page 873)

11. What is an innate behavior? It is a behavior that appears in fully functional form the first time it is performed, even though the animal may have had no previous experience with the stimuli to which it responds.

_____

12. What two things interact to cause innate behaviors?

   a. An animal's genes

   b. An animal's environment

Learned Behavior (pages 873–875)

13. What is learning? Learning is the changes in behavior that result from experience.

_____

14. List the four major types of learning.

   a. Habituation   c. Operant conditioning

   b. Classical conditioning   d. Insight learning

15. The process by which an animal decreases or stops its response to a repetitive stimulus that neither rewards nor harms the animal is called _____ habituation _____.

16. What is the advantage of habituation? Animals can spend their time and energy more efficiently by ignoring unrewarding or nonthreatening stimuli.

_____

17. Identify the type of learning illustrated below. _____ Classical conditioning _____
   What is the stimulus? _____ Bell ringing _____ What is the reward or
   punishment that is associated with the stimulus? Food is the reward.

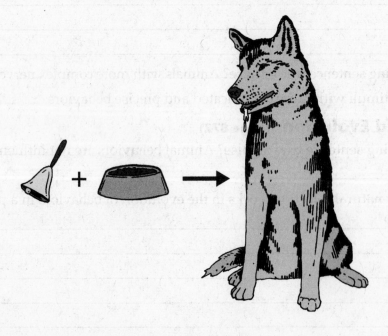

18. What is operant conditioning? <u>Operant conditioning occurs when an animal learns to behave</u>
<u>in a certain way through repeated practice, in order to receive a reward or avoid punishment.</u>

_____

19. How does a Skinner box work in operant conditioning? <u>When an animal presses a</u>
<u>button, it receives food. After the animal has done it several times, it learns that it gets food</u>
<u>whenever it presses the button.</u>

_____

20. When does insight learning occur? <u>It occurs when an animal applies something it has</u>
<u>already learned to a new situation.</u>

_____

21. Is the following sentence true or false? Insight learning is common among reptiles and
amphibians. _____<u>false</u>_____

Instinct and Learning Combined (page 876)

22. What is the purpose of imprinting? <u>Imprinting keeps young animals close to their mother,</u>
<u>who protects them and leads them to food sources.</u>

_____

23. Is the following sentence true or false? Imprinting can be changed after it has occurred.
_____<u>false</u>_____

Reading Skill Practice

When you read a section, taking notes can help you organize and remember the
information. As you read or review Section 34–1, take notes by writing each
heading and listing the main points under each heading. Do your work on a
separate sheet of paper.

Students should make note of the main points on pages 871–876. Their notes should include enough
detail to be clear and informative.

Section 34–2 Patterns of Behavior (pages 878–882)

Key Concepts

- How do environmental changes affect animal behavior?
- How do courtship and social behaviors increase an animal's evolutionary fitness?
- How do animals communicate?

Behavioral Cycles (page 878)

Match the behavioral cycle with its description.

Behavioral Cycle	Description
_a_ **1.** Dormancy	**a.** A sleeplike state that allows an animal to survive periods when food or other resources may not be available
_c_ **2.** Migration	**b.** Behavioral cycles that occur in daily patterns, such as sleeping at night and attending school during the day
_b_ **3.** Circadian rhythms	**c.** The periodic movement from one place to another and then back again to take advantage of favorable environmental conditions

Courtship (page 879)

4. Circle the letter of each sentence that is true about courtship.

   (a.) Courtship behavior helps animals identify healthy mates.

   (b.) In courtship, an individual sends out stimuli to attract a member of the opposite sex.

   c. Fireflies have an elaborate dance to indicate their readiness to mate.

   d. Courtship rituals always involve a single behavior.

Social Behavior (page 880)

5. Is the following sentence true or false? Courtship is an example of a social behavior.
   _____true_____

6. A group of related animals of the same species that interact closely and often cooperate with one another is called a(an) _____society_____.

7. What are the advantages of animal societies? Strength in numbers improves the animals' ability to hunt, to protect their territory, to guard their young, and to fight rivals.

8. How does helping a relative survive improve an individual's evolutionary fitness? Related individuals share a large proportion of one another's genes. Helping a relative survive increases the chance that the genes an individual shares with that relative will be passed along to the next generation of offspring.

Competition and Aggression (page 881)

9. What is a territory? It is a specific area that contains resources that are necessary for an animal's survival.

10. Circle the letter of each resource that animals need to survive and reproduce.
  a. odors   (**c.**) nesting sites
  (**b.**) mates   (**d.**) water

11. When does competition occur? It occurs when two or more animals try to claim one or more limited resources.

12. A threatening behavior that one animal uses to gain control over another is ____aggression____.

Communication (pages 881–882)

13. What is communication? It is the passing of information from one organism to another.

14. Is the following sentence true or false? Animals with poor eyesight often use visual signals involving movement and color. ____false____

15. Some animals communicate using ____pheromones____, chemical messengers that affect the behavior of other individuals of the same species.

16. Is the following sentence true or false? Some animals that use sound to communicate, such as dolphins, might live in places where vision is not very useful. ____true____

Vocabulary Review

Completion   *Fill in the blanks with terms from Chapter 34.*

1. The way an animal reacts to changes within itself or its environment is called
   _____behavior_____.

2. A single, specific reaction to a stimulus is a(an) _____response_____.

3. Animals that change their behavior as a result of experience are
   _____learning_____.

4. In _____classical_____ conditioning, an animal learns to make a mental
   connection between a stimulus and a reward or punishment.

5. A behavioral cycle that occurs in a daily pattern is a(an) _____circadian rhythm_____.

6. A specific area that is occupied and protected by an animal is its
   _____territory_____.

7. The passing of information from one organism to another is called
   _____communication_____.

8. The system of communication that only humans are known to use is
   _____language_____.

True or False   *In the space, write* true *if the statement is true. If the statement is false, write the term that makes the statement true.*

_____true_____ 9. A <u>stimulus</u> is any kind of signal that carries information and can be detected.

_____true_____ 10. An <u>innate behavior</u> is an instinct.

Habituation 11. <u>Insight learning</u> occurs when an animal stops its response to a repetitive stimulus that is harmless.

imprinting 12. Ducklings exhibit <u>operant conditioning</u> when they follow the first moving object they see.

_____true_____ 13. <u>Migration</u> is the periodic movement from one place to another and back again.

courtship 14. In <u>learning</u>, an individual sends out stimuli in order to attract a member of the opposite sex.

_____true_____ 15. <u>Aggression</u> is a threatening behavior that one animal uses to gain control over another.

Summary

35–1 Human Body Systems

The levels of organization in a multicellular organism include cells, tissues, organs, and organ systems. Cells are the basic units of structure and function in living things. In multicellular organisms, cells are specialized to perform certain functions. Tissues are groups of similar cells that perform a single function. There are four different types of tissues. Epithelial tissue covers body surfaces. Connective tissue supports the body and connects its parts. Nervous tissue carries messages throughout the body. Muscle tissue enables the body to move. An organ is a group of tissues that work together to perform a complex function. An organ system is a group of organs that perform related functions. Humans have 11 organ systems.

Organ systems work together to maintain stable conditions in the body. The process of maintaining stable internal conditions is called homeostasis. Homeostasis may involve feedback inhibition, or negative feedback. For example, the nervous system senses when the body cools and signals the cells to produce more heat.

35–2 The Nervous System

The nervous system controls and coordinates functions throughout the body and responds to internal and external stimuli. Messages carried by the nervous system are electrical signals called impulses. Cells that transmit impulses are called neurons. A neuron has a cell body containing the nucleus. Short branches, called dendrites, carry impulses toward the cell body. A long fiber, called the axon, carries impulses away from the cell body. A myelin sheath surrounds parts of the axon in some neurons. Impulses can jump over the myelin and travel faster.

A resting neuron is one that is not transmitting an impulse. Resting potential is the difference in electrical charge across the cell membrane of a resting neuron. An impulse begins when a resting neuron is stimulated by another neuron or by the environment. The impulse is a sudden reversal of charge across the cell membrane, called an action potential. The lowest level of stimulus needed to activate a neuron is known as the threshold.

At the end of the axon is a synapse. A synapse is the location at which a neuron can transfer an impulse to another cell. Chemicals called neurotransmitters transmit impulses across the synapse.

35–3 Divisions of the Nervous System

The nervous system has two major divisions: the central nervous system and the peripheral nervous system. The central nervous system is the control center of the body. It relays messages, processes information, and analyzes information. The peripheral nervous system carries messages back and forth between the environment and the central nervous system.

The central nervous system consists of the brain and spinal cord. Both are wrapped in layers of tissue called meninges. Between the meninges and nervous tissue is cerebrospinal fluid, which cushions and protects nervous tissue.

The brain is divided into several regions. The cerebrum controls voluntary actions. The cerebellum controls actions of the muscles. The brain stem controls basic body functions. The thalamus receives impulses from the senses and sends them to the cerebrum. The hypothalamus connects the nervous and endocrine systems.

The spinal cord connects the brain to the rest of the body. Certain kinds of information, including some reflexes, are processed directly in the spinal cord. A reflex is a quick, automatic response to a stimulus. A reflex allows your body to respond to danger immediately, without spending time thinking about a response. Animals rely heavily on reflex behaviors for survival.

The peripheral nervous system has two divisions. The sensory division transmits impulses from sensory neurons to the central nervous system. The motor division transmits impulses from the central nervous system to muscles and glands. The motor division is further divided into somatic and autonomic nervous systems. The somatic nervous system controls voluntary actions. The autonomic nervous system controls involuntary actions.

35–4 The Senses

Sensory receptors are neurons that react to stimuli in the environment and send impulses to the central nervous system. There are five types of sensory receptors. Pain receptors respond to pain. Thermoreceptors respond to temperature. Mechanoreceptors respond to pressure. Chemoreceptors respond to chemicals. Photoreceptors respond to light.

Light enters the eye through the pupil, which is a small opening at the front of the eye. Light then passes through the lens, which focuses the light on the retina. Photoreceptors called rods and cones are located in the retina. Rods are sensitive to dim light. Cones are sensitive to colors.

Sound vibrations enter the ear and create pressure waves in a fluid-filled structure called the cochlea. Sensory receptors in the cochlea send impulses to the brain. Three tiny canals in the ear, called semicircular canals, help the central nervous system maintain balance.

The sense organs that detect taste are the taste buds. Skin—the largest sense organ—contains sensory receptors that respond to temperature, touch, and pain.

35–5 Drugs and the Nervous System

A drug is any substance, other than food, that changes the structure or function of the body. Several types of drugs can affect the nervous system. Stimulants increase actions controlled by the nervous system, such as heart rate. Stimulants also increase the release of neurotransmitters in the brain. Depressants decrease actions, such as heart rate, that are controlled by the brain. Cocaine causes the sudden release in the brain of a neurotransmitter called dopamine. Opiates act like natural brain chemicals called endorphins, which normally help overcome pain. Marijuana can cause memory and concentration problems.

Alcohol is a depressant. It slows down the central nervous system. Drinking alcohol during pregnancy may cause fetal alcohol syndrome (FAS). Babies born with FAS have birth defects. People who are addicted to alcohol have a disease called alcoholism.

Addiction is an uncontrollable dependence on a drug. Drug abuse is the intentional misuse of any drug for nonmedical purposes. The best way to avoid the effects of drugs is to avoid drugs.

Chapter 35 Nervous System

Section 35–1 Human Body Systems (pages 891–896)

🔑 **Key Concepts**
- How is the human body organized?
- What is homeostasis?

Organization of the Body (pages 891–894)

1. List the levels of organization in a multicellular organism, from smallest to largest.

   a. _Cells_____

   b. _Tissues_____

   c. _Organs_____

   d. _Organ systems_____

Match the organ system with its function.

	Organ System	Function
c	**2.** Nervous system	**a.** Stores mineral reserves and provides a site for blood cell formation
a	**3.** Skeletal system	**b.** Provides oxygen and removes carbon dioxide
g	**4.** Integumentary system	**c.** Coordinates the body's response to changes in its internal and external environments
e	**5.** Endocrine system	**d.** Helps produce voluntary movement, circulate blood, and move food
i	**6.** Lymphatic/immune systems	**e.** Controls growth, development, metabolism, and reproduction
d	**7.** Muscular system	**f.** Eliminates wastes and maintains homeostasis
j	**8.** Reproductive system	**g.** Serves as a barrier against infection and injury
b	**9.** Respiratory system	**h.** Converts food so it can be used by cells
f	**10.** Excretory system	**i.** Helps protect the body from disease
k	**11.** Circulatory system	**j.** Produces reproductive cells
h	**12.** Digestive system	**k.** Brings materials to cells, fights infection, and helps to regulate body temperature

13. What are four types of tissues found in the human body? _The four types of tissues are_ _muscle tissue, epithelial tissue, connective tissue, and nervous tissue._

   _____

14. The eye is an example of a(an) ____organ____.

15. Circle the letter of the type of tissue that covers interior and exterior body surfaces.

   a. nervous

   b. connective

   c. epithelial

   d. muscle

16. Circle the letter of the type of tissue that connects body parts.

   a. nervous   **c.** epithelial

   (b.) connective   **d.** integumentary

Maintaining Homeostasis (pages 895–896)

17. The process of maintaining a controlled, stable internal environment is called
_____homeostasis_____.

18. The process in which a stimulus produces a response that opposes the original
stimulus is referred to as _____feedback inhibition_____.

19. Fill in the missing labels in the diagram to show how a thermostat uses feedback
inhibition to maintain a stable temperature in a house.

Thermostat senses temperature change and switches off heating system

Room temperature increases

Room temperature decreases

Thermostat senses temperature change and switches on heating system

20. Is the following sentence true or false? The part of the brain that monitors and controls
body temperature is the hypothalamus. _____true_____

21. What happens if nerve cells sense that the core body temperature has dropped
below 37°C? The hypothalamus produces chemicals that signal cells throughout the body to
speed up their activities, which causes a gradual rise in body temperature.

_____

22. What happens if the body temperature rises too far above 37°C? The hypothalamus
slows down cellular activities, minimizing the production of heat.

_____

Section 35–2 The Nervous System (pages 897–900)

⊂⊃ **Key Concepts**
- What are the functions of the nervous system?
- How is the nerve impulse transmitted?

Introduction (page 897)

1. What is the function of the nervous system? The nervous system controls and coordinates functions throughout the body and responds to internal and external changes.

_____

Neurons (pages 897–898)

2. How are neurons classified? Neurons are classified according to the direction in which an impulse travels.

3. What are three types of neurons?

   a. Sensory neurons _____

   b. Motor neurons _____

   c. Interneurons _____

4. Is the following sentence true or false? Sensory neurons carry impulses from the brain and the spinal cord to muscles and glands. _____false_____

5. Label the following features in the drawing of a neuron: cell body, dendrites, and axon.

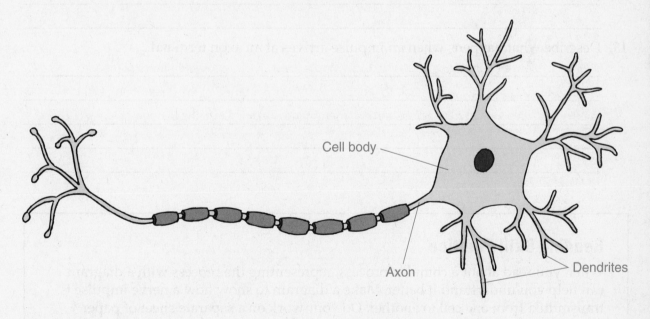

Cell body

Axon   Dendrites

6. What is the function of the myelin sheath? The myelin sheath increases the speed at which nerve impulses can travel.

The Nerve Impulse (pages 898–899)

7. The electrical charge across the cell membrane of a neuron in its resting state is called its _____resting potential_____.

8. How does a nerve impulse begin? A nerve impulse begins when a neuron is stimulated by another neuron or by its environment.

_____

_____

9. Circle the letter of the choice that describes an action potential.

    a. Reversal of charges due to the flow of positive ions into a neuron

    b. Increase in negative ions in a neuron due to the flow of potassium out of the cell

    c. Change to a negative charge due to the flow of sodium ions out of a neuron

    d. Reversal of charges due to the flow of negative ions into a neuron

10. The minimum level of a stimulus that is required to activate a neuron is called the _____threshold_____.

11. How does a nerve impulse follow the all-or-nothing principle? Either a stimulus will produce an impulse or it will not, depending on its strength.

_____

The Synapse (page 900)

12. What are neurotransmitters? Neurotransmitters are chemicals that are used by a neuron to transmit an impulse across a synapse to another cell.

_____

13. Describe what happens when an impulse arrives at an axon terminal.

    The sacs release neurotransmitters into the synaptic cleft. The neurotransmitters diffuse

    across the synaptic cleft and attach to receptors on the membrane of the neighboring cell,

    causing positive ions to rush across the cell membrane and stimulate the second cell.

_____

_____

Reading Skill Practice

When you read about a complex process, representing the process with a diagram can help you understand it better. Make a diagram to show how a nerve impulse is transmitted from one cell to another. Do your work on a separate sheet of paper.

Students' diagrams should be similar to Figure 35–8. Their diagrams should be labeled to show the relevant parts of the cells and the direction of the nerve impulse.

Section 35–3 Divisions of the Nervous System
(pages 901–905)

🔑 **Key Concepts**
- What are the functions of the central nervous system?
- What are the functions of the two divisions of the peripheral nervous system?

Introduction (page 901)

1. What is the function of the central nervous system? <u>The central nervous system relays</u> <u>messages, processes information, and analyzes information.</u>
_____

The Central Nervous System (page 901)

2. The central nervous system consists of the _____<u>brain</u>_____ and the _____<u>spinal cord</u>_____.

3. Is the following sentence true or false? Three layers of connective tissue known as meninges protect the brain and spinal cord. _____<u>true</u>_____

4. The brain and spinal cord are bathed and protected by _____<u>cerebrospinal fluid</u>_____.

The Brain (pages 902–903)

Match the part of the brain with its function.

	Part of Brain	Function
<u>c</u>	5. Cerebrum	**a.** Coordinates and balances the actions of the muscles
<u>a</u>	6. Cerebellum	**b.** Regulates the flow of information between the brain and the rest of the body
<u>b</u>	7. Brain stem	**c.** Controls voluntary activities of the body
<u>e</u>	8. Thalamus	**d.** Controls hunger, thirst, fatigue, anger, and body temperature
<u>d</u>	9. Hypothalamus	**e.** Receives and relays messages from the sense organs

10. The two hemispheres of the brain are connected by a band of tissue called the _____<u>corpus callosum</u>_____.

11. Identify the four lobes of the brain.

   a. <u>Frontal lobe</u>   c. <u>Temporal lobe</u>
   b. <u>Parietal lobe</u>   d. <u>Occipital lobe</u>

12. Is the following sentence true or false? The left hemisphere of the cerebrum controls the body's left side. _____<u>false</u>_____

13. Is the following sentence true or false? The outer layer of the cerebrum is called the cerebral cortex. _____<u>true</u>_____

14. What is gray matter, and where is it found? <u>Gray matter is densely packed nerve cell</u> <u>bodies and is found in the cerebral cortex of the cerebrum.</u>

15. The two regions of the brain stem are the _____ medulla oblongata _____ and the _____ pons _____.

The Spinal Cord (page 903)

16. What is the advantage of a reflex? It allows your body to respond to danger immediately, without spending time thinking about a response.

_____

The Peripheral Nervous System (pages 903–904)

17. Circle the letter of each choice that is part of the peripheral nervous system.

   a. cranial nerves   **c.** ganglia

   b. spinal nerves   **d.** spinal cord

18. Complete the concept map.

19. Circle the letter of each activity that is controlled by the somatic nervous system.

   a. Beating of the heart   **c.** Wiggling the toes

   b. Lifting a finger   **d.** Pulling foot away from tack

20. What does the autonomic nervous system regulate? It regulates activities that are automatic, or involuntary, such as the heartbeat.

_____

21. Why is it important to have two systems that control the same organs?

One system speeds up the activities of the organs, and the other system slows down the activities of the organs.

_____

Section 35–4 The Senses (pages 906–909)

⚷ Key Concept
- What are the five types of sensory receptors?

Introduction (page 906)

1. What are sensory receptors? They are neurons that react directly to stimuli from the environment.

2. List the five general categories of sensory receptors.

   a. Pain receptors

   b. Thermoreceptors

   c. Mechanoreceptors

   d. Chemoreceptors

   e. Photoreceptors

3. Which category of sensory receptors are sensitive to touch, sound, and motion? Mechanoreceptors are sensitive to touch, sound, and motion.

Vision (pages 906–907)

4. Circle the letter of each sentence that is true about the structures of the eye.

   (a.) Light enters the eye through the cornea.

   b. The chamber behind the cornea is filled with vitreous humor.

   (c.) The pupil changes in size to let more or less light enter the eye.

   (d.) The lens focuses light on the retina.

5. Is the following sentence true or false? The function of the iris is to adjust the size of the pupil. _____ true

6. Where are the photoreceptors located in the eye? They are located in the retina.

7. What do photoreceptors do? They convert light energy into nerve impulses that are carried to the central nervous system.

8. Is the following sentence true or false? Cones are extremely sensitive to light, but they do not distinguish different colors. _____ false

9. How do impulses travel from the eyes to the brain? They are carried by the optic nerves.

10. What are the two types of photoreceptors? Rods and cones

Name_____ Class_____ Date _____

Hearing and Balance (pages 908–909)

11. List the two sensory functions of the ear.

   a. _Hearing_____

   b. _Detecting positional changes associated with movement (balance)_____

12. Label each of the following structures in the drawing of the ear: auditory canal, tympanum, semicircular canals, and cochlea.

13. Is the following sentence true or false? The tympanum sends nerve impulses to the brain. _____false_____

14. Complete the flowchart.

Vibrations enter the ear through the ____auditory canal____.

↓

The vibrations cause the ____tympanum____ to vibrate.

↓

These vibrations are picked up by three tiny bones, called the ____hammer____, ____anvil____, and ____stirrup____.

↓

The last bone transmits the vibrations to the ____oval window____, creating pressure waves in the ____cochlea____.

↓

Tiny hair cells inside the ____cochlea____ produce nerve impulses that are sent to the brain through the ____cochlear____ nerve.

© Pearson Education, Inc., publishing as Pearson Prentice Hall.

15. What is the role of hair cells in the cochlea? In response to pressure waves in the cochlea, the hair cells produce nerve impulses that are sent to the brain through the cochlear nerve.

16. How do the semicircular canals help maintain balance? They monitor the position of the body, especially the head, in relation to gravity.

Smell and Taste (page 909)

17. Is the following sentence true or false? Your sense of smell is actually an ability to detect pressure. _____false_____

18. How does the body detect smell? Chemoreceptors in the lining of the nasal passageway respond to specific chemicals and send impulses to the brain through sensory nerves.

19. Is the following sentence true or false? Much of what we commonly call the "taste" of food and drink is actually smell. _____true_____

20. The sense organs that detect taste are the _____taste buds_____.

21. List the four different categories of tastes.

a. _____Salty_____

b. _____Bitter_____

c. _____Sweet_____

d. _____Sour_____

Touch and Related Senses (page 909)

22. What is the largest sense organ? The skin is the largest sense organ.

23. Is the following sentence true or false? The skin contains sensory receptors that respond to temperature, touch, and pain. _____true_____

24. Circle the letter of each choice that is true about the sense of touch.

(a.) Unlike the other senses, the sense of touch is not found in one particular place.

b. All parts of the body are equally sensitive to touch.

c. The greatest density of touch receptors is found on the arms and legs.

(d.) Touch is detected by mechanoreceptors.

25. Where is the greatest density of touch receptors found on the body? The greatest density is found on fingers, toes, and the face.

Section 35–5 Drugs and the Nervous System
(pages 910–914)

👁 **Key Concepts**
- What are the different classes of drugs that directly affect the central nervous system?
- What is the effect of alcohol on the body?

Introduction (page 910)

1. Is the following sentence true or false? A drug is any illegal substance that changes the structure or function of the body. _____false_____

2. Is the following sentence true or false? Among the most powerful drugs are the ones that cause changes in the nervous system, especially to the brain and the synapses between neurons. _____true_____

3. How can drugs disrupt the functioning of the nervous system? They can disrupt it by interfering with the action of neurotransmitters. _____

_____

Drugs That Affect the Synapse (pages 910–914)

Match the drug or type of drug with one way that it can affect the body.

	Drug or Type of Drug	Effect on the Body
e	4. Stimulant	a. Acts on pleasure centers of brain
d	5. Depressant	b. Destroys liver cells
a	6. Cocaine	c. Reduces pain
c	7. Opiate	d. Decreases heart rate
f	8. Marijuana	e. Increases blood pressure
b	9. Alcohol	f. Causes lung damage

10. Circle the letter of each choice that is a stimulant drug.
   (a.) nicotine   (c.) amphetamine
   (b.) cocaine   d. codeine

11. Circle the letter of each choice that is a depressant drug.
   (a.) alcohol   (c.) tranquilizer
   (b.) morphine   (d.) barbiturate

12. Cocaine causes the sudden release in the brain of a neurotransmitter called _____dopamine_____.

13. Is the following sentence true or false? The most widely abused illegal drug is marijuana. _____true_____

14. Circle the letter of each choice that is a result of long-term use of marijuana.
   (a.) Loss of memory   **c.** Increase in testosterone
   (b.) Inability to concentrate   **d.** Cirrhosis of the liver

15. Is the following sentence true or false? Alcohol is one of the most abused legal drugs.
_____true_____

16. What is fetal alcohol syndrome, or FAS? FAS is a group of birth defects caused by the
effects of alcohol on the fetus.
_____

17. People who have become addicted to alcohol suffer from a disease called
_____alcoholism_____.

18. How does long-term alcohol use affect the body? It destroys cells in the liver and can lead
to cirrhosis of the liver and liver failure.
_____

Drug Abuse (page 914)

19. The intentional misuse of any drug for nonmedical purposes is referred to as
_____drug abuse_____.

20. An uncontrollable dependence on a drug is known as _____addiction_____.

21. What is psychological dependence on a drug? It is a mental craving, or need, for the drug.
_____

22. When does physical dependence on a drug occur? It occurs when the body cannot
function without a constant supply of the drug.
_____

23. How can drug use increase the transmission of HIV, the virus that causes AIDS?
Many users inject drugs for maximum effect. HIV can be spread rapidly from person to person
when drug users share contaminated needles.
_____

Chapter 35   Nervous System

Vocabulary Review

Completion   *Fill in the blanks in the table.*

Tissue Type	Function
Epithelial	1. Covers body surfaces
Connective	2. Supports the body and connects its parts
Nervous	3. Carries nerve impulses
Muscle	4. Enables the body to move

True or False   *Determine whether each statement is true or false. If it is true, write* true *in the space provided. If the statement is false, change the underlined word or words to make the statement true.*

___true___ **5.** The process by which organisms keep internal conditions relatively constant is called <u>homeostasis</u>.

___neurons___ **6.** Cells that transmit nerve impulses are known as <u>meninges</u>.

___axon___ **7.** The long fiber that carries impulses away from the cell body of a nerve cell is the <u>dendrite</u>.

___threshold___ **8.** The lowest level of stimulus needed to activate a neuron is called the <u>action potential</u>.

___true___ **9.** The location at which a neuron can transfer an impulse to another cell is referred to as a(an) <u>synapse</u>.

___cerebrum___ **10.** The part of the brain that controls voluntary actions is the <u>brain stem</u>.

___thalamus___ **11.** The part of the brain that receives impulses from the senses and sends them to the cerebrum is the <u>hypothalamus</u>.

___true___ **12.** Light enters the eye through a small opening called the <u>pupil</u>.

___cones___ **13.** Photoreceptors in the eye that are sensitive to colors are known as <u>rods</u>.

___stimulants___ **14.** Drugs called <u>opiates</u> increase actions controlled by the nervous system.

___addiction___ **15.** An uncontrollable dependence on a drug is known as drug <u>abuse</u>.

Answering Questions   *In the space provided, write an answer to each question.*

16. List the levels of organization in a multicellular organism, from smallest to largest.

The levels of organization in a multicellular organism, from smallest to largest, are cells, tissues, organs, and organ systems.

17. What is resting potential? Resting potential is the difference in electrical charge across the cell membrane of a resting neuron.

18. What is the function of the autonomic nervous system? The function of the autonomic nervous system is to control involuntary actions.

19. How does alcohol affect the central nervous system? Alcohol slows down the central nervous system.

20. To which type of stimulus do thermoreceptors react? Thermoreceptors react to temperature.

Summary

36–1 The Skeletal System

The skeletal system supports the body, protects internal organs, provides for movement, stores mineral reserves, and provides a site for blood cell formation. The skeleton is divided into two parts: the axial skeleton and the appendicular skeleton. The axial skeleton includes the skull, ribs, and spine. The appendicular skeleton includes all the bones associated with the arms and legs, including bones of the shoulders, hips, hands, and feet.

The bones that make up the skeletal system are living tissue. Bones are a solid network of living cells and protein fibers that are surrounded by deposits of calcium salts. A typical bone is surrounded by a tough layer of connective tissue called the periosteum. Beneath the periosteum is a thick layer of compact bone. Running through compact bone is a network of tubes called Haversian canals. These canals contain blood vessels and nerves. Inside the layer of compact bone is spongy bone. Spongy bone is quite strong and adds strength to bones without adding mass. Within bones are cavities that contain a soft tissue called bone marrow. Bone marrow can be yellow or red. Yellow marrow is made up of fat. Red marrow produces blood cells.

The skeleton of an embryo is composed almost entirely of cartilage. Cartilage is a type of connective tissue that is tough but flexible. Cartilage is replaced by bone during the process of bone formation, or ossification. Ossification starts before birth and continues until adulthood.

A place where one bone attaches to another bone is called a joint. Joints permit bones to move without damaging each other. Depending on its type of movement, a joint is classified as immovable, slightly movable, or freely movable. Immovable joints, such as the joints in the skull, allow no movement. Slightly movable joints, such as the joints in the spine, allow a small amount of restricted movement. Freely movable joints permit movement in one or more directions. Freely movable joints are classified by the type of movement they permit.

Ball-and-socket joints, such as the shoulder, allow the widest range of movement of any joint. Hinge joints, such as the knee, permit only back-and-forth movement. Pivot joints, such as the elbow, allow one bone to rotate around another. Saddle joints, such as those in the hand, allow one bone to slide in two directions.

Strips of tough connective tissue, called ligaments, hold bones together in a joint. The bony surfaces of the joint are covered with cartilage. A substance called synovial fluid forms a thin film on the cartilage and makes the joint surfaces slippery.

Bones and joints can be damaged by excessive strain or disease. Arthritis is a disorder that involves inflammation of the joints. Osteoporosis is a condition in which bones weaken. Weak bones are likely to fracture, or break.

36–2 The Muscular System

Muscle tissue is found everywhere in the body. There are three different types of muscle tissue: skeletal, smooth, and cardiac. Skeletal muscles are usually attached to bones. They appear to be striped, so they are also called striated muscles. Skeletal muscles are responsible for voluntary movements such as dancing.

© Pearson Education, Inc., publishing as Pearson Prentice Hall.

Smooth muscles line blood vessels and the digestive tract. They are not striated or under conscious control. Smooth muscles move food through the digestive tract and control the flow of blood through the circulatory system. Cardiac muscle is found only in the heart. Like smooth muscle, it is not under conscious control.

Skeletal muscle cells are called muscle fibers. Muscle fibers are composed of smaller structures called myofibrils. Each myofibril is made up of even smaller structures called filaments. Filaments can be thick or thin. Thick filaments are made of a protein called myosin. Thin filaments are made of a protein called actin. A muscle contracts when the thin filaments in the muscle fiber slide over the thick filaments.

Impulses from motor neurons control the contraction of skeletal muscles. The point of contact between a motor neuron and a muscle fiber is called a neuromuscular junction. A neurotransmitter named acetylcholine is released by the motor neuron into the synapse. Acetylcholine transmits the impulse across the synapse to the skeletal muscle cell. The more muscle cells that are stimulated to contract, the stronger the contraction.

Skeletal muscles are joined to bones by tough connective tissues called tendons. Tendons pull on bones and make them work like levers. Muscles provide the force to move the bones. Most skeletal muscles work in opposing pairs. When one muscle contracts, the other relaxes.

Regular exercise is important in maintaining the strength and flexibility of muscles. Regular exercise also strengthens bones. Strong bones and muscles are less likely to become injured.

36–3 The Integumentary System

The skin is the single largest organ of the body. It is also the largest component of the integumentary system. The integumentary system serves as a barrier against infection and injury, helps to regulate body temperature, removes waste products from the body, and provides protection against ultraviolet radiation from the sun.

The skin is made up of two main layers: the epidermis and the dermis. The epidermis is the outer layer of the skin. Cells of the epidermis produce keratin. Keratin is a tough, fibrous protein that helps keep the epidermis flexible and waterproof. The epidermis also contains cells, called melanocytes, that produce melanin. Melanin is a dark drown pigment that helps protect the skin from ultraviolet rays.

The dermis is the inner layer of skin. It contains nerves, blood vessels, glands, and other structures not found in the epidermis. The dermis works with other organs to maintain homeostasis. It helps to regulate body temperature. Sweat glands in the dermis produce sweat when the body gets too hot. When the sweat evaporates from the skin, it cools the body.

Too much sunlight can produce skin cancer. You can protect against skin cancer by wearing a hat, sunglasses, and protective clothing. You also should use sunscreen with a sun protection factor (SPF) of at least 15.

In addition to the skin, the integumentary system includes the hair and nails. Both hair and nails are composed mainly of keratin. Hair on the head protects the scalp from sunlight and cold. Hair in the nostrils and around the eyes prevents dirt from entering the body. Hair is produced by structures called hair follicles. Hair follicles are located in the dermis. Nails grow from an area called the nail root. Nails protect the tips of the fingers and toes.

Section 36–1 The Skeletal System (pages 921–925)

🖝 Key Concepts

- What are the functions of the skeletal system?
- What is the structure of a typical bone?
- What are the three different kinds of joints?

Introduction (page 921)

1. What forms the skeletal system? <u>Bones and other connective tissues, such as cartilage and ligaments, form the skeletal system.</u>

The Skeleton (page 921)

2. List the functions of the skeletal system.

   a. <u>Supporting the body</u> d. <u>Storing mineral reserves</u>

   b. <u>Protecting internal organs</u> e. <u>Providing a site for blood cell formation</u>

   c. <u>Allowing movement</u>

3. Is the following sentence true or false? Most bones act like levers on which muscles act to produce movement. <u>true</u>

4. Is the following sentence true or false? There are 106 bones in the adult human skeleton. <u>false</u>

5. Complete the concept map.

The Human Skeleton

is divided into

Axial skeleton — Appendicular skeleton

which contains — which contains

Skull — Rib cage — Arms/legs — Shoulders

Vertebral column — Pelvis

6. What is the general function of the axial skeleton? It supports the central axis of the body.
_____

Structure of Bones (page 922)

7. The two minerals that make up most of the mass of bone are _____calcium_____ and _____phosphorus_____.

8. Is the following sentence true or false? Bones are living tissue. _____true_____

Match each structure in a bone with its description.

Structure	Description
___c___ **9.** Periosteum	**a.** Network of tubes running through bone
___d___ **10.** Compact bone	**b.** Soft tissue contained in bone cavities
___a___ **11.** Haversian canals	**c.** Tough layer of connective tissue surrounding bone
___e___ **12.** Spongy bone	**d.** Thick layer of dense bone beneath the periosteum
___b___ **13.** Bone marrow	**e.** Bone with a latticework structure

14. Cells that produce bone are called _____osteoblasts_____.

Development of Bones (pages 922–923)

15. The skeleton of an embryo is composed almost entirely of a type of connective tissue called _____cartilage_____.

16. The network of fibers in cartilage is made from two proteins called _____collagen_____ and _____elastin_____.

17. Circle the letter of each sentence that is true about cartilage.

a. It contains blood vessels.   **c.** It cannot support weight.

(**b.**) It is dense and fibrous.   (**d.**) It is extremely flexible.

18. Cartilage is replaced by bone during the process of bone formation called _____ossification_____.

19. Is the following sentence true or false? By adulthood, all the cartilage in the body has been replaced by bone. _____false_____

Types of Joints (page 924)

20. What is a joint? A joint is a place where one bone attaches to another.
_____

21. List the three classifications of joints, based on their type of movement.

a. Immovable

b. Slightly movable

c. Freely movable

22. What are examples of immovable joints? Examples are the places where the bones in the skull meet.
_____

23. Is the following sentence true or false? The joints between the two bones of the lower leg are slightly movable joints. _____true_____

24. Identify the type of freely movable joint represented in each of the drawings below.

Ball-and-socket joint   Hinge joint   Pivot joint

25. Is the following sentence true or false? Ball-and-socket joints permit the widest range of movement. _____true_____

Structure of Joints (pages 924–925)

26. Circle the letter of each sentence that is true about the structure of joints.

   (a.) Cartilage protects the ends of bones as they move against each other at joints.

   (b.) Ligaments hold bones together at joints.

   c. Synovial fluid prevents the ends of bones from slipping past each other at joints.

   d. A bursa is a swelling caused by inflammation of a joint.

Skeletal System Disorders (page 925)

27. Inflammation of a bursa is called _____bursitis_____.

28. A serious disorder that involves inflammation of one or more joints is
_____arthritis_____.

Section 36–2 The Muscular System (pages 926–931)

🔑 Key Concepts
- What are the three types of muscle tissue?
- How do muscles contract?
- Why is exercise important?

Types of Muscle Tissue (pages 926–927)

1. List the three different types of muscle tissue.

   a. Skeletal _____ b. Smooth _____ c. Cardiac _____

2. Is the following sentence true or false? Each type of muscle has the same function.
   _____false_____

3. Is the following sentence true or false? Skeletal muscles are usually attached to bones.
   _____true_____

4. Circle the letter of each sentence that is true about skeletal muscles.
   (a.) They have striations.
   (b.) Most of them are consciously controlled by the central nervous system.
   (c.) Their cells have just one nucleus.
   d. Their cells are long and slender.

5. Circle the letter of each sentence that is true about smooth muscle cells.
   (a.) They are spindle-shaped.
   (b.) They can function without nervous stimulation.
   c. They have two or more nuclei.
   (d.) They are connected by gap junctions.

6. What are three functions of smooth muscles? Smooth muscles move food through your digestive tract, control the way blood flows through your circulatory system, and increase or decrease the size of your pupils.
   _____
   _____

7. Is the following sentence true or false? Cardiac muscle cells always have two nuclei.
   _____false_____

8. Complete the table that compares and contrasts the three types of muscle tissue.

TYPES OF MUSCLE TISSUE

Muscle Tissue Type	Striated/Not Striated	What It Controls
Skeletal	Striated	Voluntary movements
Smooth	Not striated	Involuntary movements
Cardiac	Striated	Heartbeat

Muscle Contraction (page 928)

9. Circle the letter of the choice that lists the muscle structures from largest to smallest.

   a. Myofibrils, filaments, muscle fibers

   (b.) Muscle fibers, myofibrils, filaments

   c. Muscle fibers, filaments, myofibrils

   d. Myofibrils, muscle fibers, filaments

Match each type of muscle filament with the protein it contains.

Type of Filament	Protein It Contains
__b__ 10. thick	a. Actin
__a__ 11. thin	b. Myosin

12. The filaments are arranged along the muscle fiber in units called _____sarcomeres_____.

13. Is the following sentence true or false? When a muscle is relaxed, there are only thin filaments in the center of a sarcomere. _____false_____

14. How does a muscle contract according to the sliding-filament model of muscle contraction? __The thin filaments in the muscle fiber slide over the thick filaments.__

15. The energy for muscle contraction is supplied by _____ATP_____.

Control of Muscle Contraction (page 929)

16. Complete the flowchart to show the missing steps in the stimulation of a muscle cell by a neuron.

Diffusion of acetylcholine across synapse

produces

Impulse in membrane of muscle cell

causes

Release of calcium ions within the fiber

affects

Regulatory proteins

allow

Actin and myosin filaments to interact

17. Is the following sentence true or false? Impulses from motor neurons control the contraction of skeletal muscles. _____true_____

18. The point of contact between a motor neuron and a skeletal muscle cell is a(an) _____neuromuscular junction_____.

19. What terminates a muscle contraction? _An enzyme produced at the axon terminal destroys_ acetylcholine at the neuromuscular junction and consequently terminates the contraction.
_____

20. Is the following sentence true or false? A single motor neuron can form synapses with many muscle cells. _____true_____

21. What is the difference between a strong muscle contraction and a weak muscle contraction? _More muscle cells are stimulated to contract in a strong muscle contraction than_ in a weak muscle contraction.
_____

How Muscles and Bones Interact (page 930)

22. Is the following sentence true or false? Individual muscles can pull in only one direction. _____true_____

23. Circle the letter of the term that refers to the tough connective tissue joining skeletal muscle to bone.

    a. cartilage   **b.** ligament   (**c.**) tendon   **d.** bursa

24. If bones are like levers, what functions as a fulcrum? _The joint functions as a fulcrum._

25. What does it mean for muscles to "work in opposing pairs"? _When one muscle in the_ pair contracts, the other relaxes.

Exercise and Health (page 931)

26. Why is regular exercise important? _It maintains muscular strength and flexibility._
_____

Reading Skill Practice

When you read a section with many details, writing an outline may help you organize and remember the material. Outline Section 36–2 by first writing the section headings as major topics in the order in which they appear in the book. Then, beneath each major topic, list important details about it. Title your outline *The Muscular System.* Do your work on a separate sheet of paper.

In their outlines, students should use the blue heads as their major topics. Under each topic, they should list enough details to make the topic clear and informative.

Section 36–3 The Integumentary System
(pages 933–936)

⬤ **Key Concept**
- What are the functions of the integumentary system?

Introduction (page 933)

1. Circle the letter of each choice that is part of the integumentary system.

   (a.) skin   **c.** cartilage

   b. bones   **(d.)** nails

The Skin (pages 933–936)

2. The most important function of the skin is _____protection_____.

3. List the four functions of the integumentary system.

   a. _Serving as a barrier against infection and injury_

   b. _Regulating body temperature_

   c. _Removing waste products from the body_

   d. _Protecting against ultraviolet radiation_

4. The largest component of the integumentary system is the _____skin_____.

5. The outer layer of skin is called the _____epidermis_____.

6. Is the following sentence true or false? The inner layer of the epidermis is made up of dead cells. _____false_____

7. Label the structures of the skin.

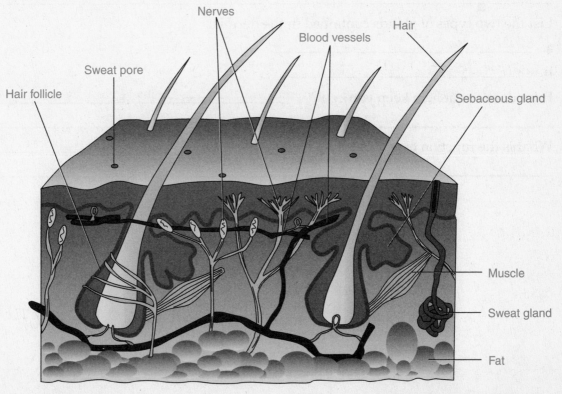

Nerves

Blood vessels

Hair

Sweat pore

Hair follicle

Sebaceous gland

Muscle

Sweat gland

Fat

Match each term with its definition.

	Term	Definition
_a_	**8.** keratin	**a.** Tough, fibrous protein
_c_	**9.** melanin	**b.** Inner layer of the skin
_b_	**10.** dermis	**c.** Dark brown pigment

11. Circle the letter of each sentence that is true about melanocytes.

(**a.**) Melanocytes are cells that produce melanin.

(**b.**) Most people have roughly the same number of melanocytes in their skin.

c. All melanocytes produce about the same amount of melanin.

d. Most people have the same distribution of melanocytes in their skin.

12. Is the following sentence true or false? The epidermis contains blood vessels.

_____false_____

13. Circle the letter of each type of structure that is found in the dermis.

(**a.**) blood vessels   (**c.**) glands

(**b.**) nerve endings   (**d.**) hair follicles

14. How does the dermis help regulate body temperature? When the body needs to conserve heat, the blood vessels in the dermis narrow, helping to limit heat loss. When the body needs to lose heat, the blood vessels widen, bringing heat from the body's core to the skin and increasing heat loss.

15. List the two types of glands contained in the dermis.

a. Sweat glands

b. Sebaceous glands

16. How does sweat help keep you cool? When sweat evaporates, it takes heat away from your body.

17. What is the function of sebum? It helps to keep the epidermis flexible and waterproof.

Hair and Nails (page 936)

18. The basic structure of human hair and nails is _____keratin_____.

19. List the two functions of head hair.

    a. Protecting the scalp from ultraviolet light _____

    b. Providing insulation from the cold _____

20. How does hair in the nose and ears and around the eyes help protect the body?

    It prevents dirt and other particles from entering the body through the nose, _____

    ears, and eyes. _____

    _____

21. Hair is produced by cells called _____hair follicles_____.

22. Is the following sentence true or false? Hair is composed of cells that have died.

    _____true_____

23. What causes hair to grow? Rapid cell growth at the base of the hair follicle causes hair to grow.

    _____

24. What is the nail root? It is an area of rapidly dividing cells near the tips of the fingers and toes

    where the nails grow. _____

    _____

Chapter 36   Skeletal, Muscular, and Integumentary Systems

Vocabulary Review

Crossword Puzzle   *Complete the puzzle by entering the term that matches each numbered description.*

```
              1
              c
    2       3
    k       h a v e r s i a n
4       |   |
e       e   r
5           6
p e r i o s t e u m
i       a   s   i
d       t   s   7           8           9
e       i   i   l i g a m e n t
r       n   f   a   |       y   |       e
m           i   g   |       o   |       e
i           c   e   |       s   10      n
s           a       |       i   d e r m i s
            t       |       n   o   |   e
12                              n   |   l
    j o i n t                       |   a
            o                       |   n
13                                  |   i
a c t i n                               n
```

Across

3. type of canals in bone that contain blood vessels and nerves
5. tough layer of connective tissue that surrounds bone
7. tough connective tissue that holds bones together in a joint
10. layer of skin that contains glands and blood vessels
12. place where one bone attaches to another bone
13. protein found in thin muscle filaments

Down

1. type of connective tissue that is replaced by bone as a person grows
2. protein found in hair and nails
4. layer of skin where melanocytes are located
6. process in which cartilage is replaced by bone
8. protein found in thick muscle filaments
9. tough connective tissue that joins skeletal muscle to bone
11. dark brown pigment in skin

Completion   *Fill in the blanks with terms from Chapter 36.*

The three different types of muscle tissue are _____ skeletal _____,

_____ smooth _____, and _____ cardiac _____. Skeletal muscles are controlled by motor neurons. A motor neuron and a skeletal muscle cell meet at a point called

a(an) _____ neuromuscular junction _____. The motor neuron releases a neurotransmitter,

called _____ acetylcholine _____, which transmits the impulse to the muscle cell.

Summary

37–1 The Circulatory System

The human circulatory system consists of the heart, blood vessels, and blood. Together with the respiratory system, the circulatory system supplies the body's cells with nutrients and oxygen and removes carbon dioxide and other wastes from the body.

The heart is located near the center of the chest. It is composed almost entirely of muscle. The thick layer of muscle that forms the walls of the heart is called the myocardium. Contractions of the myocardium pump blood through the circulatory system.

The heart is divided into right and left halves by a wall called the septum. Each half of the heart has two chambers, for a total of four chambers. The upper two chambers, or atria (singular: atrium), receive blood entering the heart. The lower two chambers, or ventricles, pump blood out of the heart. The right side of the heart pumps blood from the heart to the lungs. This pathway is the pulmonary circulation. The left side of the heart pumps blood to the rest of the body. This pathway is the systemic circulation. Flaps of connective tissue, called valves, between chambers prevent blood from flowing backward in the heart.

Each heart contraction begins in a small group of cardiac muscle cells called the pacemaker. From the pacemaker, the impulse travels through the rest of the heart, causing the heart to contract.

When blood leaves the heart for the body, it passes into a large blood vessel called the aorta. As blood flows through the rest of the circulatory system, it moves through three types of vessels: arteries, capillaries, and veins. Arteries are large vessels that carry blood away from the heart. From arteries, blood flows into capillaries, the smallest vessels. Capillaries bring nutrients and oxygen to the cells and absorb carbon dioxide and other wastes. From the capillaries, blood flows into veins and is returned to the heart. Large veins contain valves that keep blood moving toward the heart.

The pumping of the heart produces pressure. The force of the blood on artery walls is called blood pressure. Blood pressure keeps blood flowing through the body. Blood pressure is controlled by the autonomic nervous system and the kidneys.

Diseases of the circulatory system, called cardiovascular diseases, are leading causes of death. Two causes of these diseases are high blood pressure and atherosclerosis, in which fatty deposits build up in arteries. Both high blood pressure and atherosclerosis force the heart to work harder and can lead to heart attack and stroke. Cardiovascular diseases are easier to prevent than cure. Prevention includes exercising regularly, eating a low-fat diet, controlling weight, and not smoking.

37–2 Blood and the Lymphatic System

Blood is a type of connective tissue containing dissolved substances and specialized cells. Blood is almost half cells and just over half fluid. The fluid portion of blood is called plasma. Plasma is mostly water. Proteins in plasma help to clot blood and fight infections.

Cells in blood include red blood cells, white blood cells, and platelets. Red blood cells transport oxygen. A protein called hemoglobin in red blood cells binds to oxygen and carries it throughout the body. White blood cells guard against infection, fight parasites, and attack bacteria. There are many types of white blood cells. White blood cells known as lymphocytes produce antibodies. Antibodies are proteins that help fight infection. Platelets—along with plasma proteins—make blood clotting possible. Platelets cluster around a wound and release proteins called clotting factors, leading to the formation of a clot.

As blood circulates, some fluid leaks from the blood into surrounding tissues. This fluid is called lymph. The lymphatic system consists of a network of vessels, lymph nodes, and organs. This system collects lymph and returns it to the circulatory system. The lymphatic system also helps absorb nutrients and fight infection.

37–3 The Respiratory System

In biology, the word *respiration* is used in two ways. Cellular respiration, as you may recall, is the release of energy from the breakdown of food molecules in the presence of oxygen. The other meaning of respiration is the exchange of gases between an organism and the environment. The human respiratory system brings about the exchange of oxygen and carbon dioxide between the blood, the air, and tissues.

The respiratory system consists of the nose, pharynx, larynx, trachea, bronchi, and lungs. Air from the nose enters the pharynx, a tube in the throat. Air moves from the pharynx into the trachea. At the top of the trachea is the larynx, which contains the vocal cords. From the trachea, air passes into two large passageways in the chest called bronchi (singular: bronchus). Each bronchus leads into one of the lungs. Within each lung, the bronchus subdivides into smaller passageways, called bronchioles. The bronchioles continue to subdivide until they reach millions of tiny air sacs called alveoli (singular: alveolus). Each alveolus is surrounded by capillaries. Oxygen crosses the thin capillary walls from the alveolus into the blood. Carbon dioxide in the blood crosses in the opposite direction into the alveolus.

Breathing is the movement of air into and out of the lungs. At the bottom of the chest cavity is a muscle called the diaphragm. When the diaphragm contracts, the chest cavity becomes larger. This creates a partial vacuum in the chest. Air pressure causes air to rush in and fill the lungs. When the diaphragm relaxes, the chest cavity becomes smaller. Increased pressure inside the chest forces air back out of the lungs.

The rate of breathing is controlled by the level of carbon dioxide in the blood. This level is monitored by the medulla oblongata in the brain. As the carbon dioxide level rises, the medulla oblongata sends nerve impulses to the diaphragm, causing it to contract. This results in breathing.

Tobacco smoke harms the respiratory system. Three of the most dangerous substances in tobacco smoke are nicotine, carbon monoxide, and tar. Nicotine is a stimulant that increases heart rate and blood pressure. Carbon monoxide is a poisonous gas that blocks the transport of oxygen by blood. Tar contains substances that cause cancer. Smoking can cause emphysema, which is loss of elasticity in the tissues of the lungs. Smoking can also cause lung cancer and heart disease. Passive smoking means inhaling the smoke of others. Passive smoking is damaging to nonsmokers, especially young children. Quitting smoking can improve a smoker's health. The best solution, however, is not to begin smoking.

Chapter 37 Circulatory and Respiratory Systems

Section 37–1 The Circulatory System (pages 943–950)

🔑 **Key Concepts**
- What are the structures of the circulatory system?
- What are the three types of blood vessels in the circulatory system?

Functions of the Circulatory System (page 943)

1. Why do large organisms require a circulatory system? Most of their cells are not in direct contact with the environment, so they cannot rely on diffusion. Therefore, they need a circulatory system to transport substances from one part of the organism to another.

2. What is a closed circulatory system? It is one that has a circulating fluid contained within a system of vessels.

3. List the three components of the circulatory system.
   a. Heart
   b. Blood vessels
   c. Blood

The Heart (pages 944–946)

4. Is the following sentence true or false? The heart is composed almost entirely of muscle. true

Match each heart structure with its description.

	Structure	Description
b	5. pericardium	a. Thick layer of muscle in the walls of the heart
a	6. myocardium	b. Sac of tissue that encloses and protects the heart
c	7. atrium	c. Upper chamber of the heart
d	8. ventricle	d. Lower chamber of the heart

9. Dividing the right side of the heart from the left side is a wall called a(an) ____septum____ .

10. Is the following sentence true or false? The heart functions as four separate pumps. ____false____

11. Complete the table about the circulatory system.

THE CIRCULATORY SYSTEM

Name of Circulatory Pathway	Side of Heart Involved	Route Blood Follows
Pulmonary circulation	Right side	From heart to lungs
Systemic circulation	Left side	From heart to rest of body

12. What happens to blood when it reaches the lungs? Carbon dioxide leaves the blood, and oxygen is absorbed.

13. Why is the blood that enters the heart from the systemic circulation oxygen-poor?
The cells of the body have absorbed much of the oxygen the blood once contained and loaded
the blood with carbon dioxide.

14. Circle the letter of each sentence that is true about blood flow through the heart.

(a.) Blood enters the heart through the right and left atria.

b. Blood enters the heart through the right and left ventricles.

c. Blood flows from the ventricles to the atria.

d. Blood flows out of the heart through the right and left atria.

15. Flaps of connective tissue called _____valves_____ prevent blood from flowing backward in the heart.

16. Each heart contraction begins in a small group of cardiac muscle cells called the _____sinoatrial, or SA,_____ node.

17. Cells that "set the pace" for the beating of the heart as a whole are also called the _____pacemaker_____.

Blood Vessels (pages 946–947)

18. Complete the concept map.

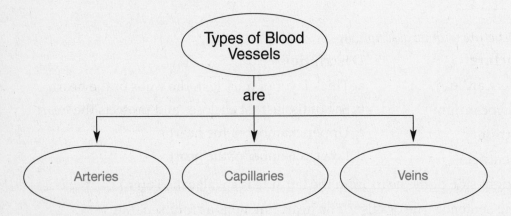

19. Circle the letter of each sentence that is true about arteries.

a. Most carry oxygen-poor blood.   **c.** They have thin walls.

(b.) They can expand under pressure.   (d.) The largest is the aorta.

20. The smallest blood vessels found in the body are the _____capillaries_____.

21. What work is done in the capillaries? They bring nutrients and oxygen to the tissues and
absorb carbon dioxide and other waste products.

22. What keeps blood flowing toward the heart in the largest veins? Valves keep
blood flowing toward the heart.

Blood Pressure (pages 948–949)

23. The force of blood on the walls of arteries is known as _____ blood pressure _____.

24. Is the following sentence true or false? Blood pressure increases when the heart relaxes.
_____ false _____

Match each type of blood pressure with the force it measures.

Type of Pressure	Force It Measures
__b__ **25.** systolic	**a.** Force of the blood when the ventricles relax
__a__ **26.** diastolic	**b.** Force of the blood when the ventricles contract

27. A typical blood pressure reading for a healthy person is _____ 120/80 _____.

28. How does the autonomic nervous system regulate blood pressure?
It releases neurotransmitters that cause the smooth muscles in blood vessel walls to
relax when blood pressure is too high or to contract when blood pressure is too low.

29. How do the kidneys regulate blood pressure? They remove more water from the blood and
thereby reduce blood volume when blood pressure is too high.

Diseases of the Circulatory System (pages 949–950)

30. A condition in which fatty deposits build up on the walls of arteries is called
_____ atherosclerosis _____.

31. High blood pressure also is called _____ hypertension _____.

32. Is the following sentence true or false? High blood pressure increases the risk of heart attack and stroke. _____ true _____

33. Circle the letter of each sentence that is true about heart attack.
(a.) It is caused by atherosclerosis in the coronary arteries.
(b.) It occurs when part of the heart muscle begins to die.
(c.) Its symptoms include nausea and chest pain.
(d.) It requires immediate medical attention.

34. Is the following sentence true or false? A stroke may be caused by a clot in a blood vessel leading to the brain. _____ true _____

35. List three ways of avoiding cardiovascular diseases.
a. Getting regular exercise
b. Eating a balanced diet
c. Not smoking

Section 37–2 Blood and the Lymphatic System
(pages 951–955)

🔑 **Key Concepts**
- What is the function of each type of blood cell?
- What is the function of the lymphatic system?

Blood Plasma (page 951)

1. The straw-colored fluid portion of blood is called _____plasma_____.
2. Plasma is about 90 percent water and 10 percent ___dissolved gases, salts, nutrients,___ ___enzymes, hormones, waste products, and plasma proteins.___

Match each type of plasma protein with its function.

	Type of Protein	Function
__b__	3. albumin	a. Helps blood clot
__c__	4. globulin	b. Regulates osmotic pressure and blood volume
__a__	5. fibrinogen	c. Fights viral and bacterial infections

Blood Cells (pages 952–954)

6. List the three components of the cellular portion of blood.
   a. _Red blood cells_   b. _White blood cells_   c. _Platelets_
7. What is the role of red blood cells? _Red blood cells transport oxygen._
8. What is hemoglobin? ___Hemoglobin is an iron-containing protein that binds to oxygen in the___ ___lungs and transports it to tissues throughout the body.___

9. Is the following sentence true or false? Mature red blood cells have two nuclei.
   _____false_____

10. Circle the letter of each sentence that is true about white blood cells.
    (a.) They contain nuclei.
    (b.) They attack foreign substances.
    c. They contain hemoglobin.
    (d.) They are also called leukocytes.

11. Is the following sentence true or false? Most white blood cells live for an average of 120 days. _____false_____

12. White blood cells that engulf and digest foreign cells are called ___phagocytes___.

13. What does a sudden increase in the number of white cells tell a physician?
    The body is fighting a serious infection.

14. List the two components of blood that make clotting possible.

a. <u>Plasma proteins</u>   b. <u>Platelets</u>

15. Number the drawings below to show the correct sequence in which a blood clot forms when a blood vessel is injured.

_____3_____   _____1_____   _____2_____

16. A genetic disorder that results from a defective protein in the clotting pathway is
_____<u>hemophilia</u>_____.

The Lymphatic System (pages 954–955)

17. What is the lymphatic system? <u>It is a network of vessels, nodes, and organs that collects</u>
<u>the fluid lost by the blood and returns it to the circulatory system.</u>
_____

18. The fluid lost by blood is called _____<u>lymph</u>_____.

19. What is the function of lymph nodes? <u>Lymph nodes act as filters, trapping bacteria and</u>
<u>other microorganisms that cause disease.</u>

Reading Skill Practice

When you read a section with difficult material, writing a summary can help you identify and remember the main ideas and supporting details. Write a concise paragraph summing up the material under each heading in Section 37–2. Each of your paragraphs should be much shorter than the text under that heading in your book. Include each of the highlighted, boldface vocabulary terms in your summary. Do your work on a separate sheet of paper.

In their summaries, students should correctly use the highlighted, boldface vocabulary terms as they briefly describe the structure and function of blood plasma, blood cells, and the lymphatic system.

Section 37–3 The Respiratory System (pages 956–963)

🗝 Key Concepts
- What is the function of the respiratory system?
- How does smoking affect the respiratory system?

What Is Respiration? (page 956)

1. The process by which oxygen and carbon dioxide are exchanged between the lungs and the environment is known as _____respiration_____ .

The Human Respiratory System (pages 956–958)

2. What is the basic function performed by the human respiratory system? _It brings about_ the exchange of oxygen and carbon dioxide.

_____

3. Label each of the following structures in the drawing of the human respiratory system: nose, pharynx, larynx, trachea, bronchus, and lung.

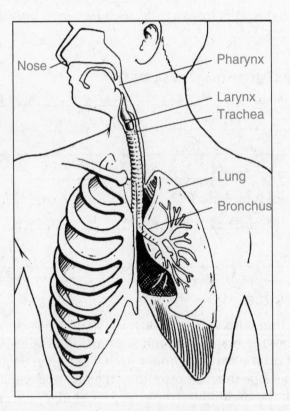

4. Circle the letter of the choice that lists the respiratory structures from largest to smallest.
   a. Alveoli, bronchioles, bronchi   (c.) Bronchi, bronchioles, alveoli
   b. Bronchioles, bronchi, alveoli   d. Bronchi, alveoli, bronchioles

5. What prevents food from entering your trachea? _A piece of cartilage called the epiglottis_ covers the entrance to the trachea when you swallow.

_____

Match each structure of the respiratory system with its description.

	Structure		Description
c	**6.** pharynx	**a.**	Tiny air sacs where gas exchange occurs
f	**7.** trachea	**b.**	Tiny projections that sweep trapped particles and mucus away from the lungs
b	**8.** cilia		
e	**9.** larynx	**c.**	Tube that serves as a passageway for both air and food
d	**10.** bronchi	**d.**	Large passageways in the chest that lead to the lungs
a	**11.** alveoli	**e.**	Structure at the top of the trachea that contains the vocal cords
		f.	Passageway between the pharynx and bronchi

Gas Exchange (page 958)

12. Gas exchange occurs in the _____alveoli_____.

13. Describe the process of gas exchange. _Oxygen dissolves in the moisture on the inner surface of the alveoli and then diffuses across the thin-walled capillaries into the blood. Carbon dioxide in the bloodstream diffuses in the opposite direction._

14. Circle the letter of each sentence that is true about gas exchange.

(**a.**) It is a very efficient process.

b. Exhaled air usually contains no oxygen.

c. The lungs remove about half of the oxygen of inhaled air.

(**d.**) The lungs increase the carbon dioxide content of inhaled air by a factor of 100.

15. Why is hemoglobin needed? _Because hemoglobin greatly increases the oxygen-carrying capacity of the blood, without it the body would need far more blood to carry the same amount of oxygen._

Breathing (pages 959–960)

16. The movement of air into and out of the lungs is called _____breathing_____.

17. The large, flat muscle at the bottom of the chest cavity is the _____diaphragm_____.

18. Is the following sentence true or false? The force that drives air into the lungs comes from air pressure. _____true_____

19. What happens when you inhale? _The diaphragm contracts and the rib cage rises. This expands the volume of the chest. This creates a partial vacuum, and atmospheric pressure causes the lungs to fill with air._

20. What happens when pressure in the chest cavity becomes greater than atmospheric pressure? _Air rushes out of the lungs, and you exhale._

How Breathing Is Controlled (pages 960–961)

21. The part of the brain that controls breathing is the _____medulla oblongata_____.

22. Is the following sentence true or false? Cells in the breathing center monitor the amount of oxygen in the blood. _____false_____

23. Why do airplane passengers in emergency situations often have to be told to begin breathing pressurized oxygen? _They have no more carbon dioxide in their blood than usual,_ so the breathing center does not sense a problem.

_____

Tobacco and the Respiratory System (pages 961–963)

24. List three of the most dangerous substances in tobacco smoke.

a. _Nicotine_____

b. _Carbon monoxide_____

c. _Tar_____

25. Is the following sentence true or false? Nicotine is a stimulant drug that increases pulse rate and blood pressure. _____true_____

26. Why is carbon monoxide dangerous? _It blocks the transport of oxygen by hemoglobin,_ depriving the heart and other organs of the oxygen they need to function.

_____

27. List three respiratory diseases caused by smoking.

a. _Chronic bronchitis_____

b. _Emphysema_____

c. _Lung cancer_____

28. Circle the letter of each sentence that is true about chronic bronchitis.

(**a.**) It is characterized by swollen bronchi.

b. It occurs only in heavy smokers.

(**c.**) It can make stair climbing and similar activities difficult.

d. It is unrelated to smoking.

29. What is emphysema? _It is a loss of elasticity in the lungs._

30. Circle the letter of each sentence that is true about lung cancer.

(**a.**) Its most important cause is smoking.

(**b.**) It is often deadly.

c. It cannot spread to other parts of the body.

d. It is usually detected early enough for a cure.

31. Circle the letter of each way that smoking affects the cardiovascular system.

(a.) It constricts the blood vessels.

(b.) It causes blood pressure to rise.

(c.) It makes the heart work harder.

(d.) It causes heart disease.

32. Inhaling the smoke of others is called _____passive smoking_____.

33. Why is passive smoking particularly harmful to young children? __Their lungs are still__
__developing.__

34. Why is it so hard to quit smoking? __Nicotine is a powerful, addictive drug.__

_____

35. What is the best solution for dealing with tobacco? __The best solution is not to begin smoking.__

_____

Reading Skill Practice

When you read a section with many details, writing an outline may help you organize and remember the material. Outline Section 37–3 by first writing the section headings as major topics in the order in which they appear in the book. Then, beneath each major topic, list important details about it. Title your outline *The Respiratory System*. Do your work on a separate sheet of paper.

In their outlines, students should use the blue heads as their main topics. Under each topic, they should list enough details to make the topic clear and informative.

Vocabulary Review

Matching   *In the space provided, write the letter of the definition that best matches each term.*

  d   **1.** pulmonary circulation

  a   **2.** systemic circulation

  j   **3.** aorta

  e   **4.** capillary

  h   **5.** atherosclerosis

  b   **6.** plasma

  f   **7.** hemoglobin

  c   **8.** platelet

  i   **9.** pharynx

  g   **10.** larynx

  l   **11.** artery

  m   **12.** vein

  k   **13.** lymph

a. path of blood from heart to body

b. fluid part of blood

c. cell fragment that helps blood to clot

d. path of blood from heart to lungs

e. smallest type of blood vessel

f. protein in blood that carries oxygen

g. structure containing vocal cords

h. buildup of fat deposits on artery walls

i. tube in throat through which air passes

j. largest artery

k. fluid that is lost by the blood

l. blood vessel that carries blood away from the heart

m. blood vessel that carries blood toward the heart

True or False   *Determine whether each statement is true or false. If it is true, write* true *in the space provided. If the statement is false, change the underlined word or words to make the statement true.*

  trachea   **14.**   Air moves from the pharynx into the <u>bronchus</u>.

  alveoli   **15.**   The tiny sacs where gas exchange takes place are the <u>lymphocytes</u>.

  true   **16.**   The <u>diaphragm</u> is a muscle that enables breathing.

  emphysema   **17.**   Loss of elasticity in the lungs is called <u>lung cancer</u>.

  nicotine   **18.**   The stimulant drug in tobacco smoke is known as <u>tar</u>.

Writing Descriptions   *In the space provided, describe each structure of the heart.*

19. myocardium   Thick layer of muscle that forms the walls of the heart

20. atrium   Upper chamber of the heart that receives blood entering the heart

21. ventricle   Lower chamber of the heart that pumps blood out of the heart

22. valve   Flap of connective tissue between chambers that prevents blood from flowing backward in the heart

23. pacemaker   Small group of cardiac muscle cells that starts each heart contraction

Summary

38–1 Food and Nutrition

Cells use the chemical energy stored in food to meet their energy needs. The amount of energy in food is measured in calories. Scientists refer to the energy stored in food as dietary Calories with a capital C. The number of Calories you need each day depends on your size and level of activity.

Nutrients are substances in food that supply the energy and raw materials the body uses for growth, repair, and maintenance. Nutrients include water, carbohydrates, fats, proteins, vitamins, and minerals.

Every cell in the human body needs water, because many of the body's processes take place in water. Simple and complex carbohydrates are the main source of energy for the body. Carbohydrates include sugars, starches, and fiber. Fats are formed from fatty acids. The body needs fatty acids to make cell membranes and certain hormones. Deposits of fat protect body organs and insulate the body. Proteins are formed from amino acids. Proteins supply raw materials for growth and repair of the body. In addition, many hormones are proteins. Vitamins are organic molecules that help regulate body processes. They include water-soluble vitamins and fat-soluble vitamins. A diet lacking certain vitamins can have serious consequences. Minerals are inorganic nutrients that the body needs, usually in small amounts. Examples of minerals are calcium and iron.

The Food Guide Pyramid can help people select a balanced diet. The pyramid classifies foods into six groups. It also indicates how many servings from each group should be eaten every day to maintain a healthy diet. Foods at the base of the pyramid should make up the major portion of the diet. Foods at the top of the pyramid should be used in small amounts.

38–2 The Process of Digestion

The function of the digestive system is to break down food into simpler molecules that can be absorbed and used by the cells. The human digestive system is a one-way tube that includes the mouth, pharynx, esophagus, stomach, small intestine, and large intestine. Other structures—including the salivary glands, pancreas, and liver—add secretions to the digestive system.

Digestion starts in the mouth. The teeth tear and crush food. This begins the process of mechanical digestion. Mechanical digestion is the physical breakdown of large pieces of food into smaller pieces. Salivary glands in the mouth secrete saliva, which contains the enzyme amylase. Amylase breaks down starches into sugars. This begins the process of chemical digestion. Chemical digestion is the breakdown of large food molecules into smaller molecules.

The chewed clump of food that is swallowed is called a bolus. It passes through the pharynx and into the esophagus. The esophagus is a tube that connects the throat with the stomach. Muscle contractions, called peristalsis, squeeze the food through the esophagus.

Food from the esophagus empties into the stomach. The stomach is a large muscular sac. Both chemical and mechanical digestion take place in the stomach. Glands in the lining of the stomach produce an acid and the enzyme pepsin. The acid and pepsin work together to begin the chemical digestion of protein. Stomach muscles also contract to churn and mix the stomach contents. This mechanical digestion produces a liquid mixture called chyme.

From the stomach, chyme passes into the small intestine. Most of the chemical digestion and absorption of food occurs in the small intestine. Enzymes from the pancreas help digest starch, protein, and fat. A liquid called bile from the liver dissolves and breaks up fat droplets. The lining of the small intestine also produces several enzymes that help break down carbohydrates and proteins. Nutrients are absorbed by cells lining the surface of the small intestine.

The surface area is greatly increased by tiny fingerlike projections called villi (singular: villus). By the time chyme reaches the end of the small intestine, virtually all the nutrients have been absorbed.

Chyme next enters the large intestine. The primary function of the large intestine is to remove water from the undigested material. After most of the water has been removed, the remaining waste passes out of the body.

Digestive system disorders include peptic ulcers, diarrhea, and constipation. Peptic ulcers are caused by bacteria. Diarrhea occurs when too little water is removed from waste in the large intestine. Constipation occurs when too much water is removed.

38–3 The Excretory System

During normal metabolism, cells produce wastes such as carbon dioxide and urea. Excretion is the process by which the body eliminates these wastes. The main organs of excretion are the kidneys. The kidneys play an important role in homeostasis. They remove waste products from blood, maintain blood pH, and control water content of blood.

The two kidneys are located in the lower back. Blood containing wastes enters the kidneys. The kidneys remove urea, excess water, and other substances from the blood.

Some of the substances are later returned to the blood. The wastes are excreted. The purified blood leaves the kidneys and returns to circulation. The basic unit of function of a kidney is the nephron. Each nephron is a small independent processing unit.

Blood goes through two separate processes in a nephron: filtration and reabsorption. Filtration removes wastes from the blood. It occurs in a structure of the nephron known as the glomerulus. The glomerulus is enclosed within another structure called Bowman's capsule. Reabsorption returns some of the filtered materials back to the blood. These materials include food molecules and water.

The fluid that remains is called urine. Urine contains urea, excess salts, and other substances. Some of the water is removed from the urine in a structure called the loop of Henle. A tube called the ureter leaves each kidney and carries urine to the urinary bladder. The urinary bladder is a saclike organ that stores urine until it can be released from the body. Urine passes from the body through a tube called the urethra.

The kidneys are controlled by hormones and by the composition of the blood. If the blood becomes too concentrated, the kidneys return more water to the blood. If the blood becomes too diluted, the kidneys return less water to the blood.

A person can survive with only one kidney. If both kidneys fail, the person must receive a kidney transplant or undergo dialysis in order to survive. Dialysis purifies the blood by passing it through a filtering machine.

Section 38–1 Food and Nutrition (pages 971–977)

⊂▬ **Key Concepts**
- What are the nutrients your body needs?
- Why is water such an important nutrient?

Food and Energy (page 971)

1. Cells convert the chemical energy in glucose and other molecules into
_____ATP_____ .

2. The energy stored in food is measured in units called _____Calories_____ .

3. Is the following sentence true or false? Your body can extract energy from almost any type of food. _____true_____

4. Besides supplying fuel, what are other important functions of food? Food supplies the raw materials used to build and repair body tissues and to manufacture proteins that regulate cellular reactions, the phospholipids in cell membranes, and DNA and other substances that the body needs but cannot manufacture.
_____
_____

5. What is the study of nutrition? It is the study of food and its effects on the body.
_____
_____
_____

Nutrients (pages 972–975)

6. Substances in food that supply the energy and raw materials your body uses for growth, repair, and maintenance are called _____nutrients_____ .

7. List the six nutrients that the body needs.

   a. Water _____   d. Proteins _____

   b. Carbohydrates _____   e. Vitamins _____

   c. Fats _____   f. Minerals _____

8. Circle the letter of each sentence that is true about water as a nutrient.

   (a.) Water is the most important of all nutrients.

   (b.) Every cell in the human body needs water.

   (c.) Many of the body's processes take place in water.

   (d.) Water makes up the bulk of bodily fluids, including blood.

Name_____ Class_____ Date _____

9. How is water lost from the body? <u>It is lost in sweat, exhaled breath, and urine.</u>
_____

10. If enough water is not taken in to replace what is lost, _____<u>dehydration</u>_____
can result.

11. Complete the concept map.

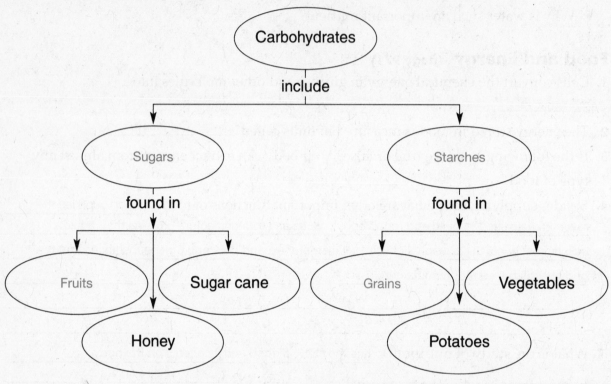

12. Why do you need fiber in your diet? <u>It supplies bulk that helps muscles keep food and</u>
<u>wastes moving through your digestive and excretory systems.</u>

13. Circle the letter of each choice that is a function of fat.
   (a.) Protecting body organs   (c.) Storing energy
   (b.) Insulating the body   d. Transporting oxygen

14. List four increased health risks associated with a diet high in fat.
   a. <u>High blood pressure</u>   c. <u>Obesity</u>
   b. <u>Heart disease</u>   d. <u>Diabetes</u>

15. Circle the letter of each choice that is a function of protein.
   (a.) Supplying raw materials for growth and repair
   (b.) Making up enzymes
   c. Helping the body absorb certain vitamins
   d. Producing cell membranes

16. The eight amino acids that the body is unable to produce are called
   _____<u>essential</u>_____ amino acids.

© Pearson Education, Inc., publishing as Pearson Prentice Hall.

Match each vitamin with its function.

	Vitamin	**Function**
d	**17.** A	**a.** Preventing cellular damage
b	**18.** D	**b.** Promoting bone growth
a	**19.** E	**c.** Repairing tissues and healing wounds
c	**20.** C	**d.** Promoting growth of skin cells

Match each mineral with a food that supplies it.

	Mineral	**Food**
b	**21.** calcium	**a.** Table salt
d	**22.** zinc	**b.** Dairy products
a	**23.** chlorine	**c.** Eggs
c	**24.** iron	**d.** Seafood

Nutrition and a Balanced Diet (pages 976–977)

25. Label the missing food groups in the Food Guide Pyramid.

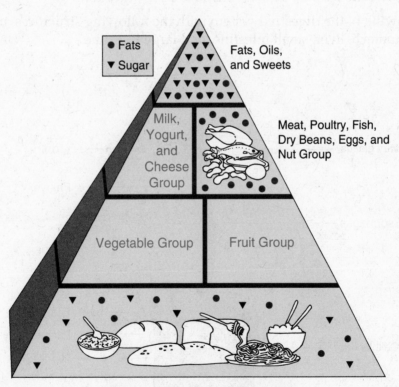

Section 38–2 The Process of Digestion
(pages 978–984)

🔑 Key Concepts
- What are the organs of the digestive system?
- What is the function of the digestive system?

Introduction (page 978)

1. What is the function of the organs of the digestive system? Their function is to help
   convert foods into simpler molecules that can be absorbed and used by the cells of the body.
   _____
   _____

The Mouth (pages 978–979)

2. The physical breakdown of large pieces of food into smaller pieces is referred to as
   _____mechanical_____ digestion.

3. The breakdown of large food molecules into smaller molecules that can be absorbed
   into the bloodstream is called _____chemical_____ digestion.

4. Label the drawing of the digestive system with the following structures: mouth,
   esophagus, stomach, liver, small intestine, and large intestine.

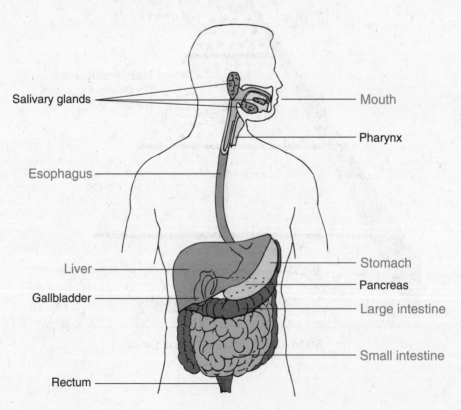

5. What is the role of teeth in digestion? <u>They do much of the mechanical work of digestion by</u> <u>cutting, tearing, and crushing food into small fragments.</u>

_____

_____

The Esophagus (page 980)

Match each term with its definition.

	Term	Definition
<u>b</u>	**6.** bolus	**a.** Contractions of smooth muscle that aid in swallowing
<u>c</u>	**7.** esophagus	**b.** Clump of chewed food
<u>a</u>	**8.** peristalsis	**c.** Food tube connecting the mouth and stomach

9. Is the following sentence true or false? The pyloric valve prevents the contents of the stomach from moving back up into the esophagus. _____<u>false</u>_____

The Stomach (pages 980–981)

10. Circle the letter of each sentence that is true about the stomach.

(**a.**) It produces hydrochloric acid.

b. It produces trypsin.

(**c.**) It helps in the mechanical digestion of food.

d. It produces amylase.

11. Is the following sentence true or false? Pepsin cannot work under the acidic conditions present in the stomach. _____<u>false</u>_____

12. A mixture of stomach fluids and food is referred to as _____<u>chyme</u>_____.

The Small Intestine (pages 981–982)

13. Where does most chemical digestion take place? <u>It takes place in the duodenum, the first</u> <u>of three parts of the small intestine.</u>

_____

14. Circle the letter of each sentence that is true about the pancreas.

(**a.**) It produces amylase.

b. It produces sodium bicarbonate.

(**c.**) Its enzymes help break down lipids and nucleic acids.

d. It produces lactase.

15. What role does the liver play in digestion? <u>It produces bile, which dissolves and disperses</u> <u>the droplets of fat found in fatty foods so that enzymes can reach the fat molecules and break</u> <u>them down.</u>

_____

16. Bile is stored in a small pouchlike organ called the _____<u>gallbladder</u>_____.

Use the table to answer the questions.

Digestive Enzymes			
Enzyme	**Site of Action**	**Site of Production**	**Nutrient Digested**
Amylase	Mouth	Salivary glands	Carbohydrate
Pepsin	Stomach	Lining of stomach	Protein
Lipase	Small intestine	Pancreas	Fat
Amylase	Small intestine	Pancreas	Carbohydrate
Trypsin	Small intestine	Pancreas	Protein
Lactase	Small intestine	Lining of small intestine	Carbohydrate
Maltase	Small intestine	Lining of small intestine	Carbohydrate
Sucrase	Small intestine	Lining of small intestine	Carbohydrate
Peptidase	Small intestine	Lining of small intestine	Protein

17. Where are the majority of digestive enzymes active? _The majority of digestive enzymes_ _are active in the small intestine._

18. Which organ or gland produces the greatest number of different digestive enzymes? _The greatest number of different digestive enzymes are produced by the small intestine._

19. Which digestive enzyme has more than one site of action and production? _Amylase_ _has more than one site of action and production._

20. Which digestive enzymes are active at a site different from the site where they are produced? _Lipase, amylase, and trypsin are active in the small intestine but produced by the pancreas._

21. Which nutrient is digested by more enyzmes than any other nutrient? _Carbohydrates_ _are digested by more enzymes than any other nutrient._

Absorption in the Small Intestine (pages 982–983)

22. Name the two parts of the small intestine where nutrients are absorbed.

a. _Jejunum_

b. _Ileum_

23. Projections that cover the folds of the small intestine are called _____villi_____.

24. Is the following sentence true or false? Molecules of undigested fat and some fatty acids are absorbed by lymph vessels called lacteals. _____true_____

25. Is the following sentence true or false? The appendix plays an important role in human digestion. _____false_____

The Large Intestine (page 984)

26. What is the primary job of the large intestine? _The primary job is to remove water from_ _undigested material._

Digestive System Disorders (page 984)

27. A hole in the stomach wall is known as a(an) _____peptic ulcer_____.

28. When something happens that interferes with the removal of water by the large intestine, a condition known as _____diarrhea_____ results.

Reading Skill Practice

When you read about a complex process, representing the process with a flowchart can help you better understand and remember it. Make a flowchart to show how food travels through the digestive system and is broken down into simpler molecules that the body can use. For more information on flowcharts, see Appendix A of your textbook. Do your work on a separate sheet of paper.

Students' flowcharts should show the organs that food passes through during digestion, starting with the mouth and ending with the large intestine. They should also indicate which nutrients are broken down in each organ.

Section 38–3 The Excretory System (pages 985–989)

⊂⊃ **Key Concepts**
- What are the functions of the kidneys?
- How is blood filtered?

Functions of the Excretory System (page 985)

1. The process by which metabolic wastes are eliminated is called _____excretion_____.

2. List four organs that are used for excretion.

   a. _Skin_____ c. _Kidneys_____

   b. _Lungs_____ d. _Liver_____

3. List three ways that the kidneys help maintain homeostasis.

   a. _Regulating water content and volume of blood_____

   b. _Maintaining blood pH_____

   c. _Removing waste products from blood_____

The Kidneys (pages 986–988)

4. Circle the letter of each sentence that is true about the kidneys.

   (a.) They are the main organs of the excretory system.

   (b.) They are located on either side of the spinal column.

   c. They remove excess water and waste products from the urine.

   d. They receive blood through the renal vein.

Match each term with its definition.

	Term	Definition
_d_	5. ureter	a. Saclike organ where urine is stored
_a_	6. urinary bladder	b. Functional unit of the kidney
_e_	7. renal medulla	c. Outer part of the kidney
_c_	8. renal cortex	d. Tube that carries urine from the kidney to the urinary bladder
_b_	9. nephron	e. Inner part of the kidney

10. Is the following sentence true or false? Nephrons are located in the renal medulla.
   _____false_____

11. What ends up in the collecting duct? _Waste products removed from the blood end up there._

12. List the two processes involved in blood purification.

   a. _Filtration_____ b. _Reabsorption_____

13. The small network of capillaries in the upper end of the nephron is referred to as the _____glomerulus_____.

14. The glomerulus is enclosed by a cup-shaped structure called the ___Bowman's capsule___.

15. Complete the Venn diagram.

Filtration   Reabsorption

Process that removes substances from blood

Processes that take place in the nephron

Process that returns substances to blood

16. The materials that are filtered from the blood are collectively called the
_____filtrate_____.

17. List six materials that are filtered from blood.

a. Water   c. Glucose   e. Amino acids

b. Urea   d. Salts   f. Vitamins

18. Which substances are removed from the filtrate and reabsorbed by the capillaries?
Nutrients such as amino acids, glucose, and fats are reabsorbed.

19. What happens during the process of secretion? Substances such as hydrogen ions are
transferred from the blood to the filtrate.

20. Circle the letter of each sentence that is true about urine.

a. It is the material that remains after reabsorption.

b. It contains only urea and water.

c. It is concentrated in the loop of Henle.

d. It is released from the body through the urethra.

Control of Kidney Function (page 988)

21. How are the activities of the kidneys controlled? They are controlled by the composition of
blood and by hormones released in response to the composition of blood.

22. Is the following sentence true or false? As the amount of water in the blood increases,
the rate of water reabsorption in the kidneys increases. _____false_____

Homeostasis by Machine (pages 988–989)

23. Is the following sentence true or false? Humans cannot survive with only one kidney.
_____false_____

24. The removal of wastes from blood using a machine is called _____dialysis_____.

Vocabulary Review

Completion   *Fill in the blanks with terms from Chapter 38.*

1. The main source of energy for the body comes from _____carbohydrates_____.

2. Nutrients that are formed from fatty acids and glycerol are _____fats_____.

3. _____Proteins_____ are needed for growth and repair of structures such as skin and muscle.

4. Saliva contains the enzyme _____amylase_____ that breaks the chemical bonds in starches.

5. The contractions that push food through the esophagus into the stomach are called _____peristalsis_____.

6. Organic molecules that help regulate body processes are called _____vitamins_____.

7. The tube that connects the throat with the stomach is the _____esophagus_____.

8. The organ that produces bile is the _____liver_____.

9. The mixture of partly digested food that leaves the stomach is called _____chyme_____.

10. The lining of the small intestine is covered with fingerlike projections called _____villi_____.

11. The primary organ of excretion is the _____kidney_____.

12. The functional units of the kidney are called _____nephrons_____.

13. The process of filtration takes place in a structure called the _____glomerulus_____.

14. The saclike organ that stores urine is the _____urinary bladder_____.

15. Urine leaves the body through a tube called the _____urethra_____.

16. The cuplike structure that encases the glomerulus is called _____Bowman's capsule_____.

17. Urea is primarily concentrated in the _____loop of Henle_____.

Summary

39–1 The Endocrine System

The endocrine system consists of glands that release secretions into the bloodstream. The secretions are called hormones. Hormones are chemicals released in one part of the body that travel throughout the body and affect cells elsewhere. Hormones bind to specific chemical receptors on cells called target cells. In addition to endocrine glands, there are exocrine glands, such as sweat glands. Exocrine glands release their secretions through ducts directly to tissues and organs.

There are two types of hormones. Steroid hormones can cross cell membranes of target cells, enter the nucleus, and turn genes on or off. Nonsteroid hormones cannot cross cell membranes. Compounds called secondary messengers carry the messages of nonsteroid hormones inside target cells. A wide range of cells also produce hormonelike substances called prostaglandins that affect only nearby cells.

The endocrine system is regulated by feedback mechanisms that help maintain homeostasis. For example, the level of a hormone in the blood may be the feedback that signals a gland to produce more or less of the hormone. Two hormones with opposite effects may work together to maintain homeostasis. This is called complementary hormone action.

39–2 Human Endocrine Glands

Human endocrine glands include the pituitary gland, hypothalamus, thyroid gland, parathyroid glands, adrenal glands, pancreas, and reproductive glands.

The nine pituitary hormones either directly regulate body functions or control the actions of other endocrine glands.

Hormones from the hypothalamus control the pituitary gland. The thyroid gland regulates metabolism. Hormones produced in the parathyroid gland help regulate calcium levels in the blood. The adrenal gland produces hormones that help the body deal with stress. The pancreas secretes insulin and glucagon. Insulin and glucagon keep the level of sugar in the blood stable. If the pancreas fails to produce, or properly use, insulin, diabetes mellitus occurs. Reproductive glands, or gonads, produce gametes. Gonads also secrete sex hormones that produce male and female physical characteristics.

39–3 The Reproductive System

Sex hormones produced by the gonads of an embryo cause the embryo to develop into either a female or a male. Sex hormones also cause puberty to occur. Puberty is a period of rapid growth and sexual maturation that usually begins between ages 9 and 15. At the end of puberty, the male and female reproductive organs are fully developed and able to function.

The main function of the male reproductive system is to produce and deliver sperm. The main organs of the male reproductive system are the testes, which are held in a sac called the scrotum. In the testes, sperm are produced in tiny tubes called seminiferous tubules. Sperm then mature in a structure known as the epididymis. They leave the epididymis through a tube called the vas deferens, which merges with the urethra. The urethra is the tube in the penis that leads to the outside. Sperm are ejected from the penis by contractions. This is called ejaculation.

The main function of the female reproductive system is to produce eggs and prepare the female body to nourish an embryo. The main organs of the female reproductive system are the ovaries. Each ovary contains thousands of follicles. A follicle is a cluster of cells surrounding a single egg. The follicle helps the egg mature. About once a month, an egg matures and is released from the ovary. The egg moves through the Fallopian tube, where it can be fertilized if sperm are present.

After a few days, the egg reaches the uterus. The uterus is connected to the outside of the body by a canal called the vagina.

One egg develops each month during the menstrual cycle. The cycle is controlled by hormones. It has four phases: follicular phase, ovulation, luteal phase, and menstruation. During the follicular phase, an egg matures in its follicle and the uterus is prepared to receive a fertilized egg. Then, the egg is released from the ovary. This is called ovulation. The luteal phase follows. During the luteal phase, the follicle turns into a structure called the corpus luteum. If the egg has been fertilized, it implants in the lining of the uterus. If the egg has not been fertilized, it passes through the uterus without implanting, and menstruation occurs. During menstruation, the lining of the uterus falls away and leaves the body through the vagina.

Diseases that are spread during sexual contact are called sexually transmitted diseases (STDs). STDs can be caused by bacteria and viruses. Common STDs include chlamydia, syphilis, gonorrhea, and AIDS. Abstinence is the only sure way to avoid being infected with STDs.

39–4 Fertilization and Development

Fertilization is the process of a sperm joining an egg. A fertilized egg is called a zygote. The zygote undergoes repeated mitosis and soon develops into a hollow ball of cells called a blastocyst. About a week after fertilization, the blastocyst embeds itself in the lining of the uterus. This is called implantation.

The cells of the blastocyst begin to specialize in a process called differentiation. Some cells migrate to form three cell layers. This process is called gastrulation. The three layers eventually develop into the different organs of the embryo. Researchers are just beginning to understand what controls the development of specialized cells and organs. Gastrulation is followed by neurulation, or the development of the nervous system. As the embryo develops, membranes also form to protect and nourish it. One of these membranes develops into the placenta. The mother and embryo exchange gases, food, and waste products across the placenta.

After eight weeks of development, the embryo is called a fetus. By the end of three months, most of the major organs are fully formed. During the remaining six months before birth, the organ systems mature, and the fetus grows in size and mass.

Childbirth occurs when hormones stimulate the mother's uterus to contract. The contractions push the baby from the uterus and out through the vagina. Twins are born if more than one egg was fertilized or if one zygote split into two embryos during early development.

Growth and development continue throughout infancy and childhood. Adolescence begins with puberty and ends with adulthood. Development continues during adulthood. The first signs of aging usually appear in the thirties.

Chapter 39 Endocrine and Reproductive Systems

Section 39–1 The Endocrine System (pages 997–1002)

🔑 **Key Concepts**
- What is the function of the endocrine system?
- How does the endocrine system maintain homeostasis?

Introduction (page 997)

1. What makes up the endocrine system? The endocrine system is made up of glands that release their products into the bloodstream.

2. What do the products of the endocrine system do? They deliver messages throughout the body.

Hormones (page 997)

3. Chemicals released in one part of the body that travel through the bloodstream and affect the activities of cells in other parts of the body are called __hormones__.

4. How do hormones affect the activities of other cells? Hormones bind to specific chemical receptors on other cells.

5. Cells that have receptors for a particular hormone are referred to as __target cells__.

6. Is the following sentence true or false? Cells without receptors are not affected by hormones. __true__

7. Is the following sentence true or false? Generally, the body's responses to hormones are quicker and shorter lasting than the responses to nerve impulses. __false__

Glands (page 998)

8. An organ that produces and releases a substance, or secretion, is called a(an) __gland__.

9. What is an exocrine gland? An exocrine gland is a gland that releases its secretions through ducts directly to the organs that use them.

10. Glands that release sweat, tears, and digestive juices are considered __exocrine__ glands.

11. What is the function of the parathyroid glands? Their function is to regulate the level of
calcium in the blood.

_____

_____

Match the endocrine gland with the hormone it produces.

	Endocrine Gland	**Hormone It Produces**
b	**12.** Pineal	**a.** Glucagon
d	**13.** Thyroid	**b.** Melatonin
a	**14.** Pancreas	**c.** Epinephrine
e	**15.** Thymus	**d.** Thyroxine
c	**16.** Adrenal	**e.** Thymosin
g	**17.** Ovary	**f.** Testosterone
f	**18.** Testis	**g.** Estrogen

19. The hormone that regulates metabolism is _____thyroxine_____.

Hormone Action (page 999)

20. List the two general groups into which hormones may be classified.

   a. Steroid hormones

   b. Nonsteroid hormones

21. Circle the letter of each sentence that is true about steroid hormones.

   (a.) They are lipids.

   b. They cannot cross cell membranes.

   (c.) They help regulate gene expression.

   (d.) They can enter the nucleus.

22. Is the following sentence true or false? Steroid hormones are produced from
cholesterol. _____true_____

23. Circle the letter of each sentence that is true about nonsteroid hormones.

   (a.) They are proteins, small peptides, or modified amino acids.

   b. They can cross cell membranes.

   (c.) They rely on secondary messengers.

   (d.) They cannot enter the nucleus.

24. Is the following sentence true or false? Secondary messengers may include calcium
ions, cAMP, nucleotides, and fatty acids. _____true_____

Prostaglandins (page 1000)

25. Hormonelike substances produced by other kinds of cells and tissues are called
_____prostaglandins_____.

26. Why are prostaglandins known as "local hormones"? <u>They generally affect only nearby</u>
<u>cells and tissues.</u>

27. Is the following sentence true or false? Some prostaglandins cause smooth muscles to
contract. _____<u>true</u>_____

Control of the Endocrine System (pages 1000–1001)

28. When does feedback inhibition occur? <u>It occurs when an increase in any substance "feeds</u>
<u>back" to inhibit the process that produced the substance in the first place.</u>

29. Fill in the missing labels in the diagram to show how the thyroid gland is regulated by
feedback controls.

Inhibition

Hypothalamus → TRH → Anterior pituitary → TSH → Thyroid → Thyroxine

30. Circle the letter of each event that occurs when core body temperature begins to drop.

   a. The hypothalamus produces less TRH.

   (b.) More TSH is released.

   c. Less thyroxine is released.

   (d.) Metabolic activity increases.

31. Is the following sentence true or false? As you lose water, the concentration of
dissolved materials in the blood falls. _____<u>false</u>_____

Complementary Hormone Action (page 1002)

32. What is complementary hormone action? <u>It refers to the joint control of part of the body's</u>
<u>internal environment by two hormones with opposite effects.</u>

33. Is the following sentence true or false? Calcitonin increases the concentration of
calcium in the blood. _____<u>false</u>_____

34. If calcium levels drop too low, the parathyroid glands release _____<u>PTH</u>_____.

35. How does PTH increase calcium levels? <u>PTH stimulates the intestine to absorb more</u>
<u>calcium from food, causes the kidneys to retain more calcium, and stimulates bone cells to release</u>
<u>some of the calcium stored in bone.</u>

36. Why is the regulation of calcium levels so important? <u>If calcium levels drop below their</u>
<u>normal range, blood cannot clot, muscles cannot contract, and transport across cell membranes</u>
<u>may fail.</u>

Section 39–2 Human Endocrine Glands (pages 1003–1008)

⊂▭⊃ **Key Concept**
- What are the functions of the major endocrine glands?

Introduction (page 1003)

1. List seven major glands of the endocrine system.

   a. Pituitary gland   e. Adrenal glands

   b. Hypothalamus   f. Pancreas

   c. Thyroid gland   g. Reproductive glands

   d. Parathyroid glands

Pituitary Gland (page 1003)

2. Describe the pituitary gland and its location. The pituitary gland is a bean-size structure that dangles on a slender stalk of tissue at the base of the skull.

3. List the two parts of the pituitary gland.

   a. Anterior   b. Posterior

4. In general, what is the role of pituitary gland hormones? They directly regulate many body functions and control the actions of several other endocrine glands.

Hypothalamus (page 1004)

5. Is the following sentence true or false? The hypothalamus controls the secretions of the pituitary gland. _____true_____

6. What influences the activity of the hypothalamus? Its activity is influenced by the levels of hormones in the blood and by sensory information collected by other parts of the nervous system.

7. In what way is the posterior pituitary an extension of the hypothalamus?
   The cell bodies of the neurosecretory cells of the posterior pituitary are in the hypothalamus.

8. Is the following sentence true or false? The hypothalamus has direct control of the anterior pituitary. _____false_____

Match each pituitary hormone with its action.

	Hormone	Action
e	**9.** ADH	**a.** Stimulates ovaries and testes
b	**10.** FSH	**b.** Stimulates production of eggs and sperm
a	**11.** LH	**c.** Stimulates release of hormones from adrenal cortex
d	**12.** GH	**d.** Stimulates protein synthesis and growth in cells
c	**13.** ACTH	**e.** Stimulates the kidneys to reabsorb water

14. What are releasing hormones, and what do they do? <u>They are hormones produced by the</u>
<u>hypothalamus and secreted directly into blood vessels. They are carried by the circulatory system</u>
<u>to the anterior pituitary, where they control the production and release of hormones.</u>

Thyroid Gland (page 1005)

15. Where is the thyroid gland located? <u>It is located at the base of the neck and wraps around</u>
<u>the upper part of the trachea.</u>

16. Is the following sentence true or false? The thyroid gland regulates reproduction.
<u>false</u>

17. List the two hormones produced by the thyroid.

  a. <u>Thyroxine</u>   **b.** <u>Calcitonin</u>

18. What does thyroxine do in the body? <u>It regulates metabolic rates of nearly all the cells of the</u>
<u>body.</u>

19. Production of too much thyroxine leads to a condition called
<u>hyperthyroidism</u>.

20. An enlargement of the thyroid gland is called a(an) <u>goiter</u>.

21. Infants who lack enough iodine to produce normal amounts of thyroxine suffer from
a condition called <u>cretinism</u>.

22. How can cretinism usually be prevented? <u>It can usually be prevented by the addition of</u>
<u>small amounts of iodine to table salt or other items in the food supply.</u>

Parathyroid Glands (page 1005)

23. How does parathyroid hormone regulate calcium levels in the blood? <u>It increases the</u>
<u>reabsorption of calcium in the kidneys and the uptake of calcium from the digestive system.</u>

Adrenal Glands (page 1006)

24. What is the general role of the adrenal glands? <u>The general role is to help the body prepare</u>
<u>for and deal with stress.</u>

25. The outer part of the adrenal gland is called the <u>adrenal cortex</u>, and
the inner part is called the <u>adrenal medulla</u>.

26. Is the following sentence true or false? The release of hormones from the adrenal
medulla is regulated by the sympathetic nervous system. <u>true</u>

27. Complete the table about adrenal gland hormones.

HORMONES OF THE ADRENAL GLAND

Part of Adrenal Gland	Hormones It Produces	Role of the Hormones
Adrenal cortex	Corticosteroids	Regulating minerals, metabolism
Adrenal medulla	Epinephrine, norepinephrine	Producing "fight or flight" response

Pancreas (pages 1007–1008)

28. Is the following sentence true or false? The pancreas is both an endocrine gland and an exocrine gland. _____true_____

29. What is the role of insulin and glucagon? __They help to keep the level of glucose in the__ blood stable.

30. When the pancreas fails to produce or properly use insulin, a condition known as _____diabetes mellitus_____ occurs.

31. _____Type I diabetes_____ is an autoimmune disorder that usually develops in people before the age of 15.

32. People with what type of diabetes produce low to normal amounts of insulin? _____Type II_____

Reproductive Glands (page 1008)

33. List the two important functions served by the gonads.

a. __Production of gametes__   b. __Secretion of sex hormones__

34. The female gonads are the _____ovaries_____, and the male gonads are the _____testes_____.

Reading Skill Practice

Taking notes can help you identify and remember the most important information in a section. Take notes on Section 39–2 by writing the main headings and under each heading listing the most important points. Do your work on a separate sheet of paper.

Students should list all the headings and under each heading add enough additional information to make the topic clear and informative.

Section 39–3 The Reproductive System (pages 1009–1015)

Key Concepts

- What are the main functions of the male and female reproductive systems?
- What are the four phases of the menstrual cycle?

Sexual Development (page 1009)

1. Circle the letter of each sentence that is true about sexual development before birth.

   a. Testes and ovaries begin to develop during the first six weeks.

   b. Male and female reproductive organs develop from the same tissues in the embryo.

   c. The testes produce testosterone, and the ovaries produce estrogen.

   d. Hormones determine whether the embryo will develop into a male or a female.

2. What is puberty? _Puberty is a period of rapid growth and sexual maturation during which the_ reproductive system becomes fully functional._____

3. How does the hypothalamus begin puberty? _It signals the pituitary to produce increased_ levels of FSH and LH, which affect the gonads._____

The Male Reproductive System (pages 1010–1011)

4. Is the following sentence true or false? The release of FSH and LH stimulates cells in the testes to produce testosterone. _____true_____

5. Circle the letter of each term that refers to a structure of the male reproductive system.

   a. testes

   b. Fallopian tube

   c. vas deferens

   d. urethra

6. The testes are contained in a sac called the _____scrotum_____.

7. Why do the testes remain outside the body cavity? _The temperature is lower outside the_ body cavity, and lower temperature is important for proper sperm development._____

8. Is the following sentence true or false? Sperm are produced in the vas deferens. _____false_____

9. The structure in which sperm fully mature and are stored is the _____epididymis_____.

10. The tube that leads to the outside of the body through the penis is the _____urethra_____.

11. Label the drawing of a sperm with the following structures: head, nucleus, midpiece, and tail.

Head

Tail

Nucleus

Midpiece

12. A nutrient-rich fluid called seminal fluid, when combined with sperm, forms _____semen_____.

The Female Reproductive System (pages 1011–1012)

13. Circle the letter of each choice that is a structure of the female reproductive system.

(a.) ovary (c.) uterus

b. epididymis (d.) vagina

14. Is the following sentence true or false? The ovaries usually produce only one mature ovum each month. _____true_____

15. Clusters of cells surrounding a single egg are called primary _____follicles_____.

16. The hormone that stimulates a follicle to grow and mature each month is _____FSH_____.

17. Is the following sentence true or false? Fertilization takes place in the uterus. _____false_____

The Menstrual Cycle (pages 1013–1014)

18. Circle the letter of each sentence that is true about the menstrual cycle.

a. It lasts an average of 3 to 7 days.

(b.) It is controlled by hormones.

(c.) It prepares the uterus to receive an egg.

(d.) It has four phases.

19. Is the following sentence true or false? The level of estrogen falls at the start of the follicular phase of the menstrual cycle. _____false_____

20. During the luteal phase, the follicle turns yellow and is now known as the _____corpus luteum_____.

© Pearson Education, Inc., publishing as Pearson Prentice Hall.

21. Is the following sentence true or false? The chances that an egg will be fertilized are the greatest during the first two days of the luteal phase. _____true_____

Match each phase of the menstrual cycle with the event that occurs then.

	Menstrual Phase	Event
__b__	**22.** Follicular phase	**a.** Egg travels through Fallopian tube.
__d__	**23.** Ovulation	**b.** Follicle develops.
__a__	**24.** Luteal phase	**c.** Lining of uterus is shed.
__c__	**25.** Menstruation	**d.** Egg is released from ovary.

26. What triggers menstruation to occur? __Declining levels of estrogen trigger menstruation.__
_____

27. Is the following sentence true or false? A new cycle begins with the last day of menstruation. _____false_____

Sexually Trasmitted Diseases (page 1015)

28. Diseases spread from one person to another during sexual contact are known as _____sexually transmitted diseases_____.

29. Is the following sentence true or false? Viral infections can be treated with antibiotics. _____false_____.

30. The most common STD is _____chlamydia_____.

Reading Skill Practice

When you read a section, taking notes can help you organize and remember the information. As you read or review Section 39–3, take notes by writing each heading and listing the main points under each heading. Do your work on a separate sheet of paper.

Students should make note of the main points on pages 1009–1015. Their notes should include enough detail to be clear and informative.

Section 39–4 Fertilization and Development
(pages 1016–1024)

👓 **Key Concepts**
- What is fertilization?
- What are the stages of early development?
- What is the function of the placenta?

Fertilization (pages 1016–1017)

1. The process of a sperm joining an egg is called __fertilization__.

2. Is the following sentence true or false? A fertilized egg is known as a zygote. __true__

Early Development (pages 1017–1020)

Match each term with its definition.

	Term	Definition
b	**3.** Morula	**a.** Organ that nourishes the embryo
c	**4.** Blastocyst	**b.** Name of embryo when it is a solid ball of about 64 cells
e	**5.** Implantation	**c.** Name of morula when it is a hollow ball of cells
f	**6.** Gastrulation	**d.** Membrane that surrounds and protects the embryo
d	**7.** Amnion	**e.** Process in which the blastocyst attaches to the wall of the uterus
a	**8.** Placenta	**f.** Process of cell migration that produces three cell layers

9. Is the following sentence true or false? The first few cell divisions take place in the Fallopian tube. __true__

10. After eight weeks of development, the embryo is called a(an) __fetus__.

11. Is the following sentence true or false? Most of the major organs and tissues are fully formed by the end of three months of development. __true__

Control of Development (page 1020)

12. Is the following sentence true or false? The fates of many cells in the early embryo are not fixed. __true__

Later Development (page 1021)

13. What changes occur during the last three months of fetal development? __The fetus doubles in mass, and the lungs and other organs undergo changes to prepare them for life outside the uterus.__

Childbirth (pages 1022–1023)

14. Is the following sentence true or false? The process of childbirth begins when the hormone calcitonin is released from the posterior pituitary gland. __false__

© Pearson Education, Inc., publishing as Pearson Prentice Hall.

15. The series of rhythmic contractions of the uterine wall that force the baby out through the vagina is known as _____labor_____.

16. What stimulates the production of milk in the breast tissues of the mother? It is stimulated by the pituitary hormone prolactin.

Multiple Births (page 1023)

17. If two eggs are released and fertilized by two different sperm, _____fraternal_____ twins result.

18. If a single zygote splits apart to produce two embryos, _____identical_____ twins result.

Early Years (pages 1023–1024)

19. Is the following sentence true or false? A baby's birth weight generally triples within 12 months of birth. _____true_____

20. Is the following sentence true or false? Infancy refers to the first year of life. _____false_____

21. Circle the letter of each development that occurs during infancy.
   a. Crawling   c. Appearance of first teeth
   b. Walking   d. First use of language

22. Childhood lasts from infancy until the onset of _____puberty_____.

23. Is the following sentence true or false? Reasoning skills are not developed until adolescence. _____false_____

24. Adolescence begins with puberty and ends with _____adulthood_____.

25. What produces the growth spurt that starts at puberty? A surge in sex hormones produces the growth spurt.

Adulthood (page 1024)

26. Is the following sentence true or false? Adults reach their highest levels of physical strength and development between the ages of 25 and 35. _____true_____

27. When do the first signs of physiological aging appear in most individuals? They appear in the 30s.

Vocabulary Review

Labeling Diagrams   *Fill in each blank with the correct name of the structure from the list.*

penis   urethra   epididymis
scrotum   testis   vas deferens

1. _____Vas deferens_____

2. _____Urethra_____

3. _____Penis_____

4. _____Epididymis_____

5. _____Testis_____

6. _____Scrotum_____

Completion   *Fill in the blanks with terms from Chapter 39.*

7. Secretions of endocrine glands are called _____hormones_____.

8. Cells that have receptors for a particular hormone are known as
   _____target_____ cells.

9. The nine hormones produced by the _____pituitary_____ gland regulate body
   functions or control other endocrine glands.

10. Female gonads are referred to as _____ovaries_____.

11. The reproductive system matures during a period of rapid growth and development
    called _____puberty_____.

12. In the ovary, eggs mature in a group of cells known as a(an) _____follicle_____.

13. An egg is released from the ovary in the process of _____ovulation_____.

14. The _____vagina_____ is a canal that leads from the uterus to the outside of the
    body.

15. After an egg is fertilized, it is called a(an) _____zygote_____.

16. During _____gastrulation_____, cells migrate to form three cell layers that later
    develop into the different organs of the embryo.

17. The mother and embryo exchange gases, food, and waste products across the
    _____placenta_____.

18. After eight weeks of development, the embryo is called a(an) _____fetus_____.

Summary

40–1 Infectious Disease

A disease is any change, other than an injury, that disrupts the normal functions of the body. Diseases are produced by agents such as bacteria, materials in the environment such as cigarette smoke, or inherited conditions. Disease-causing agents are called pathogens. Diseases caused by pathogens are called infectious diseases.

In the 1800s, scientists concluded that infectious diseases are caused by microorganisms, or germs. This idea is now known as the germ theory of disease. A scientist named Robert Koch developed rules to identify the microorganism that causes a specific disease. These rules, known as Koch's postulates, are still used.

Pathogens cause disease by destroying cells, releasing toxins, or disrupting body functions. Types of pathogens include viruses, bacteria, protists, worms, and fungi. Infectious diseases can be transmitted in several ways. Many are spread from one person to another through coughing, sneezing, or physical contact. Some are spread through contaminated water or food. Others are spread by infected animals. Vectors are animals that carry pathogens from person to person.

Antibiotics are drugs that kill bacteria without harming the cells of the host. Antiviral drugs fight certain viral diseases. The best treatment for most infections includes rest, a balanced diet, and fluids.

40–2 The Immune System

The immune system is the body's main defense against pathogens. It produces cells that recognize, attack, destroy, and "remember" each type of pathogen that enters the body. This process is called immunity. The immune system has both nonspecific and specific defenses.

The skin is the most important nonspecific defense. It forms a barrier that few pathogens can get through. Mucus, saliva, and tears trap pathogens and contain an enzyme that kills bacteria. If pathogens manage to enter the body, other nonspecific defenses go to work. The inflammatory response occurs when tissue is damaged by injury or infection. Blood vessels near the site expand, and white blood cells enter the tissues to fight infection. The immune system also releases chemicals that cause a fever. The higher body temperature slows the growth of many pathogens. In addition, cells infected with a virus may produce proteins called interferons, which interfere with the growth of the virus.

If a pathogen is able to get past the nonspecific defenses, the immune system reacts with specific defenses against that particular pathogen. This is called the immune response. A substance that triggers the immune response is known as an antigen. Pathogens may serve as antigens.

There are two types of immune response: humoral immunity and cell-mediated immunity. In humoral immunity, white blood cells, called B cells, produce antibodies that travel through the bloodstream and attack pathogens in the blood. Antibodies are proteins that recognize and bind to specific antigens. In cell-mediated immunity, white blood cells, called T cells, track down and destroy abnormal or infected cells. T cells also attack the cells of transplanted organs. This is called rejection. It can be prevented with drugs. After a pathogen is destroyed, certain B cells or T cells, called memory cells, remain in the body. Memory cells can quickly respond to the same pathogen if it enters the body again. This greatly reduces the chance that the disease develops again.

Besides having a disease, immunity can be acquired in other ways. Vaccination is the injection of a weakened or mild form of a pathogen to produce immunity. This type of immunity is called active immunity. Active immunity appears after exposure to an antigen. Another type of immunity is called passive immunity. It is produced when antibodies enter the body. Antibodies may be injected to fight an infection. Antibodies also pass from mother to fetus. Passive immunity lasts only as long as the antibodies remain in the body.

40–3 Immune System Disorders

There are three types of immune system disorders: allergies, autoimmune diseases, and immunodeficiency diseases. Allergies are overreactions of the immune system to antigens such as pollen. Antigens that cause allergic reactions are called allergens. In response to allergens, the body produces chemicals called histamines, which cause symptoms such as sneezing and watery eyes. Some allergic reactions lead to asthma. Asthma is a chronic respiratory disease in which the air passages become narrower than normal. This may cause coughing and difficulty breathing.

Autoimmune diseases occur when the immune system attacks the body's own cells. For example, in Type I diabetes, the immune system attacks cells of the pancreas that make insulin. Other examples of autoimmune diseases are rheumatoid arthritis, myasthenia gravis, and multiple sclerosis (MS).

Immunodeficiency diseases occur when the normal immune response breaks down. The most common immunodeficiency disease is AIDS. It is caused by the human immunodeficiency virus (HIV). HIV can be transmitted through the exchange of body fluids such as blood. The only no-risk behavior with respect to HIV and AIDS is abstinence. At present, there is no cure or vaccine for AIDS.

40–4 The Environment and Your Health

Anything that increases the chance of disease or injury is a risk factor. Risk factors in the environment include poor air quality and solar radiation. Air quality refers to the number and types of dangerous gases and particles in the air. Water, like air, can carry dangerous substances. For example, human or animal wastes can pollute water with bacteria. Bioterrorism is a new health threat. Bioterrorism is the intentional use of biological agents, such as viruses, to disable or kill people.

Cancer is a life-threatening disease in which cells multiply uncontrollably and destroy healthy tissue. Cancer may cause a tumor. A tumor is a mass of cells growing out of control. Some tumors are not cancerous. All forms of cancer are ultimately caused by harmful mutations. Mutations may be inherited or caused by viruses, chemicals, or radiation. Chemicals that cause cancer are called carcinogens. Sources of potentially harmful radiation include sunlight and radon gas, which is found in rocks and can leak into buildings. Protecting the body from radiation and carcinogens can help prevent cancer. Other ways of maintaining health include eating a healthful diet, getting plenty of exercise and rest, abstaining from harmful activities, and having regular checkups.

Section 40–1 Infectious Disease (pages 1031–1035)

Key Concepts
- What causes disease?
- How are infectious diseases transmitted?

Introduction (page 1031)

1. Any change, other than an injury, that disrupts the normal functions of the body, is a(an) _____disease_____ .

2. What are three ways diseases can come about? Diseases can be inherited, caused by materials in the environment, or produced by agents.

_____

3. Disease-causing agents are called _____pathogens_____ .

The Germ Theory of Disease (pages 1031–1032)

4. State the germ theory of disease. Infectious diseases are caused by microorganisms, or germs.

5. Circle the letter of each scientist whose work led to the germ theory of disease.
   (a.) Koch   b. Steere   (c.) Pasteur   d. Burgdorfer

6. Is the following sentence true or false? Lyme disease is caused by bacteria.
   _____true_____

7. Circle the letter of the type of organism that spreads Lyme disease.
   a. mosquito   (b.) deer tick   c. deer fly   d. horse fly

Koch's Postulates (page 1032)

8. What are scientists trying to identify when they use Koch's postulates? They are trying to identify the microorganism that causes a specific disease.

_____

9. Number the steps in the flowchart below so they show how to apply Koch's postulates.

Pathogen identified	Pathogen injected into healthy lab mouse	Pathogen grown in pure culture	Healthy mouse becomes sick	Pathogen identified

| 1 | 3 | 2 | 4 | 5 |

Name_____ Class_____ Date _____

Agents of Disease (pages 1033–1034)

10. Is the following sentence true or false? Most of the bacteria and yeast that are found in the body are harmful and cause disease. _____false_____

11. List two ways that bacteria can produce illness.

a. Breaking down tissues   b. Releasing toxins

Match each type of pathogen with a disease caused by that type.

	Type of Pathogen	Disease
d	**12.** Virus	**a.** Athlete's foot
b	**13.** Bacterium	**b.** Anthrax
e	**14.** Protist	**c.** Tapeworm
c	**15.** Worm	**d.** Influenza
a	**16.** Fungus	**e.** Malaria

How Diseases Are Spread (page 1034)

17. List three ways that infectious diseases are spread.

a. Coughing, sneezing, or physical contact

b. Contaminated water or food

c. Infected animals

18. Animals that carry pathogens from person to person are called _____vectors_____.

19. Is the following sentence true or false? Thorough hand washing does not help prevent the spread of many pathogens. _____false_____

Fighting Infectious Diseases (page 1035)

20. Compounds that kill bacteria without harming the cells of humans or animals are called _____antibiotics_____.

21. Circle the letter of each sentence that is true about antibiotics.

(a.) They work by interfering with the cellular processes of microorganisms.

(b.) Many of them are produced by living organisms.

c. They were first discovered in the 1940s.

d. They are effective against viruses.

22. How do antiviral drugs fight viral diseases? Antiviral drugs inhibit the ability of viruses to invade cells and to multiply once inside cells.

_____

_____

_____

Section 40–2 The Immune System
(pages 1036–1042)

🔑 Key Concepts
- What is the function of the immune system?
- What are the body's nonspecific defenses against invading pathogens?

Introduction (page 1036)

1. The body's main defense against pathogens is the _____ immune system _____.

Match the type of defense with its role in the body.

Defense
Role

___b___ 2. Nonspecific
  a. Destroying harmful pathogens that enter the body

___a___ 3. Specific
  b. Preventing pathogens from entering the body

Nonspecific Defenses (pages 1036–1038)

4. What is the job of the body's first line of defense? Its job is to keep pathogens out of the body.

5. List the four components of the body's first line of defense.
  a. Skin
  b. Mucus
  c. Sweat
  d. Tears

6. Is the following sentence true or false? The body's most important nonspecific defense is the skin. _____ true _____

7. How does mucus help protect the body from disease? It traps pathogens.

8. Body secretions contain an enzyme, called _____ lysozyme _____, that kills bacteria.

9. When does the body's second line of defense come into play? It comes into play when pathogens enter the body.

10. Is the following sentence true or false? The inflammatory response is a nonspecific reaction to tissue damage caused by injury or infection. _____ true _____

11. White blood cells called _____ phagocytes _____ engulf and destroy bacteria.

12. Why does an increase in the number of white blood cells indicate that the body is dealing with a serious infection? When pathogens are detected in the body, the immune system produces millions of white blood cells to fight the infection.

13. An elevated body temperature is called a(an) _____ fever _____.

14. Circle the letter of each sentence that is true about elevated body temperature.

(a.) It kills many pathogens.

(b.) It speeds up the action of white blood cells.

  c. It decreases heart rate.

  d. It slows down chemical reactions.

15. Is the following sentence true or false? Interferon is a protein that helps fight bacterial infections. _____false_____

Specific Defenses (pages 1038–1040)

16. What is the immune response? It is a series of specific defenses that attack a disease-causing agent.

_____

17. A substance that triggers the immune response is known as a(an) _____antigen_____.

18. What are some examples of antigens? Examples include viruses, bacteria, and other pathogens.

_____

19. List the two different immune responses.

  a. Humoral immunity   **b.** Cell-mediated immunity

20. Circle the letter of each sentence that is true about humoral immunity.

(a.) It is a response to pathogens in body fluids.

(b.) It depends on lymphocytes.

(c.) It involves antibodies.

(d.) It involves plasma cells.

21. A protein that helps destroy pathogens is called a(an) _____antibody_____.

22. Is the following sentence true or false? Antibodies can fight viruses but not bacteria. _____false_____

23. Label the antigen-binding sites in the drawing below.

Antigen-binding sites

Antigen

Antibody

© Pearson Education, Inc., publishing as Pearson Prentice Hall.

24. Is the following sentence true or false? Plasma cells are specialized B cells.
_____true_____

25. What happens once the body has been exposed to a pathogen? Millions of memory B cells remain capable of producing specific antibodies to that pathogen. This greatly reduces the chance that the disease could develop a second time.

26. Circle the letter of each sentence that is true about cell-mediated immunity.
(a.) It is a defense against the body's own cells.
(b.) It involves killer T cells.
c. It involves antibodies.
(d.) It causes pathogen cells to rupture and die.

27. Is the following sentence true or false? Cell-mediated immunity is particularly important for diseases caused by prokaryotic pathogens. _____false_____

Acquired Immunity (pages 1041–1042)

28. What is vaccination? It is the injection of a weakened or mild form of a pathogen to produce immunity.

29. How do vaccines work? Vaccines stimulate the immune system to create millions of plasma cells ready to produce specific types of antibodies should you ever be exposed to the pathogen.

30. Complete the Venn diagram by labeling the two types of immunity.

_____Active Immunity_____   _____Passive Immunity_____

Is due to antigens
Lasts for life

Can result from vaccination

Is due to antibiotics
Lasts for a short time

Section 40–3 Immune System Disorders
(pages 1043–1047)

👈 Key Concepts
- What is an autoimmune disease?
- How can AIDS be prevented?

Allergies (page 1043)

1. An overreaction of the immune system caused by antigens is called a(an)
   _____allergy_____.

2. Circle the letter of each choice that is a result of allergens binding to mast cells.
   a. The mast cells release chemicals known as histamines.
   b. There is increased flow of blood and fluids to the surrounding area.
   c. Sneezing, runny nose, watery eyes, and other symptoms occur.
   d. Antihistamines are released by the mast cells.

Asthma (page 1044)

3. A chronic respiratory disease in which air passages become narrower than normal is
   called _____asthma_____.

Autoimmune Diseases (page 1044)

4. What produces an autoimmune disease? It is produced by the immune system making a
   mistake and attacking the body's own cells.
   _____
   _____

5. Complete the table about autoimmune diseases.

AUTOIMMUNE DISEASES

Autoimmune Disease	Organ or Tissue That Is Attacked
Rheumatoid arthritis	Connective tissues around joints
Type I diabetes	Insulin-producing cells of the pancreas
Myasthenia gravis	Neuromuscular junctions
Multiple sclerosis	Myelin sheath that surrounds neurons

AIDS, an Immunodeficiency Disease (pages 1045–1047)

6. Is the following sentence true or false? AIDS is a type of disease in which the immune
   system is weakened by infection. _____true_____

7. What does AIDS stand for? Acquired Immune Deficiency Syndrome

8. List some of the diseases that may be symptoms of AIDS.

   a. _A rare form of skin cancer_____

   b. _Severe fungal infections in the mouth and throat_____

9. Circle the letter of the choice that refers to the cells that are attacked by HIV.

   (a.) Helper T cells   c. Red blood cells

   b. Killer T cells   d. Helper B cells

10. Is the following sentence true or false? The body does not produce antibodies against HIV. _____false_____

11. Circle the letter of each choice that is true about the spread of HIV.

   a. It is usually spread by casual contact.

   b. It is spread only by sexual contact.

   (c.) It can be spread by sharing needles.

   (d.) It is spread only by contact with infected blood or other body fluids.

12. Is the following sentence true or false? Any sexual contact carries some risk of contracting HIV. _____true_____

Reading Skill Practice

When you read about new or difficult concepts, making a concept map can help you better understand and remember the ideas. Make a concept map that shows how immune system disorders are classified, based on the material in Section 40–3. For more information about concept maps, see Appendix A of your text. Do your work on a separate sheet of paper.

Students' concept maps should show that immune system disorders are classified as allergies, in which the immune system overreacts to antigens; autoimmune diseases, in which the immune system attacks the body's own cells; and diseases such as AIDS, in which the immune system itself is attacked.

Section 40–4 The Environment and Your Health
(pages 1049–1054)

🖭 **Key Concepts**
- What environmental factors affect your health?
- How can you maintain your health?

Introduction (page 1049)

1. A _____risk factor_____ is anything that increases the chance of disease or injury.

2. Is the following sentence true or false? Both heredity and environmental factors can affect your health. _____true_____

Air Quality (pages 1049–1050)

3. Circle the letter of each factor that is part of air quality.
   - (a.) number and concentrations of gases
   - b. amount of sunlight
   - (c.) nature and amount of tiny particles

4. Why can overexposure to carbon monoxide be fatal? _____If carbon monoxide is inhaled, it binds to hemoglobin, preventing it from carrying oxygen._____

5. _____Ozone_____ is a highly reactive form of oxygen that is produced by vehicle exhaust and factory emissions.

6. Allergic reactions can be triggered by _____dust mites, pollen, mold spores, and animal dander_____.

Water Quality (pages 1050–1051)

7. What has probably been the single most important factor in nearly doubling human life expectancy over the last century or so? _____Providing safe drinking water_____

8. Circle the letter of each of the following that can be a water pollutant.
   - (a.) human and animal wastes
   - b. carbon monoxide
   - (c.) chemicals
   - d. dust mites

Bioterrorism (page 1051)

9. The intentional use of biological agents to disable or kill individuals is called _____bioterrorism_____.

10. Why could the release of smallpox virus cause serious problems? _____Vaccination programs eliminated smallpox in humans around the world years ago. As a result, almost no one has been vaccinated against the virus for decades._____

Cancer (pages 1052–1053)

11. Circle the letter of each sentence that is true about cancer.

(a.) It is generally a life-threatening disease.

(b.) It is characterized by cells multiplying uncontrollably and destroying healthy tissue.

c. It is caused by foreign cells invading the body.

d. It is easy to treat and to understand.

12. When do cancers begin? ___Cancers begin when something goes wrong with the controls that___
___normally regulate cell growth and development.___
_____

13. A mass of growing tissue is known as a(an) _____tumor_____.

14. Is the following sentence true or false? All tumors are cancerous. _____false_____

Match the type of tumor with its description.

	Tumor Type	Description
__a__	**15.** Benign	**a.** Does not spread to surrounding healthy tissue or to other parts of the body
__b__	**16.** Malignant	**b.** Can invade and destroy surrounding healthy tissue

17. List three ways that cancer cells cause illness as they spread.

a. ___They absorb the nutrients needed by other cells.___

b. ___They block nerve connections.___

c. ___They prevent the organs they invade from functioning properly.___

18. Complete the concept map.

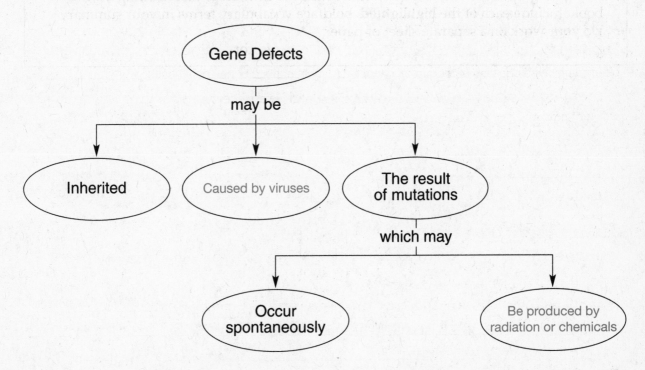

19. Chemical compounds that are known to cause cancer are called ____carcinogens____ .

20. Why is it important to detect cancer early? If cancer is detected early, there is a better chance of treating it successfully.

Maintaining Health (page 1054)

21. Give three reasons it is important to eat a healthful diet. A balanced diet provides essential nutrients. Eating foods that are low in saturated fat and cholesterol may help prevent obesity. Eating plenty of fruits, vegetables, and whole grains will help protect against certain cancers.

22. For most people, adequate rest means getting about ___eight___ hours of sleep each night.

23. ___Smoking and tobacco products___ can cause a variety of respiratory conditions as well as cancers of the lung, mouth, and throat.

24. Is the following sentence true or false? Discovering a disease early does not make it easier to treat. ___false___

Reading Skill Practice

When you read a section with difficult material, writing a summary can help you identify and remember the main ideas and supporting details. Write a concise paragraph summing up the material under each heading in Section 40–4. Each of your paragraphs should be much shorter than the text under that heading in your book. Include each of the highlighted, boldface vocabulary terms in your summary. Do your work on a separate sheet of paper.

In their summaries, students should correctly use the highlighted, boldface vocabulary terms as they briefly describe air quality, water quality, cancer, and maintenance of personal health.

Vocabulary Review

Matching   *In the space provided, write the letter of the definition that best matches each term.*

_d_   **1.** disease

_g_   **2.** pathogen

_f_   **3.** antibiotic

_a_   **4.** immunity

_k_   **5.** inflammatory response

_b_   **6.** antigen

_h_   **7.** vaccination

_c_   **8.** allergy

_e_   **9.** histamine

_l_   **10.** asthma

_j_   **11.** risk factor

_i_   **12.** vector

a. process in which the immune system produces cells that destroy pathogens or make them harmless

b. substance that triggers the immune response

c. overreaction of the immune system to antigens such as pollen

d. any change, other than an injury, that disrupts the normal functions of the body

e. chemical the body produces in response to allergens

f. drug that kills bacteria without harming the cells of the host

g. disease-causing agent

h. injection of a weakened or mild form of a pathogen to produce immunity

i. animal that carries pathogens from person to person

j. anything that increases the chance of disease or injury

k. response in which blood vessels expand and white blood cells enter infected tissues to fight infection

l. chronic respiratory disease in which the air passages become narrower than normal

Multiple Choice   *In the space provided, write the letter of the answer that best completes each sentence.*

_a_   **13.** Koch's postulates are rules for
   a. identifying the microorganism that causes a specific disease.
   b. keeping the environment safe for human health.
   c. determining which vector spreads a disease.
   d. protecting the skin from sunlight.

_d_   **14.** Nonspecific defenses include
   a. fever.
   b. interferon.
   c. the skin.
   d. all of the above.

_b_   **15.** The type of immunity that results when antibodies are passed from mother to fetus is called
   a. active immunity.
   b. passive immunity.
   c. permanent immunity.
   d. inherited immunity.

_c_   **16.** The type of immunity in which T cells attack abnormal or infected cells is known as
   a. humoral immunity.
   b. passive immunity.
   c. cell-mediated immunity.
   d. T cell immunity.

_a_   **17.** An example of an autoimmune disease is
   a. Type I diabetes.
   b. AIDS.
   c. asthma.
   d. allergy to pollen.